THE 50 SECRETS OF SELF-CONFIDENCE

The confidence to do whatever you want to do

Richard Nugent

THE 50 SECRETS OF SELF-CONFIDENCE

The confidence to do whatever you want to do

Richard Nugent

To Sam and Will. Always be confident.

CONTENTS

ABOUT THE AUTHOR

Richard Nugent is the founder of Twenty One Leadership and is a renowned keynote speaker. His approach combines the latest research in the fields of leadership, personal development and change with over ten years experience of working with demanding clients to create lasting change. He specializes in executive leadership development and coaching emerging talent.

INTRODUCTION

The importance of a book like this was captured perfectly for me by one of the contributors to it, a highly rated senior executive in one of the country's largest organizations. As a footnote to his fantastic and insightful chapter that will help others to be more confident, he added, 'It's ironic that I am doing this because I don't really feel confident'.

For most people confidence is context specific. We feel confident in some environments, with some people and in some situations but experience a complete lack of it in others. This book has been written to reverse that experience. You have the capacity to experience confidence in any situation and at any time. This book provides 50 techniques to help trigger and develop your natural confidence.

Confidence not arrogance

I have included a chapter which deals specifically with how to develop true deep confidence rather than a superficial surface version of it. It is crucial to differentiate between confidence and arrogance. It is impossible to be too confident. As you will see in the pages ahead, true confidence is humble; it helps you to share the limelight with others and is at times vulnerable. I often consider the most confident people to be those who feel comfortable with not feeling confident in a particular situation. Once you cross the line into self-importance, self-indulgence and ego-driven thinking and behaviour you have stepped out of confidence. The proper application of the techniques in this book is unlikely to lead to arrogance, but if you happen to stray across that line then take a swift step back as arrogance damages confidence.

My journey

One of the barriers to some people accessing their confidence is that they think other people can do it because of circumstance, education or even genetics. Because of this I want to be clear that I haven't always been an expert on confidence. I faced the same challenges with weight, bad skin and failed fledgling romances as most adolescents. I got my first job as a business trainer in my early twenties and while my career was fairly successful, moments of confidence were at a premium. Even my early days as a consultant were a rollercoaster of confidence-related emotions. Only in my early thirties when I discovered the fundamental secret of confidence did these peaks and troughs even out. I hope this book provides you with the same certainty that your confidence is in your hands.

How to get the most from this book

For most people this will be more of a selection box than a formal meal. Each chapter has been created so that anyone can learn from it, but undoubtedly some chapters will be more important or compelling to you. Read these first.

Remember that the whole concept of this book is to provide techniques that you can experiment with. Reading without action may lead to an unconscious increase in the amount of time you feel truly confident. By choosing a technique or two at a time and using them, I am confident that your confidence will grow significantly no matter what your starting point is!

While you will prioritize the order in which you read the chapters, I would encourage you to read the whole book. Each chapter contains valuable insights – even if you don't think the chapter title applies to you right now. For example, the chapter 'What comedy teaches you about confidence' contains some fantastic advice on how to trigger day-to-day confidence for those with no desire to tread the comedy boards.

Repetition is good

Some concepts and techniques will be repeated in various places through the book. This is completely intended. Repetition is the mother of all skill. Mastery relies at least in part on replicating good habits. If you notice a specific point is recurrent, perhaps it one that you need to learn most.

ACKNOWLEDGEMENTS

I am hugely grateful to many people for their input and support to bring this book into reality.

The wonderful contributers including Joanne Nugent, Martyn Beauchamp, Alexis Bowman, Jenny Bersin, Ray Biggs, Kevin Cherry, Steve Marriott, Graeme Carrick, James O'Connor, Nick Grantham, Haider Imam, and Brian Lumsdon and Ben Morton, my colleagues at TwentyOne Leadership.

Those who have influenced my work over recent years including Kimberley Hare, Michael Neill, Michael Heppell, Alastair Olby and Sue Bridgewater.

My wonderful support team including my Executive Assistant Jo Smith and branding expert and office buddy Ross Aitken.

The team at Hodder and in particular the superb support from Iain Campbell.

There are many more than space permits here.

Finally thank you for reading this book, applying the techniques and making the world a more confidence place.

Note: details of books cited, TED talks and other weblinks can be found at the end of the book under Further reading.

1 **THE FUNDAMENTAL SECRET OF CONFIDENCE**

Confidence is contagious. So is lack of confidence.
Vince Lombardi

If you have bought this book, the chances are that you want more confidence in certain areas of your life. In my work over the last decade I have encountered tens of thousands of people, and confidence is one of the most common development areas. I have been fortunate enough to work with professional footballers and athletes, CEOs and executives from some of the biggest and best-known brands in the world, and many, despite their apparent success, still feel they lack confidence.

By applying the tools, techniques and principles you will read on the following pages, you will have all the confidence you could ever need in any situation. You will be able to share these strategies with colleagues and clients, friends and family and, best of all, be able to trigger instant confidence whenever you need it.

You can choose to use the book in two ways: you can read it from cover to cover, applying the frameworks that are most appropriate for you; or you can use the index to guide you and use it as a toolkit to develop the areas that you feel are most important.

Whichever approach you take, the most important thing is to experiment and practise the concepts that you read. Any change comes from habit and learning it occurs through action.

Each of the secrets in this book are valuable in their own right, but all are built on the foundation of a fundamental understanding of what confidence is. Most people are brought up believing that confidence is something that they have or don't have. This is not the case; we all have it and can trigger it in an instant.

Confidence is not something you have or don't have; it's something that you do or don't do.

REALIZE THAT IT'S NOT OUTSIDE, IT'S INSIDE

Somewhere back in time someone created some particularly unhelpful language about confidence. We talk about confidence as if it is something that sits outside of us and that we get. We don't say, 'If only I could get more happy', yet we use that language about confidence. This leads to the misperception that we can only have confidence when a specific set of circumstances occur or when we have achieved certain things. We think that we will be confident when we are an expert in something or when we have lost a certain amount of weight, when we have achieved a promotion or gained a qualification. None of this is true.

Confidence is an emotional state. It is something that we feel sometimes and don't feel at other times. The various chapters outline the numerous ways in which we can feel this state more often, but it is really important to understand these strategies are triggers for the physical, mental and emotional state that we recognize as confidence.

UNDERSTANDING STATES

How long do you think states last? You might think that feelings take time to change. In fact, most emotional states last somewhere between 20 seconds and two minutes. All states are a result of an electrochemical reaction in the brain. These reactions are triggered by a combination of what you are thinking about, what you are doing with your body and your perception of the world around you.

States can be triggered in an instant and changed again in another and the great news is that you are completely in charge of your state at any time. We do, however, have certain states that we hang around in more of the time. I am sure that you can picture someone now who has a default state of miserable. They only seem to notice the negative in their world, they will always focus on what is bad or what could go wrong. They will answer a simple 'How are you?' with a low-energy, 'Oh surviving … just'. These masters of misery will even have a specific posture and way of walking that radiates gloom. It is a state that they can access easily and do so regularly.

Now think of someone who seems to be in a consistently confident state. Think about how they see the world, what do they notice most in situations and who do they surround themselves with? What kind of language do you hear them using most? Now picture them walking across a room or sitting in a meeting. I bet that their physiology is significantly different from our melancholy friend from the first example.

When you remember that confidence is a feeling we get as a result of what we think, do and say, it is easy to see how people who understand this can be confident in any situation and find it easier and easier to get into that state.

FINDING YOUR STATE OF CONFIDENCE

Everyone is confident in some area of his or her life. If you have a job, can drive, have a family, play sport, are part of a club, or if you have ever done anything well – you know how to 'do' confidence. The secret is to know what your confidence looks, sounds and feels like and then replicate it in areas where you don't do confidence as easily.

Try this experiment. Think back to a time when you felt at your most confident best. It can be in any situation. Recall it as if you were there again now. See what you saw at that time, notice what is happening around you. It is important to be in the memory rather than watching it from outside. Keep focusing on the memory and notice the kinds of things you were thinking; if you were speaking remember the words that you were using and how you were saying them. Now, as you remember this time from the past when you were at your most confident best, focus on how you were standing or moving and, most importantly, how you were feeling. Notice where the confident feelings were in your body and how those feelings moved.

Now notice that, even though you were just accessing a memory, you are feeling some of that feeling right now. This is a taste of your confidence.

The brain is an amazing piece of kit that we are gaining a greater understanding of than ever before but the one thing that it doesn't do well is differentiate between what is real and what is strongly imagined. We will explore much more of the implications and uses of this inability in other chapters; however, the most important consequence of this in relation to confidence is that when we imagine ourselves as confident the brain releases the same chemicals around the body as when we really do feel confident. As you will see in future chapters the debate about 'we fake confidence' has no practical value.

Putting it all together

Confidence is a feeling that we get as a result of what we think, what we do with our body and how we perceive the world around us. These combine to create a neurological and biological response in the body. When the right mix of chemicals has the right receptors in the body we feel confident. This means that confidence can be triggered by us at any time regardless of situation, experience or external factors.

States are completely transient, changing moment by moment. We can influence these changes through our thinking, our physiology and our language. We can create structures and habits that ensure that confidence is a state that we default to. The more time you spend in any state the easier it is to re-access this state. It is important to remember that lack of confidence, fear and doubt are states that can become habit too.

You already are confident in many areas of your life even if you don't realize it. Noticing what confidence looks, sounds and feels like for you and then replicating this in other situations is a great way to build your confidence habit. This is especially useful because the brain processes reality, imagination and memory in the same way. If you imagine or remember confidence it will trigger it in the present.

These core principles and practices underpin the practical secrets that are shared in the rest of the book. Without this understanding of what confidence is and how it is created it would be much more difficult to apply the techniques presented here. Now that you have this understanding triggering your confidence will be easier than ever before.

2 THE MYTH OF FEAR

*You can't make decisions based on fear and
the possibility of what might happen.*
Michelle Obama

If confidence is a state then what is fear? When people define it
they usually refer back to times in the past when they experienced
fear, but they don't define what it actually is. Fear is a feeling, or
we would label it a state. As with any other emotional state it is
triggered by a combination of what you do with your body, the
words and phrases that you use and, importantly, the thoughts
that you concentrate most on.

We believe that we get afraid because of other people or because
of certain situations but this is not the case. Our fear is triggered
because of what we think about certain situations or people.

Take phobias as an example. My younger brother has a phobia
of clowns. Even seeing a picture of a clown will trigger an almost
overwhelming sense of fear and the physiological reactions that
come with it including increased heart rate, body temperature
and instant perspiring. If you asked him why he is so afraid of
clowns he would tell you it was because they are weird looking
and scary and he just is. There was an instant when James
was a very small child that he saw a clown at a party and was
frightened by it. He can't actually remember that event, so it isn't
the memory of the clown that triggers fear. He has a connection
in his brain that he is scared of clowns. His fear is a result of a
thought he has, not an external event.

It is worth remembering that these kinds of thoughts seem real.
Because of this the feelings of fear that we experience feel very
real. Highly confident people have a way of experiencing this fear
and moving on from it quickly and by using the techniques in the
rest of this chapter you can too.

LEARN HOW YOU TRIGGER YOUR FEAR

The first step in escaping fear is to be clear about how you create it. In order to create the state of fear you must be imagining whatever you are thinking about going badly. For example, if you are feeling fear about a presentation you are going to do, you must be imagining this presentation going badly. It is this negative future thinking that triggers the sense of fear. Even in what appears to be a live situation it is your thinking about what is going to happen that triggers fear. If someone walks towards you in a way that you consider to be threatening, it is not their walk that creates alarm, it is what you are imagining is going to happen next that triggers those feelings. Next time you feel a sense of fear, spend a moment noticing what specifically you are thinking about. I guarantee you are imagining a situation going badly. The more vividly you are running the mental DVD through your head, the stronger your fear reaction will be. Similarly the more times you repeat these pictures and sounds in your mind, the more real they will become and so will your sense of fear.

TAKE THE ANTIDOTE

It is worth understanding at this stage that it is impossible to feel fear in the moment. Let's take the example of someone walking towards you in a threatening way. I hope this never happens to you, but if it did your fear is likely to be the result of you thinking that you are going to be attacked. However, if the worst happened you would not be feeling fear – or at least not of being attacked. You may be feeling fear about what is going to happen next – again this is future thinking.

In less extreme circumstances, such as work and social situations, the understanding that fear can't be felt in the moment is vital in providing an antidote. For example, when mentally rehearsing your presentation, if you notice the state of fear building, stop and consciously rewind the movie that has been running in your head. Now play it through your head in full sounds and colour again but with every element of the situation going brilliantly. You will notice the sense of fear fall away.

It is impossible to feel a real sense of fear while imagining any future situation going well or positively. Positive future mental rehearsal of any situation provides the antidote to fear in any situation.

USE FEAR WHEN IT IS USEFUL

Fear is a survival instinct. It is not useful to reverse every sense of fear we experience. A friend worked closely with a top security consultant in Hollywood. This personal safety expert suggested that when the rich and famous suffered personal harm it was almost always because they had ignored some warning signs that they were at risk or putting themselves in a dangerous situation.

Highly confident people don't ignore fear, but they do have a natural way of understanding when fear is rational, and when it is irrational and getting in the way of what they want to achieve.

Imagine for a moment that your state of fear is a living thing in itself. Its purpose is to get you to pay attention and take action. The action you take should be very different depending on when and where the fear shows up. Your fear appearing just as you start to walk down a dark and secluded shortcut home on your own is likely to be a signpost for a reroute. However when a sense of panic overwhelms you about a presentation you are due to make in six weeks' time then I would suggest that the attention you must pay is to prepare more fully, especially emotionally, for the event.

Putting it all together

In the same way that confidence is a state we trigger with our thoughts and physiology, our sense of fear is something that we can manage and change quickly and easily (with practice). Most of us are brought up with an understanding of fear as being something that is outside of us but instead it is our processing of a situation and, more accurately, our projection of future situations that create our own sense of fear.

The three secrets of fear that you have discovered during this chapter are:

1. You will only feel fear if you imagine something going badly or wrong.
2. It is impossible to feel fear 'in the moment'. If something bad happens the primary emotion tends not to be fear, at least not about what is actually happening.
3. You can't feel fear while imagining a situation or event going well.

The lesson from highly confident people is to reduce the occurrences of what emotional intelligence guru Daniel Goleman calls the 'amygdala hijack'. Goleman uses the term to describe emotional responses from people which are immediate, overwhelming and out of proportion with the actual stimulus. The threat response (fear) that we experience is much greater than the threat itself.

Fear in itself isn't bad. In fact it is a protection mechanism that helps us stay alive, but irrational and uncontrolled fear is unhelpful and a significant barrier to real and continued confidence. Consider the situations in which you allow your fear to become an unhelpful barrier and use the antidote in this chapter to turn your experiences around.

I would also highly recommend to parents that you help your children understand this different version of fear at as early a stage as possible. So many young people have their potential inhibited by fears that are never likely to exist anywhere but in their minds and those of their teachers and parents.

3 UNDERSTAND THE POWER OF YOUR THOUGHTS

The world as we have created it is a process of our thinking.
It cannot be changed without changing our thinking.
Albert Einstein

How much of what you understand as reality is a direct experience of what is happening in the outside world, and how much of what you experience as real is created in your head? I have asked this question at seminars and conferences up and down the country, and no one has ever answered that our experience of the world is one hundred per cent real and accurate.

Research by Shaun Achor from Harvard University suggests that around 90 per cent of what we experience is not the outside world but instead it is as a result of the lens that we see the world through.

Perhaps the fastest growing area of psychology in the world today is based on three fundamental principles of thought, mind and consciousness. These three principles (as originally defined by philosopher and author Sydney Banks) combine to create our experience. Those living by Banks's ethos are likely to suggest that 100 per cent of our experience is as a result of our thinking about world rather than the world itself.

Whichever of these schools of thought is closest to your understanding of how the world works, it is clear that what we think has a direct impact on our confidence. The thoughts we spend most time on will define our levels of confidence.

In simple terms, if you spend more time thinking about your shortcomings, what may go wrong and how people may perceive you negatively, then this will result in low confidence.

If you spend more time thinking that people are perceiving you positively, what your strengths are and the potential positive results of what you do, then the higher your confidence will be. My experience in the world of sport and business tells me that people forget these certainties of confidence.

The good news is that understanding the impact of your thinking on your confidence means that you don't always have to change your thinking to be positive. Noticing that you are wrapped up in thoughts that are moving you out of a confidence state is often enough for these thoughts to have less energy and internal influence.

NOTICE YOUR THINKING ABOUT CONFIDENCE

The first step to influencing your thinking about confidence is to notice your thinking and become more aware of the thoughts that you have which move your confidence levels up or down. The following mini-project of noticing your thinking is one that I give to every new coaching client.

The next time that you notice a specific change in the amount of confidence you are feeling, take a moment to pause and become aware of what you have been thinking about. At this stage you don't have to do anything with these thoughts – this isn't a positive thinking exercise. The aim is just to notice what you are thinking.

Here is a simple example. You are getting ready for a big social occasion. You will spend the night with people who you really want to impress. You spend considerable time getting ready and before you're due to head out you check the mirror for a final time. You aren't happy. You spend the next five minutes studying every imperfection, whether it's extra weight, signs of ageing or lack of that all important symmetry that beautiful people have. You decide that your outfit isn't complimentary so make a rushed change. Another five-minute mirror check confirms it isn't the mirror, it is you. You quickly change again, take one last opportunity to notice everything that is wrong with you and then you rush out of the door with your confidence left on the floor with your rejected clothes.

Now imagine another day. You look in the mirror, notice that you look OK and leave. On the days when we think we look good we spend a really brief period thinking about how we look and on the bad days we spend lots of time.

It is not the image in front of us that decides our confidence in these situations but the thoughts we have about those images. The same applies to any of our thinking about confidence and in order to understand this you must first get used to noticing your thinking.

CHANGE YOUR FOCUS

Imagine you are in the cinema watching a scary movie. It is the moment that the film reaches its scariest moment; the fear gets a little too much for you. What do you do? Do you keep watching ever more intently? Do you stare at the very thing that is making you feel bad and analyse why you are feeling like that? Or do you simply turn away from the screen and concentrate on something else? We know a simple change in focus in this situation is all we need to do to shift our thinking and change how we feel in that moment.

Now consider the same approach to confidence. If you notice your thinking is creating a lack of confidence, the simplest strategy is to focus on something else. If you feel your thinking, then changing your thinking will naturally change how you feel – and in an instant.

Occasionally when I share this with people who have been used to thinking about confidence in the old way – as a belief that it is built and reinforced over years – they reject the idea that simply changing focus can create more confidence. If it sounds too easy to you, I would guess that this is because your current strategy is to focus on and examine in detail the thoughts that negatively affect your confidence. The more you are used to exploring these thoughts and immersing yourself in them, the more challenging you will find it to change your focus. If this seems familiar, then use other techniques in this book to increase your confidence but make changing your focus one that you revisit and practise.

THINK ABOUT THINKING ABOUT CONFIDENCE

When you think of being confident, how do you feel? Happy, hopeful, sad, frustrated? What about when you think about a lack of confidence? How do you experience that? One of the key traits of truly confident people that I have noticed over the years is how they feel when they don't have confidence. It is a myth to think that people who are highly confident are in a constantly confident state; it is more true to say that it matters much less when they don't feel confident. They don't attach any strong meaning to their momentary confidence dip. They don't connect the absence of confidence to their performance in whatever they are trying to do and, most importantly, they don't consider it as permanent.

When you really understand the impact of thinking on your confidence, then you are able to feel a lack of confidence and experience it as nothing more than that. Confidence is a state, as is lack of confidence. Both are useful in some situations and not in others. The ability to notice when you aren't confident, to notice your thinking about it and be completely OK with that lack of confidence, is in itself the ultimate experience of confidence.

Putting it all together

We are all living in the experience of our thinking.

The thoughts that we focus on most create our perception of what is real. This understanding is crucial in becoming more confident.

The more we revisit thoughts of confidence, the more we will experience ourselves in that way. The opposite is also true. Many people have developed a strong habit of focusing on thoughts that reinforce their self-perception as unconfident.

The regular practice of noticing your thinking will help you to understand how you create your sense of confidence or your lack of it. The more you do it, the more you will notice how much of this comes from your thinking about a situation or person rather than the situation or person itself.

Noticing your thinking will take the energy out of the thought that is creating your unhelpful feeling. However, changing your focus – literally thinking about something else – will naturally interrupt the thought pattern that is creating a negative feeling.

Being comfortable with a temporary absence of confidence is a sign of confidence.

The experience of understanding that a lack of confidence is nothing more than the absence of a specific state and not something that you should link to your identity or performance is the ultimate step in understanding the power of thought and its impact on confidence.

4 WHAT CONFIDENCE IS AND WHAT IT ISN'T

Arrogance is blind to the stumbling block.
Toba Beta, *Master of Stupidity*

So far in this book we have established that confidence is a neurological and physiological state that can be triggered by a combination of what we do with our body and what thoughts we pay most attention to. You will notice that so far we have given little attention to our behaviours beyond these foundations. While we will examine the habits of interaction later in the book, it is important to remain clear that confidence is a largely inside-out experience.

Over the past ten years my clients have included CEOs and executives from multimillion pound and dollar organizations. I have worked with professional sportsmen and women at the peak of their careers who perform in front of tens of thousands of people week in and week out. You would think that these people were all masters of their self-confidence; however, too many of these people were relying on an outside-in version of confidence that is often then perceived by others as arrogance. You have probably felt it about someone in the past. That nagging sense that this is all a front, like all you are seeing of that person is a brightly coloured shell hiding the real person inside. There is a fine but significant line between self-generated confidence and this fragile superiority. Worst of all, the outside-in nature of this self-protection blocks the building of true and lasting confidence habits.

NOTICE WHEN YOU'RE AT YOUR MOST CONFIDENT

How do you know you have done something well? Is it as a result of feedback, the obvious achievement of results or do you just know? Some of us are naturally wired in such a way that we rely mainly on external sources to let us know whether we have done a good job or not. For these people the main source of understanding about their performance in any area of their life lies in the hands of others. This can be hugely challenging when it comes to building your confidence from the inside. If you are the kind of person that gets huge energy from feedback others give you, it is especially important that you build your own self-confidence routines.

A brilliant way to do this is to make a habit of noticing daily successes or moments when you have felt at your most confident. It may be useful for you to make a daily practice of writing the successes, or 'confidence moments', from the previous day as a way of setting yourself up positively for the day ahead. This will trigger states of confidence in the moment and also begin to rewire your brain to notice more of those moments as they happen.

This process can also be useful for those of us who are wired to use our own internal criteria to define whether something has been a success or not. People with this preference – known as internally referenced – know themselves better than anyone else whether they have done a good job or not. Internally referenced people don't get the same energy from feedback or external criteria as those who are externally referenced. My experience is that internally referenced people can find it easier to build a bank of positive experience; however, if they go through a prolonged period where they don't feel things are going well they can also give undue weight to these experiences.

If you have a tendency to feel that enough is never good enough or you suffer from the curse of perfectionism then it is even more important that you notice your thinking about how you have performed at a certain task in a specific situation (see Chapter 2).

BE A WEEBLE

Those of you of a certain age will remember the Weeble. The Weeble was an egg-shaped child's toy with a weight on the bottom. The marketing tagline was 'Weebles wobble but they don't fall down'. This is a great metaphor for the building of real confidence as opposed to arrogance.

People who operate from this frail, surface false confidence build it up like scaffolding around them. It holds them up in certain situations or in certain company. It often looks bold and sounds loud. It is self-important and is fuelled by talk of achievements or connections with these who are achieving.

However when the person is taken out of the comfort zone that this scaffolding is built for, it falls away leaving a vulnerable and often overwhelmed person.

By applying the knowledge and tools from this book you can be sure you are becoming a Weeble. Your internal resources provide a solid but flexible base of confidence that is with you no matter what the circumstances and even when you don't feel confident in the moment, you know that you can be with the next thought or action.

With this real base of inside-out confidence you can let go of your ego. You don't have to prove how confident you are by talking up your achievements, how much money you have or who you know. True confidence enables you to show up as your best self more often and more comfortably.

MAKE GREAT COFFEE

There is one secret of confidence that almost every book and resource I have read seems to ignore. Being brilliant at something is a great builder of confidence. I have met lots of people who are talented and try to ignore it but in general the burden of evidence becomes so great that they finally give in and allow their confidence to grow. My friend and mentor Michael Neill used to share his principles for building a great coaching business as part of his coaching seminars. Among the principles for gaining clients and developing your profile was always the line 'make great coffee'. In other words, to build a great coaching business you must give people great coaching.

We can apply the same principle to any area of life. If you lack confidence when presenting (more on this later in the book) then apply the learning from this book to grow your confidence in this area, but also develop your presentation style and skills. The better you become the more your confidence will grow. This isn't rocket science, but the role of personal and professional development is one of the pillars of confidence that is often overlooked.

Putting it all together

We all appreciate some kind of external recognition of our skills and the work that we do. When we get this appreciation it helps trigger a more powerful confidence state. It is important to hold on to the fact that confidence still comes as a result of what we do and think. The habit of focusing on success experiences or moments of confidence is hugely valuable in the process of cementing confidence as a default state.

Highly confident people aren't permanently at a 10/10 level of confidence. During my time with the business consultancy Kaizen Training, one of the attributes we would look for in a new recruit was 'the ability to light up a room but not to have to'. Truly confident people will be comfortable in the moments when stuff happens and their confidence temporarily fades. They will also be comfortable when the spotlight is on others, knowing that their turn will come and not be driven by their ego to wrestle the spotlight back.

You can only ignore the fact that you are brilliant at something for so long. Eventually the results will cancel out your lack of confidence in that particular area of your life. Think for a moment about your particular areas of professional or personal expertise. It is likely that you know 90 per cent more than 90 per cent of the people on the planet on a number of subjects. The better and more consistent results you get the more your confidence will grow.

5 THE OFFICIAL PSYCHOLOGY OF CONFIDENCE

Wanting to be someone else is a waste of the person you are.
Marilyn Monroe

We know confidence is an emotional state. We recognize that the feeling created from the biological process can be triggered instantly and anchored by habits that help this to become a default state. This understanding of confidence is quite a recent one and I think that there is value in exploring a more traditional psychological view of it.

Psychologists rarely measure confidence as a single entity. Instead they measure three factors:

- **Self-esteem** – A measure of the degree to which an individual values themselves.
- **Narcissism** – A destructive form of high self-esteem.
- **Self-efficacy** – The ability to achieve personal goals.

In various research journals there is dispute between the impacts of these various areas on the success of individuals, so the traditional view on confidence becomes a difficult one to apply in practice. The more contemporary view is that a balance of the two positive traits and the avoidance of narcissism leads to happiness and contributes to success.

An over-reliance on self-esteem alone, without any focus on the achievement of goals, can lead to shorter term confidence that is undermined by a sense of under-achievement. Many self-help books in the late 90s and early 2000s overplayed the focus on just feeling good without a need for action.

Too great a focus on the achievement of goals will lead to an uncomfortable success. We explore in other chapters of this book how an over-emphasis in this area creates the potential for our achievements to overtake the levels of genuine confidence we have in ourselves.

When we value ourselves and the contribution we make to others around us (self-esteem), and we have belief that we can succeed (self-efficacy), then we create a great breeding ground for confidence.

It is an excellent reminder that confidence is a positive and desirable state to be in and to be around. It is neither self-loving nor negative to others. Narcissism and confidence are in some ways opposites.

MAINTAIN YOUR SELF-ESTEEM

Many studies have been carried out into self-esteem over the years. These studies suggest that our baseline level of self-esteem is significantly impacted upon by environmental factors such as social class, maturation, birth order and gender. This could leave us with a belief that self-esteem can't be affected significantly; however, many studies also show that our level of self-esteem is created by our reflections of performance across a range of areas. This gives us the ability to focus on the areas of our life that we perform best in, in order to build a general self-value. It also shows the importance of learning and development in increasing our self-worth.

Take the time now to list and reflect on the areas of your life that you perform well in. For some of you this will be an easy task. For others, you may find it difficult to identify them. If this is the case, then break down the task that you are good at into smaller and smaller elements. I can find no scientific evidence that suggests that more important performance areas carry more weight in their influence of our self-esteem. In other words if you make brilliant coffee and others appreciate it, your focus on this could still impact on your self-esteem just as much as a focus on something that technically has more social significance.

AVOID NARCISSISM

At the core of narcissism is a preoccupation with one's self. Narcissism is revealed by an unhealthy focus on personal preferences, aspirations, needs, success, and how one is perceived by others. In the extreme, narcissists tend to become physically and emotionally isolated.

I would expect few narcissists to be reading a book on confidence, so a strategy for battling self-obsession seems a little unnecessary. However, this is an opportunity to highlight again that real confidence is a positive social state. Those who master genuine confidence do not need to feed their ego. They know they are fundamentally 'OK' and therefore are able to be vulnerable. Confident people are able to focus on others because of their comfort with themselves.

If at any point your future success leads you to fall into any narcissistic traits here are three simple ways to come back from the brink.

Judge all people as the same. We are all intelligent and highly functioning forms of flesh and bone powered by electricity and mysterious life force. Beyond that money, status, IQ or other means that we use to judge others are created in our own heads.

Laugh at yourself. We all do silly things. Every person has made a crazy decision or made a temporary fool of themselves. Take time to reflect on how you have made others smile through these things.

Give service in any way that you can. There are few ways to become more humble than to give what you can to others. The narcissistic way is to be so focused on self that they don't see the needs of others. My wife and I recently gave some old toys to a local women's refuge. While we were happy to help it was an incredibly humbling experience to remember how lucky we are and to see more of the challenges of others.

BUILD BELIEF IN YOUR ABILITY TO GET THE JOB DONE

Self-efficacy is one of the best defined areas in traditional psychology's view of confidence. The work of Albert Bandura gives us a great platform to understand what those high in self-efficacy do, what those with a lack of it are prone to and, most importantly, how to build it.

Bandura defines self-efficacy as 'the belief in one's capabilities to organize and execute the courses of action required to manage prospective situations'. Put simply the degree of certainty that we have the ability to do, what we need to, to achieve what we want to.

People with a strong sense of self-efficacy:

- view challenging problems as tasks to be mastered
- develop deeper interest in the activities in which they participate
- form a stronger sense of commitment to their interests and activities
- recover quickly from setbacks and disappointments.

Most people have things they want to accomplish or achieve. Most people also understand that putting these plans into action is not quite as easy. Bandura and others have found that people who have the traits of strong self-efficacy will approach goals, tasks, and challenges very differently to those who demonstrate traits of low self-efficacy.

People with a low sense of self-efficacy:

- avoid challenging tasks
- believe that difficult tasks and situations are beyond their capabilities
- focus on personal failings and negative outcomes
- quickly lose confidence in personal abilities.

Bandura also outlines how those with high self-efficacy build that characteristic. Here are four sub-strategies to help you build your belief in your ability to complete a specific task.

1. Mastery experiences. Complete the task successfully to the point that it is mastered.
2. Social modelling. Witnessing other people successfully completing the task is another important source of self-efficacy. This especially applies when observing people in a similar position who have to strive to complete the task.
3. Social persuasion. Bandura found that people could be persuaded to believe that they have the skills and capabilities to succeed. Consider who you could enlist to persuade you that you can do a particular task.
4. Psychological responses. Paying attention to how you feel before completing a task and using some of the tools contained in this book will in themselves contribute to the belief that you can achieve it. As you will have read in other chapters in this book, emotional states are often self-fulfilling.

Putting it all together

This book is full of techniques to build and solidify your confidence. These strategies have been created by modelling those who are already confident and codifying the results. Traditionalists who are rightly protective of psychology can challenge this approach and its reputation.

This chapter confirms that the techniques included in this book complement the traditional view of confidence rather than conflict with it. Indeed this alternative way of categorizing the approaches you can employ will help ensure that your confidence continues to grow. This inclusion of narcissism as a characteristic to avoid provides a boundary and sense check.

Much of the early formal research into the elements of confidence suggested that many of the factors involved were predicated on environmental factors such as upbringing.

It is clear from more recent research and social experiments that confidence comes from within and can indeed be built.

The most important person in deciding how well or easy it is to develop your confidence is you. You have to find the approaches that work for you. No book or academic can give you the exact formula, but with a small amount of effort and a fair amount of experimentation you will crack your confidence code.

6 WHO ARE YOU?

As you become more clear about who you really are, you'll be better able to decide what is best for you – the first time around.

Oprah Winfrey

To help get to grips with the concept of identity I want to start this chapter with a question. The only answer that you aren't allowed to give to this question is your own name. Here is the question.

Who are you?

If you have tried to answer that question, then you will know that it is deceptively difficult. It gets straight to the heart of your character, personality and individuality.

Your self-identity is a key factor in defining the areas of your life where confidence is likely to be naturally high and the situations in which you will have to work at it. I recently worked with a professional footballer. Despite the fact that he was married and had children, when asked to answer the identity question he clearly said that he was 'just a footballer'. It is no surprise then that he was hugely confident on the training pitch, in the dressing room and during games; however, the thought of attending a local charity event and giving a short speech about the work he did sent his confidence through the floor.

Your self-identity will define what you think you are capable of doing, what you believe about yourself and the world, and what is most important to you in situations; it even influences what you do. All of this from a concept that has grown and been defined unconsciously over the course of your life.

BE AWARE OF YOUR IDENTITIES

It is time for another identity exercise. Write down a list of the life roles that you regularly adopt.

Here are some examples of roles that I adopt.

Dad	Brother	Manager
Family bank manager	Cleaner	Taxi driver
Friend	Footballer	Writer
Coach	Gardener	Furniture construction expert

If you review your identities you will understand that what is important in some won't be in others. Your abilities in some roles will be really high, but really low in others. Some of these identities will be chosen and others will be forced upon you.

You will also appreciate that in some life roles your confidence will flow naturally and in others you will have to use the tools in this book to trigger it. This goes beyond how you perceive your abilities to do the tasks related to the role, and is defined by how you see yourself in relation to the role.

While this concept of identity impacting on confidence is not gender specific, my experience is that there are more opportunities for it to impact females than males.

A familiar example of this came from a client I worked with who had recently become a mother. Her self-identity was one of a Human Resources Director from well before her job title reflected this. She excelled in her studies and career and sure enough became the youngest HR Director in her company's history. Then, following a surprise pregnancy, she became a mother and after six months returned to work to find everything had changed. When I first met her she shared how decisions that once were easy to make required huge consideration. She felt that her values were very different and this impacted on her ability do be effective in her role. Consider for a moment the identity of a mum and the values, beliefs and capabilities that must come to the fore. Compare them to the values, beliefs and capabilities that are most important as an HR Director. They are clearly different and at times will conflict. Everyone who is a parent faces these conflicts.

ADOPT AN IDENTITY TO BOOST CONFIDENCE

This creation and change of identities is happening at a deeply unconscious level pretty much all the time. By making it more conscious then we can use our different life roles to increase our confidence in many different situations. You are effectively borrowing your confidence from one area of your life and applying it in another.

Revisit the list of life roles you created earlier. Which of these would you consider that you are most confident in? When you are in this role and feeling highly confident, what is that like? Where in your body do you feel that confidence? How does that confidence manifest in your thinking and how you behave?

Now think of another of your life roles. Imagine applying that confidence in that role. What impact would that have? How would you be acting if you adopted the confidence from the previous identity to that role?

Making this thought process part of your preparation for specific situations will be a powerful way to ensure that your confidence is consistent and feels congruent as you are simply expanding your natural confidence.

CREATE ASPIRATIONAL IDENTITIES

My friend, coach and mentor Michael Neill helped me learn a valuable lesson about self-identity a number of years ago. He shared a story of being challenged about a strapline on his website. It read 'one of the world's best success coaches', and a close friend suggested the he remove 'one of' from all his literature. For a brief time Michael protested, arguing that there was no sure-fire way of measuring his abilities and results against others. When he was finally convinced to make the change he immediately found that he thought and operated differently as the need to inhabit his new identity of 'the world's best success coach' took hold.

This is just one of many examples of people I have met living into a new and aspirational identity. Don't wait until you are completely comfortable with a self-identity before thinking about how you would operate if that were true.

As I write this book, if I adopt the identity of a coach who coaches on confidence I notice that my beliefs are that I can write some useful tips and ideas, that it is important that I do my best to make them simple to follow and that I need to work hard to write a great book. Frankly it doesn't feel inspiring.

Now, what if I adopt the identity of 'the world's foremost expert on helping anyone master confidence in every area of their life'? I have already noticed a change in how I feel inside. I believe that I have enough knowledge, tools, techniques and useful information for two books and that every person who reads it will improve their life by applying what they read. It is my duty to get this knowledge out there so I've suddenly got huge energy to get the best of what I know down in writing. Just by exploring a different identity I have a totally different experience of my confidence about writing even though that identity may not be completely true. Of course, if I write the world's most amazing book then that identity could become a self-fulfilling prophecy!

How can you apply this in your life? Explore it in your identities around work, parenting or relationships.

Putting it all together

Your self-identity influences which values, beliefs and capabilities are prevalent at any particular time. We all have different identities and we will experience more or less confidence in these identities at different times in our lives. By becoming really aware of which of these versions of our personality we operate in most often and in which we are more resourceful we can borrow confidence from one area of our lives and apply it in another.

This exploration of the different versions of ourselves can be extended by considering what identities it would be useful for us to live into. It is important not to be completely incongruent when exploring new identities but instead to think about how we can stretch and expand what is there already.

This is a great time to stop and ask the question 'who am I when I am at my best?'

7 YOU AND YOUR VALUES

*Too many people over value what they are not
and under value what they are.*
Malcolm S. Forbes

Personal values are a representation of what is really important to us in life. While this book aims to share the secrets of highly confident people, in this chapter I can share with certainty a common trait of the unconfident. Living with behaviours that contravene your values will drain your sense of confidence.

This applies in relationships when the things that are most important to one partner aren't important to the other. In business, employees who are forced to operate under a set of values that they don't share will quickly become disengaged. Families who don't have a set of shared values – explicit or implicit – will quickly fall apart.

The first challenge for most people is that they don't have the opportunity to define what their values are. You will intuitively know what is most important to you, but it is unlikely that you will have defined your values clearly and even less likely that you have shared them with others.

Having a network of people around you who share the same sense of what is really important in work, relationships or life will naturally give you confidence. Their behaviours are more likely to be congruent with yours. The choices they make will align with yours and even if they have different character traits you have the foundation of a solid relationship.

When my wife and I analysed a number of our key character traits it confirmed that we are on opposite ends of the scale on many of them. She likes detail, I like the big picture. She likes certainty, I like variety. She does most of her thinking on the inside, I form ideas out loud. The list goes on and on. So what has held us together through over a decade of marriage? A shared view on what is most important really.

UNCOVER YOUR VALUES

We have established that your values are a representation of what is most important to you really. I have encountered lots of processes over the years to elicit personal values and my favourite is still the simplest. It is most powerfully done in an environment you are comfortable in and at a time that you won't be interrupted.

Take five or ten minutes to answer the following question: *what is most important to me really?* Typically people will list somewhere between four and eight things. They shouldn't be materialistic things. If your list includes your shiny new car then I would suggest that you aren't thinking deeply enough. Don't over-analyze as you are writing, go with whatever comes up first. I find that intuition plays a useful part in the process.

Once you have your list then take a further moment to review each one and get clear on what that actually means to you. Here are some examples from my values.

Honesty: Be straightforward in conversations. This doesn't mean being rude, but I love people with whom what you see is what you get. The opposite of this is lying and that is likely to create hurt or anger.

Variety: Trying new things and going to new places is important and gives me energy. Routines have their place but not routine for the sake of it.

Family: This is one of the most difficult for me to articulate because family is the single most important thing to me. My children, wife, parents and siblings form the cornerstones upon which everything else is built.

If you have followed this simple process you now have a clear articulation of your values. By being consciously aware of what is most important to you, you will notice others demonstrating their values through their actions and decisions.

THE POWER OF COMMONLY SHARED VALUES.

I have already shared one example of the power of shared values in relationships. I'm not suggesting the first-date protocol of comparing lists of what is important really, but it is worth paying attention to the things that a new partner seems to make a priority and compare this with your values. I think it is perfectly acceptable, in fact desirable, to have a values-led conversation in an established relationship. This can be especially useful during challenging times in a partnership. Temporary lapses in behaviour can be overcome, but differences in value sets are a much greater challenge.

In business, the impact of shared values is equally clear. Research carried out by James Kouzes and Barry Posner found that discussing personal values in organizations creates a significantly greater sense of engagement among employees than discussing the company's values. (*The Leadership Challenge*, Kouzes and Posner).

My work in organizations has led to the certain belief that company values should be a representation of the most commonly shared values of the people in that organization. When this is the case the values will naturally come to life and be lived and breathed throughout the business. In coaching senior executives I always recommend that if their values don't at least overlap with their company's values they should leave the organization before this incongruence drains their energy and confidence, and negatively impacts on the business.

Your values strongly influence your behaviours and decisions. Surrounding yourself with people who share your values naturally validates your behaviours and decisions, and reinforces your sense of confidence.

TURN VALUES INTO BEHAVIOURS

Now that you are clear on the things that are most important to you really, use them to drive your behaviours. What should you be doing more of if these are your values? What must you do less of? One of the biggest drains on confidence is the sense that you have to do things or behave in ways that are in conflict with your values.

If you are a leader of a team or organization, use the shared values of that entity to define which behaviours are acceptable and which aren't. For example in my organization one of our values is 'balance'. This is a representation of the shared values the team have around the importance of work–life balance, health and family. When we make decisions about which projects to work on these values drive our behaviour and influences our decisions. If a project is long or particularly intense then it is a must that the team member takes specific recovery time during and after it. It is also OK for any team member to turn down a project to honour the value of balance.

Putting it all together

Values are the things that are most important to us really and form the basis of much of our unconscious decision making. Living a life at odds with your values will guarantee you unhappiness and lead to a lack of confidence. Spending too much time with people who don't share your values has the same impact. Over time your values may shift and this leaves you with choices to make about how and where you spend your time. Be brave in these choices as they can define how fulfilled your life is.

To the uninitiated, values can seem somewhat fluffy but as your understanding of values grows so will your appreciation of their importance. One of the most interesting challenges is to avoid judging those whose value set is different from yours. These people can seem odd and give you the sense of a distorted view of life. The reality is that they just hold different things to be important than you do. When you begin to see this more clearly and accept it then your confidence will make a significant leap.

Remain clear as to what your values are. Work on building friendships, relationships and careers that allow you to live these values more freely, and encourage others to do the same. Values-led relationships and organizations are always the most successful. Ensure yours are among these.

8 IT'S NOT ALL ABOUT YOU

Listening is a positive act: you have to put yourself out to do it.
David Hockney

It is a common misconception that confident people have to be the life and soul of every room at all times. When I started my career as a business consultant, one of the behaviours I was measured against was 'can light up a room but doesn't have to'. I think this articulates the approach of the genuinely confident. They know they can bring energy and be at the centre of a conversation, but don't feel that they have to be. The inability to share the limelight often has its roots in the fear that you won't be able to step out of another's shadow. On other occasions it can be a lack of social intelligence which leaves others sensing an overbearing nature. I experienced this at a recruitment event I led with a group of colleagues. One of the participants had a particularly strong CV and track record. On paper he seemed too good to be true. Unfortunately during the event he showed this to be the case. In every group exercise, and during breaks at lunch, he dominated the conversation and gave others little opportunity to contribute to the discussion. While this showed a surface confidence, it also demonstrated a lack of awareness especially as we were looking for as many good candidates as possible. In the final wrap up of the day he again monopolized the open session, asking three questions in quick succession, and on each occasion he addressed me as Robert despite us having several one-to-one conversations and him having full information on each assessor.

Confidence isn't dominating or overpowering. The confident person knows when to focus their attention on others and be a conduit for that person's confidence. While this chapter will largely concentrate on specific strategies to do this, the first step is to set a clear intention within yourself that you are going focus your attention on others. For many people this doesn't happen naturally and it takes patience and conscious effort especially in situations where others are vying for attention.

My experience is that the long-term impact is positive. Confident people don't have to light up the room, because they are secure in the knowledge they can at any time. It is those who lack confidence that court attention, as if it is the last time they will ever experience it.

SEE THEM

How often do you begin an interaction with the sole intent of tuning into the other person? In my formative years in learning and development I was subject to many training courses where I was encouraged to actively listen. This often included making notes, listening for the intent behind the words, giving non-verbal signals that I was listening and various other techniques. In isolation these aren't bad things to do, but they can get in the way of the purpose of listening – to fully understand what is being said. I have noticed a clear pattern in the most confident people that I work with. They are able to listen with an intensity which means that I can feel they are listening without them saying anything. I would highly recommend developing this talent. While it starts before the interaction that I mentioned earlier in the chapter, it requires a quieting of the mind while the other person is speaking. There will be times when you want to repeat back some of what they have said to clarify that you are receiving the message, but it is important to trust that focusing fully on them will lead you to be able to do this without making copious notes.

Exercise your ability to stay focused and connected with what they are saying until you are able to demonstrate that you are doing this without saying a word. The chances are you will know you are doing this brilliantly when people begin to give you praise and feedback on how brilliant a listener you are.

CONFIRM THEY MAKE SENSE

How do you demonstrate that you really understand where someone is coming from? How do you show that what they are saying makes sense? The most common way that I hear people demonstrating what they think is empathy is to tell a similar story about themselves as their partner in communication has told. This can often play out into conversation that feels semi-competitive. Person A shares a tale of the long hours they work and how their boss doesn't appreciate them. Person B says they know how they feel as they too are working exceptionally long hours, aren't appreciated by their boss and their partner is complaining that they don't see them. Person A then describes how it is going to get worse as the work is going to get busier and there is no more budget for extra staff. They will probably have to work 12-hour days every day just to keep on top of things. Person B agrees and says that that is the norm for them and they are now taking work home to do at the weekend. And so the conversation continues.

Now imagine if person B's first response was, 'Really, that must be tough. How do you manage to stay motivated when you are working that hard?' I am sure that you can see how this will change the dynamic of the conversation. It is a great demonstration of confidence to give the feeling that you know exactly where another person is coming from without making the conversation about you. This ability to relay information back or use phrases like 'that makes sense', 'I can understand why you might feel like that' or 'I can see where you are coming from' shows that you are not only listening but you appreciate their world view. Notice that it doesn't mean you share their world view. You can empathize with an individual's position without agreeing with them.

TAKE THE LIMELIGHT WHEN IT HELPS OTHERS

The ability and willingness to really hear others and give them the limelight is hugely valuable, but so is knowing when to step back into it. This understanding of when to step back in is something that highly confident people seem to develop naturally.

If you haven't got to grips with this yet, then the key question is one of purpose. For example, if you are in a one-to-one conversation where someone is sharing the challenges in their relationship, ask yourself what is the purpose of them sharing this? If it is just to be heard, then the first two strategies in this chapter are likely to be enough. If you feel that they are engaging with you for advice and guidance, follow these two strategies, and then confidently step in with your ideas or experience.

In group situations the choice about when to step into the spotlight can still be made with the same purpose question. What is your purpose for being there and what is the others' purpose? If your purpose is connection with others in that meeting or at that event, then you will achieve that much more easily by focusing on the first two strategies in this chapter because people will perceive you as a good listener who understands them. If the purpose is to raise your profile or influence a decision then, while strategies one and two remain important, you need to be ready once you have stepped into their world to share your viewpoint or experience confidently.

Putting it all together

One of my most influential coaches once suggested to me that the only way to be truly confident is to first be completely vulnerable. While many people place vulnerability in the same category as weakness I experience it as the willingness to not always be right and being comfortable with imperfection. A differentiation between surface confidence or arrogance and deep genuine confidence is the ability to really listen and show genuine empathy without the ego getting in the way. For some of you this will be natural and the challenge will be the third strategy in this chapter, knowing when to step forward and shine in any particular situation. However, for many people reading this book, the challenge will come in feeling comfortable with in the first two strategies. When I train leaders in organizations in the art and magic of coaching, I find that the most common struggle for them is not to give their immediate answers and suggestions. When I work with professional footballers, those with the strength to focus on what is best for the dressing room and the team rather than act on what their ego is telling them are in the minority.

Many of the strategies contained in this book will help you to light up any room and shine in any situation. Practise these strategies until your natural in-built confidence radiates, but remember that this doesn't mean you always have to light up the room. The truly confident person knows that they can but that they don't have to.

9 ESCAPE THE PRISON OF YOUR BELIEFS

Just as no one can be forced into belief,
so no one can be forced into unbelief.
Sigmund Freud

When I first started in the field of personal change, 'shifting beliefs' was the thing to do. My first trainer in the field was pretty obsessed by getting everyone he worked with to focus on identifying, explaining and then working on deep-rooted personal beliefs. Looking back now, it was a pretty problem-focused approach to the subject (see Chapter 16 to learn more about problem focus and solutions focus). I find the more you ask people to explore their limiting beliefs the more limiting beliefs they seem to notice or develop.

It is much more helpful to understand what beliefs are and where they come from. They then seem to be so much easier to move and sometimes just disappear without any real intervention.

Beliefs are simply stories that we learn or are taught about the world. If personal beliefs are an area you haven't explored before, the important part of the last sentence is 'stories'. Beliefs by nature are not true or fixed. In some cases these stories are repeated either by others to the point where they feel like they are real or absolute, but even most set beliefs held by one person will not be shared by others.

As human beings we are built to make meaning and build belief systems. What many in the self-development arena seem to forget is that we are also built to quickly change our beliefs. Most people in Western cultures will have believed in some version of Santa Claus as a child. If you did you will remember that every bit of evidence that you noted proved beyond doubt that he existed. The very moment that you knew he didn't everything changed and every piece of evidence demonstrated irrefutably that he didn't. Your beliefs changed and you noticed a different set of data.

Whether you are looking at your beliefs about yourself, your ability to do something or even your confidence itself, you don't need a complex neurological process to change them, you just need three steps:

1. See your beliefs for what they are.
2. Get evidence that disproves the belief.
3. Repeat.

BE AWARE OF YOUR BELIEFS

Beliefs are stories that we develop and hold onto that form rules and boundaries for our lives. They are largely unconscious; we often don't know why we can't do something or think that something is wrong for us, we *just do.*

Pause for a moment to think how your key beliefs developed. Usually parents will play a key role, as will our education. Our peer group will help shape them too alongside defining experiences that we regularly revisit. The more often we relive a particular belief the more real it will appear. It is not uncommon for a client to say, 'That's not a belief, that is a fact'. There are no real beliefs – just beliefs that seem real to you at specific times in your life.

Now would be a good time to examine the areas of your life that you would like more confidence in. What beliefs do you have about these areas that may be getting in the way of your confidence? Are these beliefs about you (someone like me couldn't do this), about your ability to do it (I'm not skilled/ knowledgeable enough) or is it a belief about your confidence itself (I would be able to if only I was confident enough). Even just the process of seeing the focus of these beliefs will often take the energy out of them and make them seem less real.

TRY ON ALTERNATIVE BELIEFS

The structure of human experience is such that your beliefs
will impact on what you do, how you do things and even your
skills, knowledge and ability in certain situations. Put simply,
your capability is dimmed down when your personal beliefs get
in the way of your confidence. The flipside of this is that you
can increase your ability and alter your normal behaviour by
adopting some alternative beliefs.

Imagine that your confidence is low about an upcoming job
interview because you believe that you don't create a good
impression in formal interviews.

How will that affect how you act in the interview? How well
formed will your answers be? How agile will your thinking be
and how strong will the examples of your experience be?

Now consider what a more helpful belief would be. How would
you prepare for the interview if you believed (or acted as if you
believed) that you were brilliant in interviews? How would you
walk into the interview? How would you sit? What would your
voice be like? How would you respond to a challenging question?
What would you say when the interviewer asked, 'Have you got
any questions for us?'

Operating from different beliefs relies on the understanding that
beliefs aren't real and that they can change. The good news is
that you don't have to change a belief forever before you act as
if it has changed. This will make perfect sense if you have read
the earlier chapters about your brain's inability to differentiate
between what is real and strongly imagined.

You can explore alternative beliefs and the impact that they will
have on your capability and behaviour in any area of your life.
Remember it is an experiment in changing your thinking. It may
not feel immediately comfortable but it will help your brain to
notice different data about what is true about you and the world
you operate in, which will then help you to form new more
helpful beliefs more easily.

JUST DO IT

The chances are that you are imagining the famous Nike swoosh and conjuring images of sports stars in their prime, but were these superstars always brilliant? Michael Jordan was the primary face of the company's advertising for many years and it was in a Nike ad that his most famous quote first appeared.

> I've missed more than 9000 shots in my career. I've lost almost 300 games. 26 times, I've been trusted to take the game winning shot and missed. I've failed over and over and over again in my life. And that is why I succeed.
> *Michael Jordan*

My invitation to you is not to wait until you are perfect before you test the limits of your self-belief. If your belief shows up as 'I can't' or 'I will never be able to', then why not just do it. If you don't have the confidence to write a book because you 'can't write', get a pen and paper and write a paragraph for the bin. If you 'couldn't ever' speak in front of a group', get your best friends together and ask them to listen to you while you stand and share a story from your favourite ever holiday. The aim is not to be the best writer or speaker in the world, but simply to disprove the limiting belief that will stop you ever developing your skills in this area.

Susan Jeffers explores this approach in great detail in the fantastic *Feel the Fear and Do it Anyway* (first published 1987). My favourite guideline from this book is: 'The only way to get rid of the fear of doing something is to go out and do it.' While it may not be the only way, I would agree that it is the quickest way. There is more on taking action later in this book.

Putting it all together

One of the key barriers to being at your confident best is your limiting beliefs. Understanding that your beliefs are neither universally true nor permanent is a brilliantly useful starting point for change. Beliefs should not be regarded as good or bad, but instead as helpful or not. While I would advocate developing an understanding of the beliefs that are getting in the way of your confidence, avoid deeply searching for limiting beliefs as you may just develop some that were not there before.

Highly confident people are very able to work around limiting beliefs about their abilities in certain situations. Some will explore other beliefs that may be more helpful to what they want to achieve, while others will simply act in spite of their beliefs.

Many people will see their beliefs as the bars to a prison of low confidence. The initial step is not to change their beliefs but to get them to understand that the prison only exists in their minds. When this kind of mental construct is created the only answer is to try and fight our way out. By developing an understanding that beliefs are just another type of thought you are thinking regularly, then it becomes easy to develop new beliefs or act in spite of them.

10 PERFECT YOU

You're lucky enough to be different, never change.
Taylor Swift

A reflection on my school days has helped to crystallize my thoughts about the perfection or otherwise of human beings. I didn't have a terrible education, my schools were good and I was a decent student. Yet no matter how hard I tried or how well I performed there was always something else I was being told I should do better. At six years old I remember being told I was a silly, silly boy, at eight that I needed to try harder and at eleven I was informed that I would never amount to anything. I don't think that these were particularly bad teachers, but they are examples of a culture that sets us up to focus on and look for our imperfections.

Sadly this often continues into adulthood. As you can imagine I am a huge advocate of personal development, but this should never imply that you need fixing or are broken. Some approaches to therapy and psychology seem to imply the opposite. My absolute belief is that personal development is about making something wonderful even better. You are a diamond and applying the learning from this book simply helps to polish that diamond.

I always operate from a helpful belief that everyone has all of the resources they need to achieve what they want to achieve. That includes you. No matter what challenges you have faced during your life, they do not define you or limit what you can achieve. However difficult circumstances are for you, you are still fundamentally OK. You might not feel OK now and I am not invalidating or being dismissive of the scale of the problems that you or anyone else may face, but I think it is fundamentally unhelpful to think that you can't recover from these challenging times. You can recover, most people do and throughout any difficulties human beings remain fundamentally perfect.

I am aware that while people feel out of touch with a sense of perfection, it is particularly difficult to trigger their state of confidence. That is what this chapter is designed to do, to help you focus on everything that is right with you and keep you connected with your ideal inner state.

I AM ALRIGHT

It's only right to start this section with a question from my coach and mentor and one of the greatest coaches on the planet, Michael Neill: 'How many babies do you know that are in therapy?'

Provided they are fed and watered, the human baby's natural state is one of wellbeing. I like to think of it as a state of being completely OK. Not OK in the British 'not too bad' sense, but instead one of perfection. Everything is completely OK.

This is a great place to start, but on the journey to feeling a genuine deep confidence it is even more powerful to realize that this state of wellbeing never leaves us. It is your default state and always there for you to access. You may not always be aware that it is there as life's challenges and your thinking about them get in the way of your connection with it but the core sense of 'I am alright' is alive in everyone.

I would encourage you to focus on this the next time your confidence seriously wavers. At the moment when a lack confidence creeps in, notice where in your body you actually do feel OK. You will find it somewhere and once you notice it there that sense of OK will start to spread through your body again.

FOCUS ON EVERYTHING THAT IS RIGHT WITH YOU

What is your best physical feature? How about your finest character trait? I would like to think that you could identify one of each, but if you were going list everything that is great about you how easy would you find it? Many people find it much easier to think about their flaws than their qualities and here-in lies a key confidence challenge. If you only notice what you perceive to be wrong with you, then confidence is never likely to be a state you remain in for long.

One of my favourite experiences of exploring this was with a professional footballer who had a reputation for being arrogant and difficult to manage. I asked him to list as many positive character traits as possible and all of the physical aspects that he was proud of. The lists were reasonably long but he hadn't realized that he had changed to listing negatives halfway through.

If focusing on everything that is right with you is a challenge now is a great time to make your list. Include both positive physical attributes and character traits. There are three things to look out for when you are completing this exercise:

1. How many attributes did you manage to list?
2. How comfortable did you find completing the exercise?
3. Is there anything on the list that surprised you?

Highly confident people don't write lists but they are just as comfortable in focusing on their positive characteristics and anything they want to improve.

AVOID PERFECTIONISM

Over the years I have arrived at the conclusion that perfectionism is a curse. I've worked with and coached many perfectionists and been married to one for over a decade! I am yet to meet one who enjoys their necessity for perfection.

The *Oxford English Dictionary* describes a perfectionist as 'a person who refuses to accept any standard short of perfection'. In other words, only 100 per cent right is right. The challenge is of course that life and the world aren't perfect. So to constantly strive for it will usually leave people feeling tired, disappointed and let down.

If this resonates with you, then working to reduce the desire for flawlessness will be incredibly useful. What in your life would it be useful to be less of a perfectionist in? Start with something simple that wouldn't matter to anyone but you (one of my clients took three months to get over the fact they weren't allowed to hang their clothes in order of both size and colour, so even this can be a challenge). Then work up to recognizing the positive traits in the imperfection of yourself and others.

I am not saying that highly confident people are sloppy, shoddy or are completely happy with their flaws and those of others. In some instances I appreciate perfectionism. I once was invited to work with a nuclear energy business and I really appreciated their obsession with perfection. However, I do also see the price perfectionists pay for their dedication to everything being just right. As well as the drag on energy the challenge in decision-making and the frustration with not being able to just get things done, it also damages confidence in many instances.

Putting it all together

One of the most challenging personal development exercises I have ever been given was to look in the mirror every day for a month and tell myself that I loved myself. I haven't gone so far as to give you this exercise – it was particularly stretching for me – but I do remember it triggering a useful train of thoughts about just what there was for me to love about me. All too often others will point out our imperfections and all too often we will then continue to focus on those imperfections while forgetting about the positive attributes.

It is this kind of thinking that clouds our connection with our default state. This state of being blissfully OK stays with us throughout our lives. No matter how things are in life you are fundamentally perfect as you are. While self-improvement is a good thing, especially the building of a constant and consistent state of confidence, this doesn't mean that you are in any way lacking. It simply shows that you have the ability to make your amazing self even better.

11 THE DETAIL OF YOUR CONFIDENCE

If you're presenting yourself with confidence, you can pull off pretty much anything.

Katy Perry

If by now you aren't crystal clear in your understanding that confidence is a state, then I'd recommend that you go back to the start and read Chapter 1 again. This fundamental understanding really is the foundation of mastering your confidence.

Having a deeper awareness of what your confidence is like will put you on the fast track to self-assurance whenever you need it. This chapter will help you to become really familiar with the component parts of your personal version of the state of confidence and how it shows up in your body and mind.

For a moment, I would like you to focus on your memories. I am certain, because of my understanding of the brain, that if you think of your most powerful memory it will be a rich and multi-faceted memory. It will have detail to it and you are likely to experience that memory in all of the senses – even though it is just in your head. In order for memories to be strong they must be multi-sensory when they are created. In exploring and understanding this detail and how it aligns to your mental states you can understand more about your confidence.

To prepare for the rest of this chapter I would like you to revisit a specific memory. I would like you to think about your favourite holiday ever. Now go to a specific time or moment from that holiday. Focus on the memory for a moment. Notice the pictures that you are making in your head. What are the colours like? Are they bright or dull? Are the pictures moving or still? Do they have a frame around them or do they surround you? What else do you notice when you focus on the pictures?

Now notice the sounds in the memory. Where in your head do you hear the sounds? In front of you, behind you, to the side or all around? Notice the volume, pitch and tone of the sounds.

Finally notice the feelings that this memory has generated. Where in your body are you noticing the feelings? Be really specific. What direction does it seem that the feelings are moving? Do the feelings have a texture or temperature?

The ability to notice feelings in this detail will help you to understand your confidence more than ever before.

EXPLORE YOUR DETAIL DIFFERENCES

In order to quickly understand the differences between your sensory focus when you are confident compared to when you aren't, try this experiment. It will be most effective if you can familiarize yourself with the questions, then close your eyes when doing each part of the exploration.

Think of an event in the past when you felt less than confident. Really associate into it, and see it through your own eyes, as if it were happening now. Notice what the pictures are like:

- Are they moving or still?
- How successful are you seeing yourself being?
- What are the colours, contrast and brightness like?

Now focus on the sounds.

- What kinds of things are you hearing? Are they supportive or not?
- Notice the volume and pitch of what you can hear.
- Also notice where the sounds are coming from.

Finally take notice of what feelings this has generated in you.

- Are they familiar?
- What would you label them as?
- Where specifically in the body are they?
- Are they moving or still? Do they have a shape?

Having noticed the pictures, sounds and feelings that you were focusing on, change your physiology completely for a moment before moving onto the second part. Stand up and move around, even sitting in a different position will help. When you've shaken off the feeling of unconfident, then you're ready to move on to the next part.

Now think of an event in the past in which you felt supremely confident. Again associate into it, see it through your own eyes, as if it were happening now.

Now notice what the pictures are like.

- Are they moving or still?
- How successful are you seeing yourself being?
- What are the colours, contrast and brightness like?

Again move onto the sounds.

- What kinds of things are you hearing? Are they supportive now?
- Notice the volume and pitch of what you can hear.
- Also notice where the sounds are coming from.

Now take notice of what feelings this has generated in you.

- Are they familiar?
- What would you label them as?
- Where specifically in the body are they?
- Are they moving or still? Do they have a shape?

You will have quickly noticed some specific differences in the sensory detail between confident and unconfident. When I first worked with a professional footballer using this framework he quickly found himself running a number of negative 'strategies'. His internal pictures were all of the situation going badly. He was performing poorly and others were showing a much higher level of ability. His internal dialogue had switched to negative and critical, he was hearing himself complain, and imagining his manager pointing out his weaknesses. Finally he had a significant knot in his stomach – no surprise bearing in mind what he was focusing on!

I then had him focus on the experience that he had full confidence in. Within seconds his internal pictures had changed. In addition to the internal pictures now showing success and the whole scenario going well, they were also brighter and clearer; mentally it was a sunny day! The auditory tape had changed too; now his internal dialogue was positive and supportive as was the imagined language of those around him. Finally, and most interestingly for me, the knot had moved. Rather than the intense feeling in his stomach, it was now an equally intense feeling in his chest – the same one he gets whenever he is excited!

USE THE DETAIL FOR INSTANT CONFIDENCE

This client found his key focus differences for fear and excitement and confident and unconfident. The differences between the two will vary from person to person, but what remains the same is your ability to change the focus.

This is a great time to remember that the brain does not differentiate time easily. The same neural networks are fired up when we remember a time from the past and when we imagine a time in the future. This ambiguity in the brain means that we can apply the learning from this chapter in three ways:

1. **In the moment.** If you notice that you are running your unconfident sensory programmes, then you can change them. In the example of the footballer this would include imagining the sun shining brighter, some really positive self-talk and making sure that knot moved from his stomach up to his chest to trigger his feeling of confidence and excitement.

2. **To feel at your brilliantly confident best about future events.** When you think about a situation in the future, which set of strategies do you notice kicking in? By ensuring you are seeing, hearing and feeling the event in the detail of your confidence, you are dramatically increasing the likelihood of being confident when the time comes.

3. **To change how you feel about events from the past.** If you take an event from the past and change the details of that memory to those that would be triggered in a confident memory, then you can begin changing how that memory is stored and its emotional impact. This is particularly useful and worth practising if you have a specific memory that consistently impacts on your overall confidence.

SPIN YOUR FEELINGS

There is one additional technique that can help change the detail of your state of confidence in seconds. Some years ago when I began studying modern psychologies, I observed a couple of leaders in the field of Neuro-Lingustic Programming helping clients to spin their feelings to great effect.

This involved the person being coached in identifying the direction that a feeling was moving in their body and changing its direction to influence the emotional state connected to it.

Try this on the feeling you associated with the less confident memory from the earlier experiment. When you notice which way the feeling is moving imagine gently slowing it down and then getting it to move in the opposite direction. As you do this you'll notice a different, more useful state being triggered. If you practise this ahead of time you will also be able to do it live as you approach challenging situations and no one else will ever know.

Putting it all together

Every state that we experience has its own detail. Our internal pictures will have different degrees of clarity, movement and intensity. Sounds will appear in different places around our heads and change in volume tone and cadence. Feelings will appear to move differently through the body starting in different places and have different textures. By building our awareness of the detail of our confidence we can learn to master it as a state to access and intensify at any moment. We can switch quickly away from a lack of confidence and even change our experience of an event from the past. While this requires some time, attention and practice, the benefits are huge especially if confidence has been a long-term issue and prior to reading this book you thought that it would take some outside influence to build it. I would also particularly recommend mastering this practice if confidence directly affects your performance in your job. I have coached professional athletes, performers and public speakers through the process with huge rewards.

12 CONFIDENCE COMES FROM CALM

Be like a duck. Calm on the surface, but always paddling like the dickens underneath.
Michael Caine

It is fascinating to see the reactions of those I work with to the notion of relaxing. In the late 20th century relaxation in the Western world was often seen as the domain of those with hippie tendencies. While there is a greater acceptance in the 21st century of the benefits of purposeful relaxing most still see it as an extra-curricular lack of activity to fit around normal life.

If this sounds familiar to you, a quick examination of relaxing should reset your attitudes and move you to slowing down in more areas of your life.

I want to make clear that being pro-calm doesn't mean being anti-busy or even anti-fast. The thought that calm and quick are opposites is a result of the 20th-century view of calm. Dictionary antonyms of calm include *frenzied*, *turbulent*, *violent* and *wild*. It's possible to be energetic and calm. My family have been involved in the RNLI for most of their lives and I have seen my eldest brother working in the gravest of emergency situations at sea. He is completely focused with a sense of calm but with absolute urgency.

This chapter shares tips to restore calmness and to relax without having to retreat under a tree for days to meditate. I see relaxation and calmness as siblings from the same family. Relaxation generally has a slower pace to it. Both have health benefits in their combating the impact of stress-related issues such as sleep and eating disorders, problems with the skin and longer term health issues affecting the heart. All of these will inhibit your confidence. By practising the tips in this chapter you will see other positive results too. You are likely to find yourself thinking more clearly and remaining more rational when under pressure.

I would recommend reading this chapter in an environment where you can experiment with the tips given here quickly. Ideally this would be in a fairly quiet private space. If this isn't possible the first time you read it, then be sure to revisit another time when you can.

BREATHE CALMLY

Some years ago I attended a workshop on breaking through mental barriers in business. All was going well until the facilitator suggested that the group of around 100 people learn some breathing techniques. I associated this method of relaxation with weekend retreats rather than business programmes. I was very wrong.

This simple technique helps me to sleep when travelling and to prepare for large presentations. I have used it to calm myself before I settled my baby to sleep and to get ready for some very tough one-to-one conversations. Clients have credited this technique with increasing their run rate (cricketers), having more energy during games (footballers) and being able to face a barrage of questions from a tyrannical managing director. Best of all it is short and very easy.

Get ready by sitting in a chair, in a position that is comfortable for you, with both feet flat on the floor. When you are comfortable follow this process:

1. Breathe in for your own count of eight.
2. Hold the breath in for your own count of eight.
3. Breathe out for your own count of eight. Make sure you breathe all of the air out; you might need to 'push' it out.
4. Hold, with no air in for your own count of four.
5. Repeat steps 1–4 twice more.

That is the whole technique! It is very simple and very powerful.

You will find the more you practise, the calmer it will help you to be. I find it even more powerful if I can close my eyes when I am going through the 8-8-8-4 process, but if that isn't possible then focus on the breathing pattern.

Here are just a few examples of situations where it will help:

- Before a presentation. It will relax you and help regulate your breathing to allow you to deliver the presentation more effectively and powerfully.
- Whenever you feel overwhelmed.
- Before you start a key task to help you focus and work more effectively.
- Before you exercise.
- To relax at the end of the day.
- To prepare for a difficult discussion or meeting at home or work.
- Any other time it would be useful to be focused and relaxed.

USE MUSIC TO RELAX

How does music impact on your mood? My guess is that you have a piece of music that, if you hear it, automatically lifts your mood and energy levels. But do you have a piece of music that automatically relaxes and calms you? Music has a huge impact on our biology. In simple terms, our brainwave patterns and heart rate will align with the beats per minute of any piece of music we are listening to. This is known as entrainment. While musical preference can be a factor, it is important to know that you don't have to love a piece of music for it to have a relaxing effect on you. Baroque music and, more specifically, music with a tempo of 60 beats per minute, has long been considered to be ideal for inducing relaxing states. Scientists in Manchester, England, recently claimed to have made the most relaxing tune in history. The song, called 'Weightless' and compiled by Marconi Unicorn, induced a deeper state of relaxation than any other they tested.

I would highly recommend creating your own relaxation playlist. Technology can really help us with this. You can make technically fantastic relaxation playlists by searching for music with a bpm of 60. A quick Google search will provide you with a huge choice. You can also use a music download system like iTunes or Amazon to create a specific playlist for your mp3 or mp4 player. If you do have strong musical preferences then I would recommend that you keep your selection quite neutral although there are more contemporary tunes that can be relaxing, these include 'Mellomaniac' (Chill Out Mix) by DJ Shah, 'Watermark' by Enya, 'We Can Fly' by Café Del Mar and 'Airstream' by Electra.

SWITCH STUFF OFF

The final relaxation strategy in this chapter is very practical but usually completely overlooked in the modern world in which we live. We live in the most stimulated environment in history. Multitasking is the norm. There are evenings where I have found myself watching television while reading emails on my laptop and posting on social media on my telephone. I have clients for whom this is the norm yet they wonder why they find it a challenge to relax.

Research has shown that night time light exposure suppresses the production of melatonin which is the major hormone that controls sleep and wake cycles. A suppression of melatonin can also have longer reaching impacts on your weight, heart and immune system. The type of light typically emitted by devices such as iPhones, tablets, LCD televisions and computer screens is close to the peak sensitivity of melatonin suppression. Add this science to the fact that when we are looking at tablets, smartphones or computers it is typically to engage in things that will stimulate our brains and even our relaxing TV watching will usually be a stimulating drama or comedy, so it is easy to see that we are making real relaxation difficult.

So the strategy is simple. Switch it off. We are a generation that has forgotten that switching off a mobile device does not mean we miss things; it means that we can get to it another time. Many people have the capacity to record their favourite television drama, yet feel the need to stay up and watch it.

Essentially I am saying that you should put yourself back in control of your choices and be aware of what really works for you and what doesn't. If you find it a challenge to relax, then try switching off your technology earlier and taking a relaxing bath and notice the difference.

Putting it all together

Confidence rarely looks rushed. Even at times of challenge the highly confident person appears composed. They are able to be fully activated, aware and alert when required and able to relax, switch off and are calm when the time is right. We live in a world where busy is the norm and you may be one of many people who find it challenging to take your foot off the proverbial gas. The ability to relax, though, is a desirable attribute and if you regularly find yourself stressed or over-activated for the task at hand or the environment that you are in, then I would highly recommend that you use this chapter to begin the journey to make calm a state that you are in more of the time. Confidence is a state that requires clear thinking and the ninety miles an hour mind-chatter of a person who is always on full and struggles to sleep are rarely a good mix. So when would be a good time to start to relax?

13 INNATE CONFIDENCE

You can't connect the dots looking forward, you can only connect them looking backwards. So you have to trust that the dots will somehow connect in your future. You have to trust in something: your gut, destiny, life, karma, whatever. Because believing that the dots will connect down the road will give you the confidence to follow your heart, even when it leads you off the well-worn path.

Steve Jobs

Have you ever wondered how tiny seeds can grow into huge trees that last thousands of years? I don't mean the process of converting food and light but how that tree knows it needs to do that? How does an acorn know how to grow into an oak rather than a pine? How does your mouth know when to water? I know why we sweat, but not how my body learned to do it. I have never had to force my body to do it; it just does. Even the simplest of processes like blinking. Have you ever considered how the eyelids of a tiny baby know how to do this at just the right time and at just the right pace?

When you consider these small and seemingly insignificant examples, it begins to become apparent there is some kind of intelligence to the universe and to us as human beings. Most people agree that there is some kind of greater force at play. Some think it is a spiritual one, some call it nature, others believe in a range of forces that control the flow of our life and destiny.

What I am sure of is that you, like everyone else, have an innate intelligence and confidence that does its best to take care of you. I am pretty sure that you have never had to concentrate on a cut to make it heal. Over time it just will. If you are a mother, the fear of having a child must at some point have been overridden by the confidence that you could do it.

The realization that this innate intelligence is alive in you and everyone and everything around you will play a huge part in cementing your confidence. When you listen calmly enough and well enough to what your intuition is saying you will always do the right thing. This chapter aims to help you to hear that still small voice within more of the time, but first, if you still doubt your innate intelligence please pause for a moment and pay attention to your breathing.

How do you know how to do that?

CONNECT WITH YOUR INTELLIGENCE

One of the defining factors in the most confident people I work with is that they are easily able to tell the difference between the type of mind-chatter that runs around our heads whenever there is pressure, or a decision, to be made and their real intelligence. Learning this distinction is a huge step to securing your genuine long-term confidence.

If you aren't easily aware of this intuitive voice or feeling, then take the first step now to try to connect with it.

1. Sit comfortably in your seat or lie comfortably in your bed.
2. Place the book somewhere that you can read it with out holding it.
3. Notice any chatter that is going on in your mind. Pay attention to the pitch, pace and tone of that internal voice.
4. Now become aware of your breathing. For a minute or so just pay attention to its gentle rise and fall.
5. Notice the sensations of your body against your chair or bed, for example the feeling of your arms against the arms of chair or the backs of your legs touching your bed.
6. Become aware of the feeling of blinking as it happens.
7. Spend another moment experiencing these newly noticed sensations.
8. Now notice how you are noticing them. Beyond any mind-chatter that is still there and beyond your body's physical connection with the environment you have an awareness of yourself. Pay attention to it. Notice what that is like for you.

Even the most sceptical clients that I take through this exercise get a pleasant surprise when they notice the first step to a real connection with the intelligence that has guided you through the best times of your life.

PUT YOUR INNATE INTELLIGENCE INTO ACTION

Think of a decision that you have been wrestling with for some time. Why have you found it hard to move forward with it? My guess is that your internal chatter has got in the way of your more intelligent self. Having just completed the previous exercise you may already have a clearer idea of the next step. If not run through the exercise again and when you reach the final step of the process ask yourself the question, 'What is the best next step?' Notice what occurs to you, not from the mind-chatter but from the other awareness.

This isn't to say that every time you have a decision to make that you have to stop and relax into a chair. I am simply helping you to make a distinction that the highly confident seem to do easily. When you connect more readily to your innate intelligence you are able to make better decisions and take better actions.

The next time you are in a challenging situation with your family, pay attention to your more intelligent self, ignoring the mind-chatter that inevitably starts in these situations. Act based on that intuitive voice and notice the difference in your response and the impact on the situation.

In challenging business meetings listen past the mind-talk that can confuse or ignite situations for the stiller guide that will help you make a more valuable contribution. It is not always easy, especially if you haven't been aware of it before, but it is always valuable for you and others.

SEE THE INTELLIGENCE OF OTHERS

You will have people in your life who always seem to be at their most intelligent best. They always seem to know the right thing to do and are at ease making even the biggest decisions.

Then there will be others around you who don't seem to have connected with their more intelligent self for some time. They often make bad decisions or do the wrong thing even when the right thing seems blindingly obvious to everyone around them. You may find it difficult to believe they have an intuition that guides them, and it may seem like the indelible intelligence of the universe has passed them by.

As your confidence and innate intelligence grow you may find that connecting with these people becomes an increasing challenge. This is a particular issue if this person is a family member, work colleague or client. Here are three additional steps to help you be at your best around these people and even help them to tune into their intuition.

See their positive intent

Every behaviour has or once had a positive intent. It serves a purpose to that person even if we believe that purpose is misguided. For example the positive intention behind aggressive behaviour is often protection. The positive intention or purpose behind fear is usually safety. By seeing the positive intent behind behaviour we can deal with behaviour more resourcefully.

See them at their best

It is possible that you are only seeing this person when they are at their worst. In busy day-to-day life partners can see each other as they wake and pull themselves around for the day ahead and when they return home from long challenging days at work. You are likely to have work colleagues who you only meet in difficult business meetings.

Take the time to connect with people when they have the opportunities to be at their best. This may be at different times of the day or in different environments.

Feedback on the positive

Take the time to let them know specifically when you have seen them at their best. Give feedback on positive behaviours or when you think their decisions or actions have had a positive impact.

This could be just the trigger they need to understand what they do when they are at their best and to do more of it. They will appreciate you more too.

Putting it all together

In the book *Big Mind Big Heart,* Zen master Dennis Genpo Merzel says: 'There is a transcendent awareness, a Big Mind, a Big Heart, present and readily accessible to each and everyone of us. When we realize it, we see it is the source of true peace, happiness, satisfaction, courage and joy.' It is this awareness that I want to connect clients with. While peace, happiness, satisfaction, courage and joy are the most noble of pursuits I want every reader to use this intelligence to make a difference to their day-to-day, moment-by-moment activities. Connecting with your most intelligent self leads to better relationships, more successful businesses and healthier lives.

This is in no way a fluffy topic; a reader who sees this as 'tree-huggy' is missing the practical impact of being connected to the same intelligence that quite literally makes the world go around. Your innate intelligence feeds your confidence and I believe the reverse is also true. The truly confident person is more easily able to pay attention to their smartest self. This is a most amazing loop to be going around where your intuition feeds your confidence and your confidence connects you more readily with what Gandhi called your 'still small voice within'.

14 GET MORE OF WHAT YOU FOCUS ON

Optimism is the faith that leads to achievement.
Nothing can be done without hope and confidence.
Helen Keller

I'd like to start this chapter with three quick mental exercises. If it is safe to do so, stop what you are doing for a few minutes and reflect on the last 24 hours. Ask yourself the question, 'How did I do'? With no other particular criteria, just a simple review of the last day and night, how was it and how were you?

Now for a further moment, reflect on your reflections. Did you notice more of what went well or what didn't? Did you see more of the things you did well, no matter how big or small, or the things that didn't go as you would have liked?

Finally for now I would like you to cast your mind forward over the next 24 hours or so. Think about the things you will be doing. Run them through your head as if they were happening now. Notice again whether things are generally going well or badly and how you are imagining yourself doing in these situations.

Unless you are an unusually positive and confident person you are likely to have noticed some good and some bad, but it is important to be aware of where you placed the emphasis. If you noticed more things going badly and your role in those things happening, you will be negatively impacting on your confidence.

There is an important fact about the brain that those rich in confidence know and tap into to help maintain and grow that precious state.

The brain is built to follow commands that it is given.

When we focus on some data the brain will take this as a directive to find more evidence or information to prove that data to be true. When applied specifically to confidence, this means that the brain will search for more examples of what you focus on most. If in your reflection at the beginning of this chapter you thought most about the things that didn't go well and in particular your role in them, the likelihood is that your brain is currently paying more attention to situations that will negatively affect your confidence. It will also be filtering out some positive experiences that would help build your confidence.

FILTERING IN POSITIVE EXPERIENCES

Various research suggests that the brain processes a huge amount of data every second. I have seen estimates of between 20 million and 400 billion pieces of information being processed every second. However, we are only consciously aware of a small portion of these processes. The most reliable research that I am aware of suggests an awareness of around 20 pieces of information every second. Our brains are designed to filter out a huge amount of data so there are memories and live experiences that we are never aware of. People who are confident tend to notice and remember more experiences that are positive and affirming, while one of the challenges of being low on confidence is that the brain provides more data to sustain that state.

This gives more evidence to support the idea that a conscious routine of noticing what has gone well on a day-to-day basis will create a solid platform for confidence. The process of doing this will help us into that state on a more regular basis and will also help to programme the brain to notice more of the positive actions and results, which in turn will further grow our confidence.

CONNECT THE PAST, THE PRESENT AND THE FUTURE

Without being a neuroscientist you know that reflecting on certain memories triggers certain emotions. You will also be aware that your thoughts about live situations trigger certain emotions too. I am certain that at some point you have imagined yourself in a particular situation in the future with certain emotions being triggered.

When you realize that you have done this naturally it becomes unsurprising to learn that the brain does not differentiate between imagination, memory and current experience. When you remember a situation in the past when you were confident exactly the same neuro-wiring is used as when you imagine yourself being hugely confident. When you feel confident in the moment, that same wiring is activated. This knowledge is wonderfully useful in thinking your world to life. You get the same confidence boost from imagining yourself doing something confidently, as you do when you remember yourself doing something confidently.

The brain connects the activity and the feeling that you have as if it actually happened. This means a neural pathway connecting your physical ability to do whatever the activity is and the state of confidence already exists. When you come to do it you will automatically feel confident.

Practise mentally rehearsing. Regularly see, hear and feel yourself doing things confidently to create the pathway more deeply. When you do the activity and feel confident, this will reinforce it even further and even more strongly, but, you don't need to wait until the first time you do something to create the state of your confidence in the brain connected with that activity.

REHEARSE THE RIGHT PHYSIOLOGY

Candice Pert is a Nobel-nominated neuroscientist and her work has been core to my understanding of the impact of our thinking on the body and its physiology. Dr Pert is often quoted as saying 'the brain is located within and throughout the body'. Her ground-breaking work, captured in *Molecules of Emotion*, confirmed what many social psychologists and modern therapists had known for sometime – that your brain programmes your body. There are numerous sporting studies that underline the fact that mental rehearsal does even more than create states and memory paths to help you function well and confidently in certain situations. Put simply, this mental preparation programmes your physiology ahead of time.

Let's apply this to a situation that many people feel they need more confidence in – presenting to large audiences. From this chapter so far you will already know that remembering a time when you have done something similar and imagining your presentation in detail will help you feel confident and be mentally prepared. You can now be sure that by seeing yourself walking on to the stage with a straight posture and steady strides will programme your muscles and increase the likelihood of your maintaining this physiology. The mental rehearsal of hearing your voice steady, calm and powerful will again trigger an internal reaction that primes your vocal apparatus to do exactly this. Throughout the book you will learn even more about the impact your physiology has on the chemistry of your brain, but for now you can be sure that mental practice impacts significantly on your body's performance.

Putting it all together

Thinking your world to life means more than a bit of visualization. It is a way to become the pilot and the plane of your confidence. A combination of mental rehearsal of confidence in situations and detailed mental review of confident times from the past will do three crucial things:

1. Create a connection in your brain between what you want to do and the state of confidence.
2. Programme your brain to filter in more examples of you at your confident best and notice less examples of confidence lacking.
3. Prepare you physiologically for a confident experience.

The great news is that you don't have to spend hours and hours to create this programming. My experience is that short, focused sessions are better than long-winded visualizations. In fact most clients I work with report that five minutes a day just after they have woken up or when they are settling down for sleep has the biggest impact. It is important to do this thinking as if you were in the situation, seeing it through your own eyes, rather than watching yourself in the situation, as if on a TV screen. In fact this is a secret of confidence in itself. Confident people tend to see themselves performing well in an associated way (through their own eyes) and performing badly in a disassociated way (as if they were watching themselves from a distance). People who find confidence difficult to experience often have the opposite pattern. Now is a great time to ensure that your pattern is that of the confident person you are becoming.

15 CREATE A CONFIDENT FUTURE

To reach a port, we must sail – Sail, not tie at anchor – Sail, not drift.
Franklin D. Roosevelt

Before you start this chapter, make sure that you have something to write with close to hand. You are about to discover a simple but powerful tool that will significantly increase the chances of bringing any life goals to life. Whether you are working on confidence in a specific area or your confidence overall, this small shift in how you set goals and talk about the future will make a big difference.

Before I explain it in more detail, it's useful to do the following quick exercise. Choose one area of your life and write down four or five goals that would be great to achieve in that area. For example:

Life area – health and fitness:

- Lose 10 lbs.
- Exercise for 20 minutes three times a week.
- Drink 2 litres of water every day.
- Cut out processed carbs for two weeks every month.

Now write the same list but in the present tense, as if it has happened already.

Life area – health and fitness:

- I have lost 10 lbs.
- I exercise for 20 minutes three times a week, every week.
- I am fully hydrated. I drink 2 litres of water every day.
- For two weeks every month I eat completely clean, cutting out all processed food.

Review your two lists. Even though I have asked you to do this as a quick exercise, notice which list gives you more energy. Notice which list gives you the greater feeling of motivation and which list triggers more ideas of which actions to take.

There is something powerful in creating goals and aspirations in the present tense. Despite the brain's inability to differentiate well between the tenses it does react more strongly to the immediate. It will search more quickly for more data relating to a goal that is created as if it is happening now. A goal written in this tense will feel closer or more realistic. I often notice a physiological difference in clients' reactions to their goals when written in the present tense. When goals are written in the future I see clients shuffling, shaking their heads or squinting as they struggle to work out how they are going to achieve it. When the same client talks about the same goals in the present tense I see them moving forward, smiling and a small quickening in pace or movement; all from a change in tense.

YOUR CONFIDENT FUTURE HISTORY

The future history exercise is one that is brilliant and spooky. Many of the most confident and most successful people that I know use the exercise to set the scene for the year ahead in their career or life. One professional footballer credited this process as the main reason he got a £2 million transfer to a Premier League club in England.

The best thing is that the process works. The second best thing is that it is super simple. Choose a point in time in the future that is appropriate for you to set goals to. Somewhere between a year and eighteen months seems to work best for most people I work with. It is most useful to choose a specific date. It is also helpful to choose somewhere you would love to be on that date in the future. Somewhere that you love being at that time of year is best. Now choose someone in your life that you could write a letter to about what you've achieved in your life. It is useful for it to be someone significant but not someone who triggers any sort of negative emotion or embarrassment. It is worth noting that you aren't actually going to send the letter, it is simply useful for the process to have someone to write it to. If you can't think of anyone, write the letter to yourself. Now imagine you are able to fast-forward through time to that date and answer this question:

Imagine it is (your date) and you are the most confident version of yourself that you could ever have imagined being. As you sit (in your chosen place) relaxing, you realize that this genuine and almost permanent sense of confidence has positively impacted on every area of your life, including family, health, your financial situation, work and every other area of your life you can imagine. Write a letter to (your chosen person) describing your life as it is now in as much rich detail as possible. Also include some of the major milestones over the last year or so that have brought you to where you are now.

DREAM BOARDS

A development of this process is to create your future history in a visual format that you can refer to consistently. For most adults it will have been many years since you created a montage of any sort, but this is a perfect opportunity to revisit your childhood in pursuit of real confidence. As with the previous process it is useful to have a specific point in the future your dream board is created for. Then as you imagine the impact of being your most confident self, create a montage of the key ways that this will manifest. Make the dream board as a rich and engaging as possible. This is not the time to be overly logical or reserved in any way.

I know some families who create dream boards together at the beginning of a new year as a way to cement a shared set of goals for the future. Children will be even less restrained and often set even more aspirational targets; in this process that's no bad thing!

It is important to have your dream board displayed somewhere that you will see it regularly. One personal development guru recommends having it under your pillow and looking at it every morning and evening in the transition between waking and sleeping states. I prefer to have it somewhere that I will see it regularly and unconsciously. I know that my brain will continue to process the data even if I am not aware of it.

PLANNING BACKWARDS

In both the previous strategies in this chapter, we are relying on the brain to unconsciously use these aspirational goals to guide our actions towards achieving them without realizing and there is no doubt that they work for many people. If you want to be even surer of achieving your confident future then create an action plan to bring your confident future history to life. One of the challenges of action planning for many people is that the very creation of the initial small steps towards this huge end goal can in itself demotivate by presenting a stark reminder of how far you have to go.

There is an alternative process for goal setting that can in itself motivate and energize as well as helping you to find creative ways to achieve your goals.

Take one of the elements of the future history that you created in part one of this chapter.

1. Ask yourself this question: 'What was the very last step that I took just before I achieved this goal?' It may take some time to answer this at first but when you have the answer write it down.
2. Now as you think of that answer, ask the question: 'What was the very last step that happened just before this?'
3. As you answer this, ask: 'And the step before that?

Continue the process until you have worked your way back to the starting point. You will have created a whole action plan in reverse order and it will be fuller and more energizing than it would have been if you had created it in the traditional way. If you currently action plan forwards as part of your work, then this reverse process can feel a little counterintuitive; however, with a little practice you may even change how you plan your work process too.

Putting it all together

The brain is an amazing organ that we are only really just beginning to understand. One of the few things that the brain does not do well is distinguish between time frames and tenses. Exploitation of this small loophole can fast-track your journey to genuine and consistent confidence.

Highly confident people or those on the journey to becoming confident can create rich aspirational goals for the future but expressed in the present tense to positively confuse the brain's understanding of how close we are to that goal. The process of creating these future histories, whether in words or pictures, is energizing and motivating in itself.

These future histories can be supported by the creation of action plans – created from the furthest point in the future backwards in time – which will all but guarantee that what can seem like a fantasy when first created will become reality in the most natural way.

16 MAKE PERSONAL DEVELOPMENT A MUST

Absorb what is useful, discard what is not, add what is uniquely your own.

Bruce Lee

My study of the subject of confidence over the last ten years has brought me together with many wonderful people. There are few who I have learned more from and with than Steve Marriott. Steve coaches with razor-sharp precision and works with clients using a powerfully persuasive style that leaves them with no choice but to do the right thing. In this chapter Steve defines beautifully why personal development is a must and shares his strategies for doing it perfectly.

I failed.

I graduated from school in the 5 per cent of my class who made the top 95 per cent look good, and with an A-star in low confidence. If it wasn't enough that I'd 'failed', I compounded my confidence issues by continually valuing everyone else's expertise and authority above my own.

Determined to change this I embarked upon a self-improvement mission and soon found myself regularly trawling the shelves of business and self-help texts as well as following the crowd to every seminar spouting the 'latest' model and method. I learned some fantastic and helpful things. I also wasted a huge amount of time, money and effort on a lot of less useful 'development' fads. My intention in this chapter is to spare you from the dark side of development and show you three ways to make your personal development a must.

So before we begin let me offer you my own definition of 'personal development'.

Personal development should never be the endless acquisition of more and more information. Information in and of itself is relatively useless. Real personal development is all about action; your ongoing development should inspire you to think differently and more creatively, understand yourself and others more deeply, challenge your status quo and ultimately have an impact in your own life as well as the lives of others. If that isn't a recipe for confidence, I don't know what is.

Audacious? I hope so. Scary? Perhaps a little, but in a good way.

I believe personal development is a contact sport, and one that pays dividends to those who play full-out. That's not to say you should attend every seminar, high-fiving and 'Hell Yeah'-ing, and read every book as the unquestionable truth.

The 'what' you choose to develop and how is entirely your choice; whatever your preference my advice is to fully commit to it and apply your whole self to the learning.

A word of caution ... in our world of immediate reward, everyone is looking for the 'fast track' to success. I haven't discovered a magic pill to personal development but here are my strategies to make the journey more fun and help you along the way.

START WITH 'WHY?'

No this isn't a trick question. The biggest reason personal development of any kind fails is because a clear and compelling 'why' hasn't been established. Many of us find ourselves on a merry-go-round of well-meaning and misguided 'advice' and recommendations from others. Maybe your boss wants you to develop a skill or competency, perhaps you've had some 'constructive feedback', even worse you may be following the crowd, after all, if everyone else is doing it …

Your boss is just as apt to make misjudgements as you are. Feedback has a stronger foundation in opinion and judgement than fact and the crowd are rushing to Justin Bieber concerts … enough said?

Successful personal development happens when your drive and reason for doing it come from *within* rather than from external pressure. After all, to 'develop' will require personal application, doing things differently, and investing your own time and effort. All of these factors become disproportionately challenging for us when our reasons for development lie with 'others' and external pressures. When your why begins with *I WANT* then you open up a whole new dimension of self-motivation; one that is not easily diverted and rises to life's challenges.

Want is not a dirty word! Turn your *shoulds* into *musts* and then turn your *musts* into *WANTS*.

Who or what inspires you? I'm not talking about a passing interest here, what are you passionate about? What really lights your fire? By honestly answering these questions you'll gain an insight into where your continued development may lie. Choose things that are important and valuable to you, things that excite you and make a real contribution to your world. Those are the things that will get you out of bed in the morning and give you the courage to persevere where others don't.

BITE OFF MORE THAN YOU CAN CHEW!

Your personal development needs to become a habit, something you do instinctively rather than reactively. It should be compelling, exciting, audacious and a little bit scary, something you think about daily. The best way to achieve this is to use as many of your own resources as possible.

We value things we pay for, and those things we pay more for we place greater value in. When we pay with someone else's resources, we are distanced from the investment and therefore value it less. By putting your own resources on the line, you are naturally going to seek to get maximum value for your investment!

Bite off more than you can chew but not so much that you'll choke. Get out of your comfort zone and spend more money on your development than you can reasonably afford. (That doesn't mean sign your life away on the most expensive programme you can find, rather challenge yourself to make the very best 'investment', something you will work hard to provide a return on.)

Commit more of your own time than you have spare. You have the same amount of hours each day as the most successful people on the planet. Over-committing your time will make you examine and re-evaluate your daily routines more critically. Ask yourself, 'If this were my payroll, does this give me best value?' and surprise yourself at how much time you can find. Just 15 minutes a day is the equivalent of 10 hours or more per month!

The first programme I personally paid for was a significant investment of money, time and effort. Something I could little afford at the time. The result? I was fully present for every minute of the four-day seminar. I worked late into the early hours reading and re-reading the material and created habits from what I learned. Do I still remember the seminar? Yes. Do I use the learning? Absolutely and on a daily basis! Have I created a return on my cash investment? Yes … within my very next contract I won using the learning!

MAKE IT SOCIAL, MAKE IT FUN

Your development has a half-life. It's impossible to remember and deploy everything you learn. There's a lot of truth in the saying, 'If you don't use it you lose it' so the sooner you do something (anything!) with your learning, the more chance you have of hanging on to it.

Learning *with* others, especially friends and colleagues, as well as being more fun than solo learning, places a higher level of accountability for action with you; after all, you're more likely to deliver on commitments you make publicly. You can kid yourself you'll take action but your mates will hold you to it!

Support networks multiply your chances of success. Simply sharing your learnings, achievements and difficulties in a safe environment, with people who care about you or who are sharing the journey with you is one of the best learning activities around...and a huge confidence booster. Buddies are a fantastic source of encouragement, challenge and positive recognition, all vital ingredients to your retention and continuing development.

Learning *with* others is fun; learning *for* others takes your development to a whole other level. Neuroscience is showing us in real-time how our brains encode learning for others at a deeper, more emotional level.

When we learn with the goal of teaching others, retention and understanding is higher than with 'selfish' learning.

Set yourself the challenge to present your learning to someone else, or better still 'teach' it on.

Putting it all together

Your confidence is a direct product of your thinking. If that thinking is a constant reminder of your 'failures' and inadequacies in comparison to others, it should be no surprise that your confidence will suffer. If on the other hand that thinking is a constant reminder of your growth and development and improvement ... then what will be the impact on your confidence?

Growth and development – knowing you are better today than you were last year has long been advocated as a 'need' for all of us. When we stop learning, we stop growing and start dying.

Scientists and researchers are now proposing continuous learning as a defence against age-related illnesses such as Alzheimer's and dementia.

Much of this is yet to be proved by science so for me, if for no other reason than 'being alive', *active, regular* and *meaningful* personal development must be on every confident person's to-do list.

[With thanks for the material in this chapter to Steve Marriott – www.steve-marriott.com]

17 YOU WON'T GET WHAT YOU WANT IF YOU DON'T KNOW WHAT YOU WANT

There are always flowers for those who want to see them.
Henri Matisse

Whether you are in business or sport, education or parenting, the practice of setting goals for yourself or others is a familiar one. My experience is that people with a genuine and consistent sense of confidence goal-set regularly and naturally, and in a way that works best for them. The art and science of finding what works for you is certainly one of the secrets of confident people.

First let us look at why goal-setting works in the first place. Your brain is fundamentally wired to follow commands that it is given. You will see the importance of this predisposition for the brain to obey commands (up to a point) in various other chapters of this book and it is the core factor in understanding the power of goal-setting. Various research suggests that we are exposed to somewhere between 20 million and 400 billion bits of data every second. Our brain can process around 1000 every second and we are consciously aware of around 20 things every second. This deleting and filtering of information and awareness helps us to function. Without it we would effectively be in constant data overwhelm. What we focus on changes what data is filtered in and out of our awareness. I would like you to notice for a moment the temperature of your left little toe. Whatever the temperature is my guess is that you had forgotten you had a left little toe before I brought it back into your awareness. This is a simple example of this brain activity in action.

By setting confidence-related goals you will direct your brain to filter in more information that is relevant to the achievement of those goals. You will also become more aware of resources, skills and abilities that you already have at your disposal.

MAKE THE GOAL COMPELLING FOR YOU

Let me be really clear that I don't believe there is one best way to set goals. There are many systems that profess to be the best. Theories are presented and debunked in equal measure. The nature of human beings means that there will never be a one size fits all for goal-setting, but a choice of good practices that you can combine to be the best process for you.

The single most important question seems to be what will make this goal compelling for you? In some cases it will be the topic of the goal that makes it exciting for you. In others it will be the specificity of it. Some people will prefer making the goal really achievable so that progress can be reviewed, while for others the fun of the pursuit of an outrageous idealistic goal is completely energizing.

Let us explore a simple confidence-related aim to understand what makes goals compelling for you: the goal of walking into a room confidently and feeling confident.

What would have to happen to make that a compelling goal for you? Would it be the specificity of which room with which people under which circumstances? For example, walking into a boardroom full of executives to present a proposal with your heart rate and breathing remaining at a normal level.

If achievable goals energize you, you will be more motivated by setting a number of progressive goals:

Week 1: Walk into a room full of strangers while remaining calm.
Week 2: Walk into a room for a one-to-one conversation with a senior manager while remaining calm.

Week 3: Ask a question in a meeting with executives while remaining calm.

Week 4: Walk in to the room while remaining completely calm.

If you are energized by the process of working towards audacious and unrealistic goals then you might set a goal like 'stride confidently into a board meeting while completely naked and greet each person individually'. I am sure I don't need to say that the aim is not to actually do this, but the game in finding the strategies that would enable you to achieve the goal will make it easy to do something more realistic and sensible.

Choose a confidence goal that is relevant to you and write it in different ways with emphasis on different elements until you find the version that feels most compelling for you.

USE YOUR GOALS AND SHARE THEM APPROPRIATELY

In Chapter 15 we explored the power of creating pictorial representations of your future history. This can be hugely powerful for general goal-setting too. A former boss of mine had a huge collage of all of his goals for the next 12 months set out in a time line. He kept it in a prominent place in his office and was happy to share it with anyone who was interested. This sharing kept him engaged and on track and the visual element made it compelling for him.

My goals tend to be written and in my early days as a leadership consultant my confidence-related goals were a simple list of milestones. I referred to them infrequently but reviewed them monthly. This prevented me from becoming overly obsessed with them but ensured I made regular progress.

This should emphasize again that there is not one ideal format for presenting goals or for how often they should be reviewed. There will be a preferred process for you and I would encourage you to try different approaches to find the one that energizes you most.

The same applies to whether you should share your confidence goals with others. Throughout my formative years in the fields of personal development the mantra was to share your goals. The belief was that the more people you shared them with the more likely you were to follow through with the actions required to achieve that goal. In more recent times the belief has switched with social psychologists citing experiments showing that the process of sharing tricks the brain into believing you have already taken action or, worse, that scorn from others will demotivate you from following through, showing that the process of sharing goals can trick the brain into believing you have already achieved them. Having those that you share them with ridicule the goals will also demotivate and disengage.

Both of these views are relevant and over-simplistic. For example, if someone tells you that you won't achieve something, does this make you more likely to go out and prove them wrong or does it de-energize you? Do all people have the same impact on you? For each goal that you set think carefully about who would be most useful to share it with. You don't have to share any with anyone, but I usually find that there is someone in my social or business network who is likely to hold me accountable to action or motivate me to do so.

Goals should motivate and engage you into action; being mindful of how you use them and who you share them with will add fuel to them.

TRY MAKING FAILURE-BASED GOALS

The most consistent theme in studies that question the power of goals is the stress that goals or their non-achievement can cause. In my view this isn't a challenge with goal-setting, but in the goals themselves. Goals should energize and engage. They should trigger a desire to do something. If your goals do anything other than this, go back to the beginning of this chapter and revise them with the ideas and advice in mind.

It is also useful to know that some people are motivated by the desire to achieve goals and others are motivated by the desire not to fail. This doesn't change the impact of goals, but will influence how you write or create them. Think for a moment about what gives you the energy to take action. Is it the desire to move towards, having things or achieving, or is it about moving away from where you are now and not settling for what you have? If you are motivated by moving away from where you are now, then be sure to integrate that language into your goals.

Putting it all together

Well-executed goal-setting is a powerful tool in any part of life. If you are in pursuit of a strong sense of confidence, then you can only know when you have achieved what you set out to do by having goals in place that clearly define what confidence looks, sounds and feels like for you.

There is no single best formula for the creation and review of goals. You have to use the best of what we know works for some, to create the recipe that fits you perfectly. Goal-setting is a regular practice for the confident. In some cases they don't realize they do it. They consistently set and adjust their goals and take their achievement as a sign of progress. Others consciously set goals and use them as fuel for growth and success.

Goals should create energy and the most confident people understand that. They also understand that none-achievement of the goal does not mean failure. You define your goals, your goals do not define you.

18 FOCUS ON WHAT YOU CAN CHANGE

There are three constants in life ...Change, choice and principles.

Stephen Covey

Many of you will be familiar with the opening few lines of the serenity prayer:

God grant me the serenity to
accept the things I cannot change;
courage to change the things I can;
and wisdom to know the difference.

(From the 'Serenity Prayer' by Reinhold Niebuhr)

These few lines encapsulate beautifully one of the characteristics of highly confident people. They have developed the ability to focus on changing the areas of their life that they can exercise some control over, not worrying about the areas that they can't.

The perception of a lack of choice is one of the biggest inhibitors of confidence. It can be mentally paralysing and this is why I love the principle that 'any choice is better than no choice'.

Dr Stephen Covey presented a quite wonderful framework to develop this way of thinking in his seminal book *The 7 Habits of Highly Effective People*.

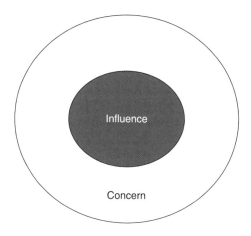

The influence circle represents all of the things that you can make a difference to in any situation or area of your life. The concern circle represents everything that causes concern that you can't do anything about. It is useful to remember that this is a model of attention as well as action.

In any area of your life the circle that you focus on will grow and the other will conversely shrink. I think this is due to both psychological and practical reasons. Research suggests we can consciously pay attention to somewhere around 20 things at a time. If we fill our conscious attention with things that would fall into the circle of concern then we have less thinking space left to notice anything we can change. This leaves us with a genuine sense that we can't change anything. Of course this is very rarely the case but it feels very real and drains confidence and certainty.

Fortunately the opposite is also true. If you consciously focus on all of the things that you can change in any situation, then the space in your thinking for the aspects that worry you but that you can't change reduces. Psychologically your circle of influence grows and your circle of concern reduces.

In addition there are practical implications. Consider for a moment you are influenced by someone who is energetic, has a 'can do' attitude and always seems to get things moving. Now contrast this with someone who is negative, constantly focuses on what is wrong and has little idea of what to do next; how likely are they to get what they want from you? It seems obvious to me that those who focus on their circle of influence are by nature going to be able to influence those around them more and have a great support network. In turn, due to their connections, they are going to have increasing ability to get things done. This further feeds their circle of influence and so on. The opposite is also true. Those who focus their attention and (ever decreasing) energy on what can't be changed are less likely to be able to influence people around them and therefore find it even more difficult to get what they want. This proves their thinking, expands their circle of concern and reduces their influence further and the cycle carries on.

A focus on what you can change fuels confidence and an increased state of confidence will fuel the sense that you can influence the world around you. This is a healthy cycle to be in. Before you continue, take a moment to reflect on where you naturally focus. If your tendency is to worry about what you can't change then this will inhibit your confidence. Use this chapter to begin to change your focus.

BE INFLUENTIAL AT WORK

Over the past ten years I have been lucky enough to work with some fantastic organizations, from global sector leaders through to companies voted as some of the top employers in the UK. Even within these organizations it is common for people to carry a sense that they can't make a difference beyond the straightforward task that they have been employed to do. Innovation is more often restricted by an individual's thinking than by a dismissive boss. More opportunities to grow relationships are missed because an individual thinks that they can't improve a connection and therefore doesn't try, than by actual disagreements in the work place.

If you are facing any significant challenges at work, then take the time now to review what you can change and separate it from what you can't. Even if the elements that you would place in the circle of influence seem small it is important to focus on them and that action.

During my development programmes I am often asked for strategies on influencing upwards. I have begun to remind participants about the serenity prayer and the circles of influence and concern. The question isn't, 'How can I influence my boss?', but, 'What can I influence my boss on?' No one is 100 per cent set on every opinion and worldview, so consider where you are able to make a difference and focus on that.

The same applies to project work. If you find yourself with a sense that a project is going off-track and there is nothing you can do about it, then take time to use the circles of influence and concern to explore where to place your energy and focus.

FOCUS ON WHAT YOU CAN DO IN RELATIONSHIPS

A coach of mine once suggested that we create our partners and relationships. He shared that whenever he had negative thoughts about things his wife did, she seemed to magically do more of those things. He experimented with writing a list of all the things that he loved about her and placed special attention on the characteristics that most endeared her to him. He never shared the list with her but would still begin to notice more and more of these wonderful traits.

There is a lesson in this when it comes to our focus in relationships. I see so many people in relationships focusing on the things in their partner that make them unhappy. I would suggest that this is unhealthy and can only lead to a suffocation of any love and connection.

I don't believe that any healthy relationship is built on a foundation of control and few survive when one partner has a drive to change the other. If you want a great relationship a great question to ask is, 'What can I influence?' The primary answer to this is you. You can influence the decisions you make, your health, how you dress, what you choose to make important and even whether to stay with someone.

These things may in turn influence others' choices and behaviours but this has to be seen as a potential outcome not a sole purpose.

I am an expert on confidence not relationships. I am lucky enough to have a wonderful wife and I've made many mistakes along the way. One thing I am certain of is that truly confident people know when to give everything they can to a relationship and when to say enough is enough.

FOCUS ON YOUR CHOICES

Have you ever had a moment when you felt that you had no choice in life? The sense that you can't influence anything is one of the quickest ways to emotionally overwhelm and will wipe out confidence. It is no surprise then that I work hard to ensure clients understand that they always have a choice. You have an ultimate choice right now. You could decide to never move again. This might not be a compelling choice, but it is a choice none the less. Eventually someone would come along and move you somehow. They may even take you somewhere warm and padded, hose you down and force you to have some food. I would like to think that the realization that you have that option will make whatever else you are doing now more compelling. As I said earlier in the chapter, any choice is better than no choice. Even in the darkest moments you have options. You decide whether to eat healthily or not. You choose to make family time more important than exercise. You choose who you spend time with and how much importance you place on the opinions of others.

There are times when it doesn't feel like you have a choice. You will often feel that you have to go to work. Even in this there is a choice. You could not go. The implications would probably be even less desirable than going, but it is still a choice.

At any moment when you feel there is no choice in life, go back to good old Dr Covey's model and work out what is in your circle of influence. Its simple power can change everything.

Putting it all together

Confident people create a cycle of influence where they are thinking about what they can do. This means they do more, which means they think they can do more and so the cycle continues. Focusing on what you can influence has the wonderful side-effect of filtering out thoughts of what you can't do anything about.

The ultimate choice that we have is what thoughts to pay most attention to. Confident people take the 'you can't do it' mind-talk with a huge pinch of salt and pay more attention to the 'let's see if we can' internal conversations. The final step is to take action . Have the courage to change the things that you can.

19 FOCUS ON SOLUTIONS

There are some four million different kinds of animals and plants in the world. Four million different solutions to the problems of staying alive.

David Attenborough

In life it is certain that problems will occur. We all have challenges to overcome and our process for examining and overcoming these problems will have significant impact on our confidence. I noticed some years ago that the most confident people in my network seemed to focus on working out solutions rather than explaining and analysing problems.

While I think there is a place for exploring problems and analysing them to prevent them happening again, I believe there is too much emphasis placed on this in most coaching, counselling and therapies. In previous chapters I have shared the concept that we can consciously pay attention to around 20 things at once. An over-emphasis on exploring life's challenges can easily lead to our awareness being completely filled by a single problem.

The antidote of this immersion in problems is solutions-focused thinking. This approach has its roots in the therapeutic approach devised by Steve de Shazer and Insoo Kim Berg and others, at the Brief Family Therapy Centre, Milwaukee. This approach values simplicity in philosophy and language and aims to discover what works in a given situation simply and practically.

One of the key elements is the absence of any focus on the problem. The attention instead is on where you are now, where you want to be and the discovery of small steps to get there.

My own experience of solutions-focused thinking is that it has positively impacted on every area of my life. For anyone whose work includes coaching, working with teams or managing change I would highly recommend *The Solutions Focus* by Mark McKergow and Paul Z. Jackson.

One of the great benefits of solutions-focused thinking is the immediacy of results. It will help you to see that you are closer to a solution than you first thought and that you can move even closer quickly and easily. This is always going to build confidence and encourage you to do more.

A SOLUTIONS-BASED GOAL

I once observed a coaching session where the coach asked the coachee, 'How do you know this is a big problem?' The reply lasted some time during which the coaching became increasingly immersed in the situation and linked together several previously unrelated problems. With one question the coach expanded the size of the problem in the coachee's mind. I stepped in at this point and asked a similarly simple question that changed the focus of the coachee's thinking completely:

'Imagine you went to bed tonight and while you were asleep a miracle happened and that problem completely disappeared. When you woke up how would you know that the miracle had happened?'

Ask yourself this question about a challenge that you have in your life right now. Answer the question in as much rich detail as you possibly can. You will notice two things. Firstly you will get really clear on where you want to get to. This is another way of creating a clear and compelling goal. Secondly you will notice a very different state compared to the state that would be generated if I asked you to explore the nature of the problem you were faced with. When you combine these two aspects, the effect is only ever going to be positive.

IDENTIFY WHERE THE SOLUTION IS HAPPENING ALREADY

Having defined the outcome it is useful to explore whether there are situations where the solution already happens. Think back to the challenge you have just been considering and answer this question: on a scale of one to ten, where ten is the ideal future you have just defined, where are you now?

In answering this question many people notice that they are closer to their desired end point than they first realized. I have coached clients specifically about confidence using this approach and having initially described how they had no confidence and it was inhibiting them in every part of their life they then scaled themselves as a five against their miracle future. When I reflect back to them that they are half way towards a future they have defined as ideal there is a palpable shift in thinking.

Now consider what has got you that high up the scale. No matter what score you initially gave yourself – even if your response was a one, reflect on what makes it a one rather than a zero. For many people analysing why a score is low rather than why it is high is counter-intuitive, however this exploration of what is already working is a key step in sorting for the positive. If we can understand what is working for us already in any challenging situation – no matter how small this may be – and do more of it, we are already on the way to tackling the issue.

TAKE SMALL STEPS TO PROGRESS

Step back for a moment to the scaling that you did against your miracle future. As you reflect on where you are now, ask yourself what would have to happen to move you just one small step up the scale. For example if you were a four out of ten what would have to happen to take you to a five?

This is a super-simple but vital step in focusing on the positive. One of the challenges with setting big goals is that they can seem so difficult to achieve. By defining the smallest steps, and then acting on them, you will see and feel the signs of progress.

Moving towards the end-goal always feeds confidence and encourages action. You may find though that the simple steps which you identify as those that will take you from a three to a four will actually move you from a three to a seven or eight. There is beauty in simplicity and there is energy in action.

Putting it all together

Over the past ten years there has been a huge wave of research in the fields of positive thinking and psychology. While some of this research requires more validation, it is clear that sorting for the positive does more than simply make you feel better. Those who are able to take a solutions-focused approach to life's challenges are likely to be more productive, more influential and get better results. The latest wave of evidence seems to suggest that positive thinking even has health benefits and my experience is certainly that those who focus mainly on the problems in their life seem to become ill more often.

One additional tip for anchoring this mindset is to reflect, review and analyse when things have gone unexpectedly brilliantly. All too often I see organizations and individuals carrying out large-scale reviews that have somehow gone wrong. This chapter has described the limitations of this already, but these limitations are turned on their heads with an in-depth analysis of what went right – especially when it wasn't predicted.

The link to confidence is a direct one. In sorting for the positive you are confirming what you can do and reducing the time and energy you have to focus on what you can't. You will retrain your brain to notice more of the positive and resourceful situations and people in your life. By applying the philosophy of the solutions-focused thinking community you will develop a framework for solving the challenges that life inevitably throws up. All of these will further endorse your psyche as someone who is able to flex and adapt in any situation and feel positive while doing it. This is the heart of real long-term confidence.

20 POSITIVITY CREATES CONFIDENCE

One love, one heart, one destiny.
Bob Marley

Pronoia (pronounced pronoya): the suspicion that the universe is a conspiracy on your behalf.

Imagine the effect on your confidence if you believed that the whole universe and everything in it was working in your favour. It might sound like a crazy thought to have, but let me give an example of someone who has the opposite belief and what their working day is like:

The alarm goes off. It is 5:45am and you have resolved to get up early, and have some breakfast before going to the gym. It is Monday and it is January, time for a new start. It is also two below zero and you forgot to reset the heating to take account of your early start. Damn that heating timer.

You decide to go to the gym tomorrow and hit snooze to have an extra 30 minutes in bed before getting up for an early start.

You wake with a start at 7:00am. The useless alarm didn't go off – granted you didn't actually press snooze, just thought about it – and it's a good job that your delightful children have got their lazy backsides out of bed. Just how did you get chosen to parent the loudest kids in living history?

You jump out of bed, stub your toe – who put that chair there? – and jump into a now luke-warm shower as the kids have used all the hot water. You wrap yourself in a damp towel and head downstairs to fumble about for the iron. Why the hell wasn't there enough time at the weekend to get a couple of shirts ironed?

You are now dressed in your roughly ironed cloths and your stress levels are heading towards the top of the scale. Of course the car is freezing and the traffic is a nightmare – it looks like every Tom, Dick and Harriet is late this morning too. Either that or they are just getting in your way specifically to irritate you. Then there are the roadworks – especially designed by the gas emergency people to make you even more unpopular with your boss and clients.

You finally arrive at the office 35 minutes late, which of course means there is more chance of being given a 100 per cent pay rise today than getting a parking space in the staff car park. Having trudged to work in the rain from the ridiculously remote overflow car park, which was strategically placed in another postcode by the planners and architects, you finally arrive to find there is already the biggest pile of files, customer complaints and requests from everyone from the Chief Executive to your most troublesome team member.

Oh and the email is down.

And the phones.

And your mobile is just about to go flat as you forgot to charge it last night.

Why does technology do that to you? It's almost as if the universe is working against you just to make life as difficult as possible and the working day has not even begun yet!

I can feel my energy levels have dropped even writing this example; it is no wonder that those of you who suffer this kind of experience every day feel so tired in the morning that you think you need a cocktail of coffee, energy drinks and sugar to get you through the day.

If you want to experience confidence more of the time, then one great option is to start showing signs of *pronoia*.

Pronoia is the unwavering belief that the whole universe and everybody and everything is conspiring to help you in every way that is possible.

Most people have an immediate response that this is plain stupid. But if you have lived even part of the example above, then you are happy to make the assumption that the universe and things within it are conspiring against you. You are also living in a world where people who you have never met are doing things to get in your way. The beliefs that you are living your life by are just as improbable as *pronoia*.

BE PRONOID

Pronoid travel includes believing that there is a special policeman travelling half a mile ahead of your car ensuring that the traffic is flowing smoothly for you. The only time he will allow you to be slowed down is when it is for your own safety. The universe will also ensure that you catch exactly the aeroplane, train or boat that you are supposed to. This will usually be the one you book, but if there is some reason for an alternative, it will do that. Trust it is the best for you.

Pronoid relationships mean that you will be with the person you are supposed to be with for exactly as long as you are supposed to be with them in order for you both to learn all of the lessons that you are meant to. You will not meet before the time is due, nor will you be allowed to stay together beyond what is right. If a relationship ends, it is for entirely good reasons, even if you cannot see that yet.

Pronoid careers work in a similar way. If you have defined what you want from your career and/or your life, the universe is making it happen right now. That means every redundancy is planned, every challenging boss you have is there for a reason, and restructures strengthen your position in the long term, if not the short term.

PLAN FOR THE BEST

Many of my coaching clients start our relationship with a belief that they should assume, and therefore plan for, the worst. This includes how they travel, how they plan their finances, relationships and more.

I am not advocating a *laissez-faire* approach to life, nor a high-risk one; I think planning is a good thing, but over-doing it leads to problems too. The brain is pretty much wired to give us more of what we focus on, so consistently planning for the worst dramatically increases the likelihood of us getting exactly that.

Thinking about relationships in a pronoid way might involve deciding what you are looking for in a relationship and putting yourself in situations where you might meet people who are looking for similar. The opposite would mean that you get really desperate and go with the next person who shows any interest in you and then blame the world for your unhappiness.

Planning a trip in a pronoid way would include checking the weather and packing based on that. If something unexpected comes along you can always buy or borrow something. Paranoid planning would mean packing for every single possible eventuality, incurring baggage charges at the airport or an aching back from carrying cases. It would also end in wondering why there is so much washing and ironing to do when you get home.

This should be straightforward, but I meet people every day who believe the world is against them and blame the results of bad decision making on that.

NOTICE RESULTS OF PRONOIA

If you have been reading this book diligently you will understand that sorting for the positive will help you to feel better, more confident and you are likely to notice different things about yourself and the world around you. What may still surprise you is that developing a positive mind set will increase your chances of success in life. Shawn Achor shares some enlightening research in his book, *The Happiness Advantage*, that demonstrates the power of sorting for the positive. For example, college freshmen who were empirically shown to be happy had a higher income 19 years earlier than their unhappy classmates. His research also suggests that happy people are 31 per cent more productive than those who are negative, neutral or stressed. An increasing amount of solid research points to the fact that pronoia, or at least training yourself to sort for the positive, will help you to make better decisions more quickly, to be more productive and potentially even earn more money.

Reflect on the results of your pronoia. Use them as fuel to build an even more pronoid approach.

Putting it all together

Most of us are brought up in a model of the world that suggests that when we have a certain amount of money or achieve a certain level of success then we will be happy. I am more certain than ever this flawed world view is a key contributory factor to a lack of confidence. Shawn Achor is among a growing band of researchers who are demonstrating that training ourselves to be positive and happy leads to success and high performance. Adopting a pronoic view of the universe is a great way to start this process. Clients who have experimented with this almost irrationally positive view of life consistently report that they are experiencing better luck than before and the ability to do more or achieve things than previously. Success and confidence shouldn't be linked but if they were, sorting for the positive is a great way to kick-start both.

21 LUCK AND CONFIDENCE

*I'm a greater believer in luck, and I find the harder
I work the more I have of it.*
Thomas Jefferson

There appears to be some connection between luck and confidence. Lucky people seem to meet their perfect partners and achieve lifelong ambitions. They have great careers and seem to win regularly at games of chance. Highly confident people seem to experience the same luck and from the outside their luck will boost their confidence. This is a perfectly rational assumption to make, but a study of the characteristics and behaviours of lucky people and a similar understanding of the highly confident shows a significant correlation. So the good news is that by reading and applying the techniques in this book you get to be more confident AND experience more luck!

It is useful at this stage to distinguish between fortune and luck. Fortune is an unknown and unpredictable phenomenon. Luck is what we experience and is predictable and influenceable. A decade ago I read a book that opened my eyes to just how subjective our luck is. I would highly recommend *The Luck Factor* by Dr Richard Wiseman. Dr Wiseman presents a simple and easy-to-follow explanation as to why some people are lucky and others unlucky. Through a set of well constructed studies and experiments he also provides a framework for anyone to experience more luck in their lives. I am in no doubt that applying the techniques in his book will lead to a greater sense of luck as well as confidence and applying his experiments will result in a greater confidence.

The number one step is to decide whether you can be lucky. Due to the nature of human experience the moment that you decide you are a lucky person, or at least experience luck, then your experience of it changes. Conversely it is extremely difficult to be lucky if you don't think you are a lucky person. And even if you are you won't notice it! It is no coincidence at all that many highly confident people also consider themselves to be at least moderately lucky.

NOTICE WHEN YOU ARE LUCKY

I am always shocked when I see people on television declaring that they have never won anything in their lives. These are often people who have already won the opportunity to be on a game show or reality TV show ahead of thousands of other people. I find it hard to believe that people can reach advanced adulthood never having won *anything*. If you are able to stop reading for a moment and list anything and everything that you have ever won, this could be from games of chance (ever won a goldfish at the funfair or a toy at an amusement arcade?) to something you have to work harder for (an award at school, swimming certificate or an accolade at work?). I surveyed a small group of people when writing this chapter. Sixty per cent responded to the question, 'Tell me something you have won' with an immediate response that they hadn't won anything before. When probed further only two per cent actually couldn't recall winning anything.

Not all of these instances will have been down to luck, but this does reinforce the idea that lucky people notice when luck happens. Unlucky people seem to delete lucky occurrences in their life.

What do you define as luck in your life? Does the moment that you met your partner count as good luck? Are you lucky to have great kids or the job that you enjoy? Do you think that the fact that you have great friends makes you lucky?

The more luck you define yourself as having, the luckier a person you are. The luckier a person you define yourself as, the more luck you will experience.

LOOK FOR THE LUCK IN YOUR BAD LUCK

One of the favourite elements of Dr Wiseman's research on luck is that lucky people see the positive in their bad luck. I see this principle played out in many people that I work with. In organizations or teams which are going through periods of change this is a major factor in defining the culture while change is taking place.

Imagine this scenario. The company you work for decides to restructure. As a result of it you retain your job at the same level and salary. Your boss, who you regard highly, leaves the organization and you now report to a former colleague who you believe is less skilled than you. Do you consider this lucky or unlucky?

What about this situation? You lose your purse or wallet. In it is some cash and your credit cards. You also have some small items of sentimental value. Having cancelled all of your credit cards you find them along with the cash and personal items in a place you hadn't checked in your house. Again do you consider this lucky or unlucky?

If you want to feel luckier in situations such as these, focus on the positive comparison to what could have been rather than the negative. In these situations that would be a realization that you could have been the one made redundant and be looking for a job just before Christmas. It's better to have a job even with a boss that you aren't sure of than to have no job at all. In situation two at least you have your cash and personal items back; most people who lose a wallet or purse never see any of it again.

Focusing on the negative comparison will help you train your brain to look for the negatives in situations and to forget experiences of good luck. This in turn can make it harder to trigger your confidence.

BUILD YOUR LUCK NETWORK

In the same way that having a network of confident people will reinforce your sense of confidence, spending time with lucky people will enhance your sense of luck.

Imagine surrounding yourself with people whose main hope in life is to solve their financial worries by playing bingo, gambling on horses and playing the lottery. Guess how lucky these people see themselves and their lives? And as you saw more data from these people that bad luck was the only luck available to them this would influence your sense of luck. I chose this example very specifically because it reflects the experience of many of the older generation I grew up with. Don't fall into that trap.

Take and make every opportunity that you can to surround yourself with people who seem to be lucky. Interact with them and learn from their luck. If they can make their own luck, then understand how they do it and apply the principles in your life. I have two friends who the rest of my social circle consider to be the luckiest people we know. It is no surprise to me that when they attend social events at the local racecourse they join together and form a betting alliance. Whether it is good planning or good fortune, these two luck conductors always finish 'up' on their flutters. While some of my friends scorn their lucky breaks, one or two smart ones spend their time looking over their shoulders and following their wagers.

Who are the luckiest people that you know career wise, in relationships or in health? How can you connect with them even more closely and make them part of your luck network?

Putting it all together

Throughout this book I have reinforced the key point that your confidence is within your control. Many people who haven't read this book will think that confidence is something which happens as a result of external factors. The same applies to luck. While nature or fortune defines where we are born and our presence at certain events we can have a huge influence on the luck that we experience.

This is both from the perspective of the amount of luck that we actually need or notice and the opportunities for good luck to happen to us. If you turn your luck radar up you will experience an increasing amount of luck. By seeing more positives in your bad luck, you refocus your brain even more on the positive, and by absorbing what others who are lucky do, you are creating more opportunities to feel the luck that they do.

The cumulative effect of this on your confidence is unquestionable. Confidence and luck form a powerful partnership. One feeds the other and, alongside the foundation techniques from the early part of this book, you will be able to have a tremendously positive influence on others around you who feel that they are lacking in either of these.

I'll leave the final words of the chapter to Dr Wiseman: 'When it comes to luck, the future is in your hands.'

And it starts right now.

22 CONFIDENCE BEFORE SUCCESS

I believe in intuitions and inspirations ... I sometimes FEEL that I am right. I do not KNOW that I am.

Albert Einstein

There is a fundamental flaw in the way that many of us think about confidence. These flaws have brought me many coaching clients over the years and caused stress to millions of people in business, sport and in personal lives.

Take the example of the million-pound footballer. I worked with a player who had already had a successful career in the second and third tiers of English football. When he secured a £1 million-plus deal to sign for a Premier League club you would expect that his confidence would shoot through the roof. After all, in a footballer's career that is classed as success and of course his long-term financial security was assured. Instead, the primary emotion he experienced throughout his first year in the top flight was insecurity.

I have seen this pattern repeated within organizations when individuals secure long worked-for promotions. Also in relationships when an individual finds their life partner and instead of confidence they experience tremendous concern about losing that partner.

Each of these examples shows that achievement doesn't necessarily lead to confidence. More often, an achievement of what we have labelled as an indicator of success will impact our ability to feel confidence. Continued success in the new role or relationship will help to reinstate that challenged confidence but this chapter, along with the rest of the book, will reinforce that the formula should be reversed. Results in every area of your life will be delivered and maintained through establishing your deep genuine confidence first. Don't get caught in the confidence trap.

BUILD CONFIDENCE TO GET WHAT YOU WANT NOT THE OTHER WAY AROUND

It is important to remember that confidence leads to success and achievement and not necessarily the other way around. Let's turn this into a very simple formula for the purpose of this section.

In this case C represents the confidence that you are building. It must be a genuine confidence rather than surface arrogance, and it must be a confidence that continues to be embedded as part of who you are. In some instances you may look to build your confidence in specific areas such as those represented in this book. In other instances you will build your confidence with a specific end goal or situation in mind.

The A in the equation represents the other things that you can do to support your success. For example, if you are preparing for a job interview then ensure that your confidence (C) is high but take action (A) to ensure that you have researched the company and role well. If your success relates to performance in a specific job then keep building and developing your confidence (C) but also take consistent action (A) on your personal development to ensure you have the skills and abilities to continue to develop the role.

Consider this simple equation for every key area of your life. Support your confidence-building with simple and consistent actions that speed up or maintain your success.

DEVELOP CONFIDENCE TO MATCH YOUR GOALS

As I have described elsewhere, goal-setting is a useful aid to confidence. To feel a sense of achievement or success you need to define what that success looks like. Consistent action is also valuable. One of the common traits of confident and successful people who I meet is that they take action rather than procrastinating. However avoiding the confidence trap requires you to let go of the assumption that being successful and action-orientated results in confidence. People who are successful without anchoring their confidence usually become stressed due to their consistent and nagging self-doubt. I often hear people in this situation talking about the sense that one day they will be found out. If you find yourself with this feeling then it is a sure-fire cue for you to bolster your confidence.

Those who are successful and take lots of action without the foundation of confidence become tired and stressed and still don't have that fundamental belief in themselves that underpins them. This is a sure-fire route to burnout.

As your goals get evermore challenging then you may need to further develop your confidence. Make this an integral part of your strategy for achieving what you want. As your success becomes even more apparent be sure to bring your confidence with you. It can be at moments of great achievement that your confidence wobbles most. Do not expect your confidence to always grow with your success. In the moments that it does then that is wonderful but don't let the moments when this doesn't happen take you by surprise.

FEEL THE FEAR AND …

The late Susan Jeffers wrote the fabulously titled self-help classic *Feel The Fear and Do It Anyway.* This title should stay with you as you continue to avoid the confidence trap. When you aren't sure what to do, do something. When fear holds you back or thoughts of 'I will when …' take hold, then move. The chapter on fear in this book (Chapter 2) will help you to understand why you are feeling the way you are and the chapter on taking action (Chapter 29) will help you to do something about it, but the sooner you do something positive the more likely you will be to notice your confidence growing and the more you will achieve what you want to achieve more quickly too.

Don't take the unhelpful mind-chatter of 'I might not be ready for this' as advice not to do it. Give yourself the opportunity to experiment with success, and while achievement doesn't guarantee you confidence, action-orientation does give fuel for more of both. What is the very next step that you could take right now that would change your perception of how successful you can be? What could you do in the next 24 hours that might be a little uncomfortable but would help get momentum? Got the answer? Then go and do it!

Putting it all together

I would love every person who reads this book to be more successful. That includes you. I would like you to be wealthier and to have more of the cool things in life that you really want. Few things would help me to be happier than to hear that you have the job, house and relationship that you want. I also want to be clear that these things are not guaranteed to give you confidence. Being in a relationship with a gorgeous man or beautiful woman is as likely to reduce your confidence as it is to increase it. A fantastic new job or the creation of your own business will give you less certainty rather than more. Even having more money can lead to more fear, not less. I am not trying to put you off success and wealth but to encourage you to prepare for it. Get confident first. Make it strong, genuine and a state that you lapse into without realizing. Take action that affects the outside world as your confidence builds and notice results.

Confidence and action will lead to achievement. Be sure to nurture your confidence as your life becomes richer (in every sense of the word) and you will continue to be fulfilled. Avoid the confidence trap at all costs and the world will remain your oyster.

23 THE PHYSIOLOGY OF CONFIDENCE

What you do speaks so loud that I cannot hear what you say.
Ralph Waldo Emerson

In November of 2012 I watched a brilliant TED Talk that would forever change my view on the power that our body has on our confidence. I want to thank Dr Amy Cuddy for her fantastic work in the field of social psychology and acknowledge the impact that has had on my work and on my clients.

Imagine being able to change how other people perceive not only your levels of confidence but also competency in just two minutes. Dr Cuddy and her colleagues at the Hellman Faculty at Harvard University found that by adopting certain poses for just two minutes significantly affected not just how individuals felt, but how others perceived them. In one of the team's most powerful experiments, individuals were brought into a laboratory and asked to adopt high or low-power poses (more on what these are later in the chapter). They then took part in a thorough and very stressful job interview. As well as being observed and videoed the interviewer was trained to give zero non-verbal feedback. When the videos of these hugely demanding interviews were sent to independent reviewers they selected all the people who had adopted high-power poses and rejected all those who had adopted low-power poses. The adoption of these simple poses allows you to be at your confident best so quickly that it can impact not just how you feel but how others perceive your capability.

I have invited hundreds of people to experiment with power poses since I began following Dr Cuddy's work, and the impact has been remarkable. Clients have shared stories of significantly better performance at work and in job interviews, being able to give keynote speeches when previously the thought of presenting to even small groups was a huge step, and even improved intimate relationships.

In that time I have only had two clients for whom power posing hasn't worked and both later admitted it was because they hadn't spent two minutes doing it. Have you got two minutes to change how others perceive you?

PRACTISE THE PHYSIOLOGY OF CONFIDENCE

Dr Cuddy provides us with a clear guide to the physiology of high-and low-power poses. As you read this section, firstly notice how you are sitting and which pose you are adopting naturally. As I describe the high-and low-power poses, shift your physiology accordingly.

Low-power poses will typically include an individual making themselves smaller and folding their hands and arms across themselves. Their heads will often be down and their shoulders will be up. If they are sitting their legs will typically be crossed quite tightly. You may occasionally see someone touching their neck. All of these combine to make the individual smaller and feel more protected.

High-power poses help the individual look bigger and more open. Typically hands or arms will be stretched out or open (imagine someone sitting with their hands clasped behind their head and with the elbows out either side of their head). Legs will be outstretched or open and if you adopt a power pose your head will be up. If you are exploring this now, find the most comfortable or natural position that you can stand while filling the largest space possible.

It is important to observe these gestures in clusters. In other words if you notice someone sitting with their arms folded please do not assume they are in a low-power pose. Look for groups of gestures and when adopting the power pose yourself demonstrate as many of the gestures as possible.

DECIDE WHEN TO POWER POSE

What is clear from Dr Cuddy's work and my experience is that the best time to use the power pose is not during an event when you want to feel high in power and low in stress but some time just before the event.

When preparing for an important meeting for example, spending two minutes in a small private space in your best power pose will get the desired result. Think for a moment in which areas of your life this would be most useful for you.

Since studying power posing many of my clients have used it to prepare for interviews, presentations, disciplinary reviews, business dinners, first dates and even to support a partner through labour!

On occasion it may be helpful to adopt a power pose live. This will typically be in a situation where another person is trying to be dominant and you want to respond in an equally dominant way. It is vital to choose these occasions carefully so as not to appear overpowering. A useful example is in a negotiation situation. In most cases I don't think it is the most desirable way to take control of the situation. My preference would be for you to use the power pose before the conversation then aim to build rapport with the other party during it. However if you find that the other party is being deliberately dominating and challenging during a negotiation then adopting a powerful physiology could be a valuable step to maintaining control.

FAKE IT UNTIL YOU BECOME IT

If you have read the early chapters of this book you will appreciate that the brain doesn't distinguish between what is real and what is made up. This means that all states are real, whether we have triggered them consciously or they have happened naturally. Cuddy underlines this in her work. She states that by using the power pose you aren't being something different but instead showing up as a better version of your natural self. You are also setting the foundations for that confident, powerful state to become a default state for you.

Try this experiment over the next month. Choose a specific situation that makes you feel out of place. It may be something simple like walking into a certain room or meeting or it may be when you meet with someone who you find slightly intimidating. For the next month ensure that before each of your chosen situations you adopt a power pose for a minimum of two minutes. After a month of doing this notice how you feel in these situations. My experience is that you suddenly realize that you feel different, less stressed and in greater control of the situation.

Putting it all together

Harvard University research has indicated that effective leaders characteristically have high testosterone and low cortisol. This chemical combination provides them with a platform upon which they are more assertive, more confident and more optimistic. They are willing to take more risks and make better decisions. The great news is that through the work of Dr Cuddy you are able to learn a technique which allows you to access this version of confidence in just two minutes. Through observing and carrying out controlled studies the team were able to establish that adopting high-power poses for just 120 seconds will lower the stress hormone (cortisol) and increase the dominance hormone (testosterone). Power poses are characterized by an open stance that fills the space around you. Your head will be up and your back straight.

The beauty of this research is that it adds more evidence and understanding to the principle that confidence is just a state which can be triggered at any time. It also confirms that by doing this on a regular basis this state becomes more of a default and changes our perspective on ourselves and the situations that we find ourselves in.

I can't recommend Dr Cuddy's TED Talk highly enough (see Further reading for a link to this talk). I will leave the final words of this chapter to her:

So I want to ask you first … both to try power posing and also I want to ask you to share the science, because this is simple. I don't have ego involved in this. Give it away. Share it with people, because the people who can use it the most are the ones with no resources and no technology and no status and no power. Give it to them because they can do it in private. They need their body's privacy and two minutes can significantly change the outcomes of their life.

Dr Cuddy

24 THE LANGUAGE OF CONFIDENCE

*Words are, of course, the most powerful drug
used by mankind.*
Rudyard Kipling

Have you ever noticed that highly confident people seem to
capture moods with nothing more than a few well-placed words?
The language of the highly confident is specific and consistent in
its make-up. Most importantly, for the context of this book, is
that their language patterns can be learned and replicated.

Confident language is concise and simple. It is specific and
engages those responding to it quickly. When highly confident
people make requests they are very clear on what they want and
spend much less time talking about what they don't want.

It is important to understand that the words and phrases we use
every day become one of the fundamental frameworks through
which we perceive the world around us. If your language tends
to be negative or problem-focused then you will programme your
brain to notice more negativity and problems. If your language is
more positive and resourceful this becomes a filter for what you
notice in the world.

This is particularly important for self-image and self-perception.
If you consistently talk about yourself in negative terms and
describe your shortcomings in detail, then this creates that
self-image regardless of how accurate it is. I often notice people
being particularly good at describing their negative traits while
speaking with energy and positivity about the strengths of
those around them. Does this sound like you? If so, a greater
awareness of your language will have a big and positive impact
on your confidence. The impact of language spreads beyond
the individual though. The culture of a team or organization
is influenced significantly by the language of its constituents.

Leaders and senior managers in particular must be acutely aware of the influence of their language patterns.

This chapter focuses on three strategies that will help you to feel more confident and those around you to perceive you as more self-assured. As with many other techniques they require some practice to change programmes and patterns that have been natural to you for many years, but stick with it as the impact is significant. In particular the degree to which you are able to influence others around to your way of thinking will increase dramatically.

SAY WHAT YOU WANT, NOT WHAT YOU DON'T WANT

Your brain is fundamentally wired to follow commands that it is given. While we have built-in safeguards to consciously choose what we do, the brain, when given a task or instruction, has a natural propensity to follow that task or instruction.

This basic wiring underpins this strategy. For example if you say, internally or externally, that you 'don't want to be scared about presenting at conferences', your brain receives this message but deletes the 'don't'. You are programming yourself to be more scared about presenting at conferences.

As you explain to a friend that you always look terrible when you are dressed for a night out you are programming your brain to notice more of what you don't like when you are ready to go out.

Use language which helps you and others focus more on what you want rather than what you don't. Here are a few examples:

- Instead of 'I am tired' say 'I'm really looking forward to a good night's sleep'.
- Instead of 'I am stressed' say 'I really need to relax'.
- Instead of 'I am terrible at this' say 'I need to get better at this'.

This is not meant to be fluffy or blandly positive. Instead it is taking advantage of your brain's natural wiring to focus on getting more of what you want rather than what you don't.

REQUEST WHAT YOU WANT FROM OTHERS

This 'towards' language can be extended to your influence on others. In fact, you do this already you just don't realize it. I recently observed a new client addressing his management team. He started his presentation by saying, 'I don't want you to be nervous about the messages I am about to share with you' (the room shuffled at this point) 'I am going to present some figures and don't worry about the fact that you might find them complicated. I know for some it might be a little bit boring but if you try not to drift off or get confused we'll get there in the end'. Hardly inspirational stuff!

When you are influencing others, choose your words carefully to increase the chances of them doing what you want not what you don't.

Here are some examples:

- Instead of 'I don't want you to worry about what I'm asking you to do' say, 'I want you to feel relaxed about what I'm asking you to do'.
- Instead of 'Don't focus on the things that have gone wrong' say, 'Focus more on what has gone well'.
- Instead of 'If we lack focus we will lose' say, 'If we focus, we will win'.

Notice that in each of these examples the message is exactly the same but positioned in a way that gives the greatest chance to focus on what is needed. Use this towards approach to influence how others feel and their likelihood to complete the task as you would like.

USE MULTI-SENSORY LANGUAGE

Memories are created in a multi-sensory way. The more rich and multi-sensory the experience, the more multi-faceted and therefore powerful the memory you will create. We can contribute to this by using multi-sensory language in conversations with others. This is particularly useful when we are making presentations or pitches that we have a chance to prepare and rehearse.

In your audience you will have people who have a preference to think and remember in pictures. Others have a preference to think and remember sounds or auditory triggers. Another section of your audience will remember the feeling that is created during a memory most of all. If you use a range of visual, hearing and feeling or movement words in your communication it will be more memorable. The more memorable it is the more confident you will be perceived.

Take a look at these two extracts from Martin Luther King's famous 'I have a dream' speech. You will notice that it is littered with seeing, hearing and feeling words and phrases.

'Let us not wallow in the valley of despair. I say to you today my friends – so even though we face the difficulties of today and tomorrow, I still have a dream. It is a dream deeply rooted in the American dream.

I have a dream that one day this nation will rise up and live out the true meaning of its creed: 'We hold these truths to be self-evident, that all men are created equal.'

I have a dream that one day on the red hills of Georgia the sons of former slaves and the sons of former slave owners will be able to sit down together at the table of brotherhood.

I have a dream that one day even the state of Mississippi, a state sweltering with the heat of injustice, sweltering with the heat of oppression, will be transformed into an oasis of freedom and justice.

This will be the day, this will be the day when all of God's children will be able to sing with new meaning 'My country 'tis of thee, sweet land of liberty, of thee I sing. Land where my fathers died, land of the Pilgrim's pride, from every mountainside, let freedom ring!'

And if America is to be a great nation, this must become true. And so let freedom ring from the prodigious hilltops of New Hampshire. Let freedom ring from the mighty mountains of New York. Let freedom ring from the heightening Alleghenies of Pennsylvania.

Let freedom ring from the snow-capped Rockies of Colorado. Let freedom ring from the curvaceous slopes of California.

But not only that; let freedom ring from Stone Mountain of Georgia.

Let freedom ring from Lookout Mountain of Tennessee.

Let freedom ring from every hill and molehill of Mississippi – from every mountainside.'

The next time you plan a presentation or meeting, think about how you can use multi-sensory language even more to engage your audience.

Putting it all together

Many people don't pay attention to the words and phrases that they use day in and day out, but your language is a significant factor in your self-confidence and others' perception of how confident you are.

Highly confident people use more 'towards language' describing what they want rather than what they don't. This helps a huge amount as our brains are built to follow commands but don't easily recognize words like 'don't'. If you tell yourself, 'Don't worry about what other people think', you will delete the first word and focus much more on the rest of the command. A slight change in your internal language will make a huge difference.

This principle transfers easily to your communication with others. Using towards commands will increase your influence and therefore your confidence.

25 CREATING A CONFIDENT IMAGE

The most courageous act is still to think for yourself. Aloud.
Coco Chanel

Too many people use image as a mask for a lack of confidence. This is not enough and will crack too easily. The hordes of young people changing their looks through needless and over-the-top plastic surgery is testament to this.

I do believe though that as you get the foundations of long-term and genuine confidence in place, your personal image and style should be a reflection and accelerator of it.

Jenny Bersin is the owner of Jenny B Style and Image Consultancy (www.jennybstyle.co.uk) and author of *Style, the Road to Freedom*. As well as one-to-one consultations she leads seminars on Perfecting Personal Effectiveness, Dressing for Success, Addressing Dressing and The Art of Fiscal Attraction. Here is her expert view on creating a confident image.

Creating an effective confident personal image is as relevant in our private lives as it is in what we choose to do for a living. Most importantly, developing a look that speaks positively of who we are gives us the opportunity to know ourselves, like ourselves and to our own selves be true. It is about speaking clearly without saying a word.

Having a perfectly clear style strategy gives us a real opportunity to be ourselves, and to present ourselves, in the way that we wish. To have an image that works well for us.

To quote Gore Vidal: 'Style is knowing who you are, what you want to say and not giving a damn.

Many of us confuse fashion with style. Fashion is a need to be identified by the labels that are worn and to be part of a crowd, however elite. Style is about shining through as an individual and is about using dress and demeanour as a celebration and an expression of who we are.

Difficulties arise in finding an image that expresses confidence when we have little, or no, direction – we need a clear and precise strategy.

Developing such a strategy gives us the chance to look at where we are and where we want to be; to signal who we are effectively and powerfully and manoeuvre change in a way that suits ourselves. Here's how:

KNOW THE IMPACT OF FIRST IMPRESSIONS

When you meet someone new it takes just three seconds for you to make that indelible first impression. With just a glance, you evaluate them. Two things happen so quickly they could almost be as one. Firstly, you notice the quality and level of energy they give out, whether they are open or closed, charming or alarming. Secondly, you respond to how they look, from their grooming to what they are wearing … and they do the same to you!

In those same three seconds, they have appraised your visual and behavioural appearance from head to toe. They have instantly analysed your dress, mannerisms and body language. You may intrigue some and disenchant others, but you will always rouse feelings in others. If they like what they see they will unconsciously tend to see the best in you and look for opportunities to say 'yes'. If they don't like what they see, the opposite is true.

Then, inside a further 87 seconds, without you having said a word, you have been appraised and decisions have been made about how good you are at your job, what your social standing is, how educated you are and how much you can be trusted. It will take six months for those first impressions to be changed.

What is the first impression that you want to create as you think about the immediacy of the impact you create? Does your current style reflect how you see yourself or how you want others to see you?

CHOOSE WHETHER TO TEASE OR PLEASE

Those who *tease* are generally of the opinion that others must take them as they find them. They may look dishevelled, disorganized and drab, but beneath they are a powerhouse of vibrancy, intelligence and diligence. They leave it to those whom they meet to be amazed and delighted when they discover the real person who lies below that dreary and unpromising surface!

Research shows that how you look affects not only how you feel about yourself but how others feel about you too. And, apparently, those who are successful not only increase their earning power but also the confidence that they have in themselves, whether at home, work or play.

Those who *please* take an easier route. Designers and creators make it their business (because it is their business!) to look as though they have flair, originality and inspired thought, whereas teachers and solicitors meet the needs of their clients by looking dependable, honest and with integrity. If they don't, those whom they meet may find it difficult to believe that they are good at what they do and worth listening to or employing.

An example, I am working with a client whose job is to guide and support senior managers into creating and effecting change within their businesses. Her role is one that is both inspirational and challenging. In terms of experience and intellect she is extremely able, BUT she sees a yawning gap. While her deeds and demeanour are spot-on her dress falls short. During her first consultation she described her choice of work dress as 'conforming, corporate, and dull'. Where does she want to be?

'Confident, self-assured, chic, original.' Easy enough to do now that she has recognized where she is and where she would like to be.

Do you want to tease or please with your personal style? Do you take an approach that is appropriate for your life and career now? Does your current wardrobe and style reflect this? How could you develop your approach further to make an even more confident statement?

DEVELOP YOUR IMAGE STRATEGY

When you look good you inspire those who you meet to have confidence in your skills. The more inspired they are, the more confident you become. The more confident you become, the more you inspire others to recognize you as a positive presence in their lives. You have clinched the art of being in demand. Being in demand will mean that you are more likely to be in a position to pick the job you want, the friends you want, the lifestyle you want.

Trying to find your own personal image is liberating. And, icing on the cake, get it right and you could be earning 8–20% more than your competitors who don't.

All you need is a simple strategy based on self-acceptance not self-criticism.

The mantra that I use with my clients is this:

SAY ... STYLE PERSONALITY ... SHAPE ... SCALE and PROPORTION ... SHADE

Understand it, implement it and you'll find developing your own effective personal style easy and effortless. Some of those who do it now ... Michelle Obama, Aung San Suu Kyi, Brian Cox, and Bob Geldof.

These are not necessarily conventionally beautiful people but they are people with direction and focus who speak about who they are and what they are and what is important to them not only in their deeds, but in their dress and demeanour too. We do not need to speak to them to know this.

If you accepted who you are completely now, what would your style be? If your style really did create the first part of the impression you want others to have about you what would it be like? What changes do you need to make?'

Putting it all together

Jenny's strategies, as outlined here, should be part of the circle of confidence. As you develop that deep sense of confidence, then your image should magnify that. As it magnifies that growing inner confidence the feedback you will get from people around you will add further weight to your confidence.

From the very beginning of this book I have made it clear that confidence must start from within. It is something you do, not something you have, and while some of the strategies are external, all are designed to anchor this true inner state of confidence. The approach to your inner style must be the same. Style is something that develops from the inside-out. The image that you want to create for the outside world must be a reflection of how you see yourself. If you just work on creating the external world without paying attention to how congruent this is, it will create a shell-like style that will break easily and at the worst possible time.

If you pay a little attention to your style by answering the questions posed in this chapter, you are likely to find that it becomes effortless for you. As Graeme Fidler formerly of Ralph Lauren, Aquascutum and Bally, said: 'Fashion you can buy – style is inherent.'

26 CONFIDENCE FROM OTHERS

Don't let people disrespect you. My mom says don't open the door to the devil. Surround yourself with positive people.
Cuba Gooding Jr

How many people can you think of who exude confidence? Who in your social network already demonstrates the characteristics of someone who is genuinely confident in a range of situations? The good news is that with a bit of study and attention you can begin to borrow their confidence traits and add them to your own.

When I deliver training sessions in confidence for mangers in sport and business, one of the things that I ask them to do is to analyse the characteristics of the most confident person that they know. Two things become really clear, really quickly. The first is that even though the individuals in the group tend to pick different people, many of the traits are very similar. Secondly, the traits are very easy to copy. When I then ask the people I am working with to consciously adopt the confidence traits that they have seen in others they find that it activates their own state of confidence. Even when they are put in a pressurized situation, like making an unprepared presentation to their fellow group members, they are able to do it in a much more assured manner when they also maintain the characteristics of their confidence mentors.

One reason for the success of these strategies relates back to a point made earlier in this book. Our brain doesn't differentiate easily between what is real and what is strongly imagined. When you adopt the traits of someone who you consider to be confident, your brain reacts to this as if the confidence is your own and happening naturally. It is useful to keep this fundamental brain wiring in place as you read through the practical strategies in this chapter and plan how you will use them.

NOTICE HOW THEY WALK INTO A ROOM

If you want to learn from the confidence of others, then analysis of their entrance into a room is a great place to start. There are some very definite patterns in how a confident person holds themselves as they enter a new environment. Pay close attention to their posture and in particular the level of their head. Scrutinize their eye contact and how they scan the room as they enter. Notice their facial expressions as they walk in and as they settle in the room. Observe the pace that they walk in at and how they sit or stand in their chosen position. The more attention you pay, the more detail you will notice. One of the things that I often look for is tension in the muscles around the jawline and eyes. This might not be something you will immediately notice, but over time it becomes very observable.

How the confident enter a room is also a metaphor for how they fill any particular space. Highly confident people seem to have a presence even if they aren't doing much. I've heard it described as an aura or energy. They just have something that brings people's attention to them which has nothing to do with how they are dressed or their physique. If this is true for the confident people who are unknowingly mentoring you, then look out for this. With attention you will notice certain things that they do which generate this quality.

MIND THEIR LANGUAGE

I would also highly recommend that you pay attention to the language patterns of your chosen subject and try them on for yourself. In Chapter 24 we looked specifically at language and building your own patterns, but modelling the patterns of others is a great place to start.

Here are some patterns to look out for:

- Do they use language that focuses on what they want or what they don't want?
- Do they spend more time talking about what has gone well or about recent failures?
- Do they have any specific verbal tics?
- How natural is their tone and their accent?
- What do you notice about their volume and pace?
- Do they pause little or often?

The aim is not to mimic them exactly but to try the patterns of language that you think create the sense of confidence in them or others. This is especially powerful if you can model the language patterns of a range of people who are confident in varying situations. The traits that are most consistent are likely to be the ones that are most important so experiment with them first.

BUILD A CONFIDENT NETWORK

While observing and modelling your confident exemplar it is really valuable to notice the people who they spend most time with. Many years ago Jim Rohn, the personal development guru, suggested that your income is likely to be an average of the incomes of the five people that you spend most time with. While I'm not sure the maths works perfectly, I think the concept is a healthy one to adopt and it lends itself perfectly to confidence. I am sure as you notice your exemplar's peer group it will be apparent that they do not feed their confidence by surrounding themselves with people who have less confidence than them. The opposite is almost always true: confident people tend to have social and business networks filled with people who are equally confident and often contain people who are even more certain of themselves.

Study how they operate in their networks and how they build them. When I am doing this kind of observation, there are small nuances to their strategies that I wouldn't have thought of which make all the difference when I apply them. One example of this came from my friend and ex-colleague Steve Marriott. Steve is an expert business coach and was in the service of a client modelling a brilliant business networker. This individual had a reputation for being the most connected person at any business event and met everyone with a confidence and certainty that left others in the shade. When Steve explored her strategies for making connections there was one very simple tactic that made a huge difference. She was always the first to arrive at an event and the last to leave. Simple as this may sound, it meant she was more likely to meet and spend quality time meeting more people. Steve passed this insight onto his clients and applied it himself with huge success.

The insight you gain may not be quite so straightforward but as in the previous strategy the more you pay attention the more that you will notice.

Putting it all together

No matter what walk of life you are from, you are surrounded by people who demonstrate genuine confidence. Whether this is at work, in your social life or even in the media, you have confident exemplars all around you. Whether the traits that highly confident people demonstrate are consciously created or have evolved over time, they still achieve the same end result. Your job in your journey to become consistently confident is to observe and explore these characteristics and experiment with them for yourself.

There are only two ways that this kind of modelling doesn't work. The first is if you do the observation and don't apply it. I have worked with clients for whom the exploration was a means to an end. Simply watching the confident person can have an impact on your state, but experimenting with applying the strategies is the jumpstart to awakening your own state of confidence. The second obstacle comes if you wait until you're in a pressurized situation to experiment with applying the strategies you've observed in others. For example, if you notice specific language patterns, try them out in situations where it doesn't matter if they don't trip off your tongue in the way that you would like.

Finally for this chapter I can't recommend enough surrounding yourself with confident people who you can learn from. It can be uncomfortable at first, but those with genuine confidence (rather than surface arrogance) should not be overwhelming. The more comfortable you are around the confident the higher your default level of confidence will be.

27 MAKE CONFIDENT DECISIONS

Freedom is the opportunity to make decisions.
Kenneth Hildebrand

Twelve frogs are idling the day away in a garden pond, each sitting on their own lily pad. Five decide to jump into the water. How many frogs are left sitting on lily pads?

If you've heard this little riddle before or are particularly astute today, you will know the answer is twelve. That's because while five frogs decided to jump, none of them actually did it! And herein lies the two parts of a confident decision.

1. Confidence in deciding what you want or need to do.
2. Confidence to follow through on your decision by taking action.

While still considering the options or possibilities open to you when taking an important decision (part one), you can put yourself under huge amounts of unnecessary pressure to take immediate action. This clouds your thinking and blocks your creativity. If you were eavesdropping on a conversation between these frogs you might hear things like:

'I've been thinking about what I should do all day and I still haven't done anything. All of the other frogs know what to do. If I don't make a decision soon, I must be a bad frog.'

Sometimes we already know what to do, yet we spend hours creating good and bad scenarios in our head of the decision playing out. It is like we are a fortune teller with a remote-controlled crystal ball where we can change the outcome again and again at the touch of a button. We become exhausted purely by the thought of taking action. These frogs might be saying things like:

'I had my frog-fingers burnt last year when I went for a swim and someone stole my lily pad. I've taken action too quickly in the past without thinking things through. I'll just stay here a bit longer.'

While your decisions don't often involve frogs, you might see similarities or patterns in the decisions you've needed to make in the past.

I have worked with many clients who wanted help with an important decision and report feeling 'a bit stuck'. Some even admit they can never make a decision, or at least it seems that way to them. On these occasions a breakthrough almost always occurs when we separate and explore each of these two parts.

We are all capable of making brilliant decisions and we do so in our own unique way. There are times when it can be useful to get a helping hand along the way to make a confident decision.

RELEASE THE PRESSURE VALVE TO YOUR DECISION

If we are in a building and hear the sound of the fire alarm, or we see someone about to put themselves in immediate danger, the situation dictates that we take immediate action. We all have an in-built mechanism that kicks in and spurs us into action, without thinking some might say. Of course in reality there is a huge amount of sophisticated neural function taking place in these moments. This includes diverting our inner resources away from 'logical reasoning' to the more primal 'fight or flight' response.

In most situations, however, we can afford a period of time to generate and assess options available to us without serious consequences. The fact that we can give ourselves permission to do so, with the pressure of action removed, can make us so much more resourceful, creative and empowered while we decide what to do.

Sometimes I will ask a client to go away and consider their decision for a whole week. The only rule is that they are not allowed to take any action at all during that week. Even if they become certain about their decision, and it is safe to do so, they must not act upon it. Invariably they come back with much greater clarity and tell me what they want to do.

This period of pressure-free time might be ten minutes during an important business meeting, 24 hours while a big-ticket is on special-offer or a week while you decide to ask for your partner's hand in marriage. You can create a period of time to research, reflect, ask advice, or simply let go and relax for a while. Whatever is right for you in that moment, you create space to generate options and make a confident decision.

Theodore C. Sorensen, advisor to John F Kennedy and author of *Decision-Making in the White House* said: 'And once I have all the options before me, then I comfortably and confidently make my decision'.

MAKE DECISIONS USING THE HEART, HEAD AND GUT

One of the most useful ways I have found to explore a decision has been developed from an exercise in Michael Neill's brilliant book *You Can Have What You Want*. Neill suggests using your head, heart and gut when exploring something important. Here are some questions that can help you. You might want to add some of your own too.

Use your head!

- Who has successfully made a similar decision before?
- What would the expert in this area advise?
- Where can you find more information?

Listen to your heart!

- What is the kindest thing to do right now?
- What would your guardian angel tell you to do?
- If you were living completely by your values, what would you do?

Trust your gut!

- What do you instinctively know to do already?
- What do you feel is right for you now?
- If a miracle happened overnight and the decision was already made, what would it be?

So you have created space without the pressure to act and generated options from which you can comfortably and confidently make your decision. When you reach the end of the period of time you've allowed, or circumstances change, then it is time to make your decision. And choose when to act.

KNOW WHEN TO ACT

So you have now made a decision, but there is still the matter of acting upon it. In his book *Think and Grow Rich*, Napoleon Hill says 'Successful people make decisions quickly, and change them very slowly, if and when they change them at all. Yes, people who make decisions go to the top. And those who don't make decisions seem to go nowhere.'

I believe the successful people Hill talks about are those who act upon their decisions. They have confidence that the conditions, circumstances and consequences are right for them to act. There are also some less-successful people who may have also made good decisions but unless they act upon them to the outside world they appear not to have decided anything.

Many people have a high setting for certainty in their lives. Doing anything that is unfamiliar or out of the ordinary can feel uncomfortable. When taking action on the back of a decision we can sometimes look for a 100 per cent guarantee that things will work out as we desire. And, of course, we can't see into the future and few outcomes can be 100 per cent guaranteed. Sometimes we will gain and there are times we might lose. All we can do is trust that we make the best decisions we can with the resources we have.

As a final test of a decision, I sometimes find the following exercise really useful to explore.

Draw a four-block grid (a large square divided into four smaller squares). Give the top left-hand square the title DO & GAIN. In that square write down what you expect to gain by taking action. Now title the bottom-left square DO & LOSE and write down the things you might lose by taking action.

The two squares to the right-hand side are to explore what you might lose or gain by not taking action. Title the top-right square DON'T & GAIN and write down what you could gain from doing nothing. Finally title the bottom-right square DON'T & LOSE and write down what you might lose from doing nothing.

One of the things this exercise can remind us is that we nearly always have complete choice of when to act upon an important decision. It also helps us ensure the time is right to act.

Putting it all together

Theodore Roosevelt once said: 'In a moment of decision, the best thing you can do is the right thing to do. The worst thing you can do is nothing.'

A confident decision comes in two parts: deciding what to do and when to take action. Taking time to generate options without the pressure to act is doing something.

Successful people know that a successful decision comes with action when the time is right and conditions are right. They know they can't predict the future and they know they won't get it right every time. They learn to trust in their ability to make good decisions.

28 MAKE MORE DECISIONS

Once a decision was made, I didn't worry about it afterward.
Harry S. Truman

What makes a good decision-maker? When working with developing leaders I ask this question regularly and the responses range from the ability to never be wrong through to assumptions about the pace of the decision-maker in processing information. While the quality of decision-making is largely judged retrospectively it is clear that confident decision-makers are comfortable making more decisions more quickly. In Chapter 27 we shared the techniques that the highly confident use to make good decisions by understanding how they make them. In this chapter we explore how the highly confident make quicker decisions. Combining your learning from these two chapters provides a powerful platform to build confidence, presence and gravitas in a range of situations and circumstances.

I often consider decision-making to be the bridge between ideas and action. You can have the best ideas, but if you take too long to cross the bridge your energy to follow that through will disappear. While I am an advocate of taking action (see Chapter 29), pacey decision-making will ensure those actions are well placed and add value to the situation.

Fast decision-making is not a lack of fear about getting things wrong. Simply, highly confident people have developed the ability to hedge their decisions. When the risk is low they tend to make quicker decisions with minimum information required. Larger decisions require more thinking but still rely more on intuition than details. Decisions that have a wider impact or greater repercussions are well considered and rely more heavily on evidence and experience. As with action-orientation it can be useful to consider decision-making as a muscle to be developed. The more you work the muscle the better it will perform. As you exercise it and stretch it the more it will build. Do not wait until a crucial life decision presents itself to develop your decision-making.

CHOOSE FROM THE MENU QUICKLY

When you eat out how do you choose your food? Do you review every option available on the menu imagining how each will look, taste and smell? Do you confer with each of your party to find out what they are having before going back to the menu again and restarting the process?

Choosing from the menu at your favourite eatery should be an enjoyable and low-risk decision. So why not speed up the process? Richard Bandler, the co-creator of Neuro-Linguistic Programming, is reputed to have a simple process for choosing from any menu. He will read down the menu until he finds something he likes and he chooses that without reading any further. Simple!

This decision-making approach is simple, useful and leaves more time for the really important things (in this case socializing). I highly recommend it. Of course the approach spreads much further than choosing food. What are the other low-risk areas of your life you can stop over-thinking and make quicker decisions in?

Here are some examples:

- Choosing between two items of clothing you want to buy. If you like them both, just pick one.
- Deciding where to go on holiday. If they all seem great just choose the one that comes first in the alphabet.
- Which task to do first. If they are equally important just do one.
- What drink to have during a night out. If you like them all, just pick the first one that comes to mind; you can always have a different one next.

These may all seem like trivial examples, but that is the point. If it isn't a big decision use it as a training ground for making decisions quickly.

CHOOSE WHAT'S NOT ON THE MENU

Let's head off to your favourite eatery again and consider another way to choose what to eat. How often do you stop and ask yourself what you would really like before you even look at the menu? Most of us are conditioned by the assumption that we can only have what we think is available. How often do you ask for something that isn't on the menu? Try it, you will be surprised how often restaurants are able to provide or create what you want.

Now think of how this simple principle of ordering 'off the menu' can apply in other areas of your life. A great example is in career decisions. I have coached many people over the years who are struggling with decisions about what they should do next. Typically the choice is between two roles that are really what they want. It is rare for people to scope out their ideal job. Being clear on what your perfect role looks like speeds up the decision-making process considerably.

Michael Neill, the renowned success coach, once gave me a coaching assignment which entailed making decisions based on only one criterion – what do I want to do now? It was fascinating both to notice my reaction to the assignment and the result.

My initial reaction was resistance. 'I can't possibly do that, it will never work' was the primary pushback. Once I realized that I was sensible, trustworthy and reasonably sane, I understood that I wouldn't ruin my life during a week of doing this. The results of the assignment were that I was able to make more decisions and be more productive. Even tasks that I had been putting off for weeks got done. The difference was that I chose to do them and felt good about it rather than feeling that I should do them and procrastinating.

I would highly recommend the experiment. If you feel unsure about whether you can trust yourself to do the right thing, use it in prioritizing your work. I am sure you will find that you can trust yourself to make more decisions without the usual turmoil.

REDEFINE BAD DECISIONS

Let us take one last visit to that restaurant. You have chosen quickly, either from the menu or off the menu. Your food arrives and you tuck in. After a few mouthfuls the disappointment sets in. It's just not quite hitting the spot. Having eaten as much as you can, you push the half-eaten meal away. My question is: does this make the original decision a bad one?

All too often I see people damaging their confidence by chastising themselves over perfectly good decisions that then haven't worked out. 'I always make bad decisions' is a familiar cry from those low on genuine confidence. Highly confident people have a different set of criteria for what makes decisions good or bad. Their focus is on the process not the outcome.

If you have made a decision in the right way and for the right reason, then that is a good decision regardless of the outcome. For example if you take a new job because the career prospects are better, the organization has a good record of staff development and you get a positive feeling for your new manager, then that is a great decision. If you don't like the job and the promises about your career prove to be false, that doesn't make the decision a bad one, it makes the company a bad one.

Consider how you define good and bad decisions. Is it on process or outcome? Reflect on key decisions that you have made over the past year and categorize them based on the quality and pace of decision-making rather than the outcome alone.

In my early twenties, I found myself in a long-term relationship that was proving unfulfilling for me. I couldn't decide whether that lack of fulfilment lay with me or my partner. She was a good person but not right for me, but at the same time I had changed and wasn't nurturing the relationship to give it the chance to grow with me. I needed to make a big decision that would define the course of my life for many years to come.

Choice one was to dedicate myself to my partner and that relationship. It would need energy, patience, understanding and sacrifice. If that was the road I was going to take, it needed to be for the long haul. The relationship would not be repaired overnight.

Choice two was to let it go. We had been together from a young age and, as difficult and scary as it felt, perhaps a fresh start would be best for both of us. Over many months I explored the options. At times I thought I had made a decision and changed my mind when it came to committing to it. I made pros and cons lists that explored every option I could conceive and despite every sensible approach to the decision I could take, I just couldn't settle.

Ultimately the five-year relationship ended on the toss of a coin. From that moment on I vowed that I would improve the pace that I made decisions at. Not because I couldn't decide, but because I really knew the decision that needed to be made but couldn't commit to it. Highly confident people make decisions quickly and well. When they have explored what they need to they commit without ever worrying about the implications of a wrong decision.

In decision-making, hindsight is rarely a helpful thing. It can fool you into thinking badly-made decisions were good ones and well thought-through decisions were bad. A well developed decision-making muscle will help you make better decisions more quickly, easily and confidently.

29 TAKE ACTION

When it is obvious that the goals cannot be reached, don't adjust the goals, adjust the action steps.

Confucius

We have already explored the fact that confidence isn't something that we have or don't have. In Chapter 1 we introduced the idea that confidence is a state. It is something that we feel at certain times and don't feel at other times and, in that respect, we can look at confidence as something that we 'do' or 'don't do'.

The actual word 'do' is a verb that is defined as performing a particular task or working on something specific. It's interesting to see that word 'state' appears in the the *Oxford English Dictionary* definition of the word: 'do': 'Do…Work on (something) to bring it to completion or to a required state'.

In order to 'do confidence' you therefore need to take action orientated towards achieving the desired outcome, the state of confidence.

Learning to access a confident state should be tackled in exactly the same way as you would tackle any big project – by breaking it down into small, bite-sized goals.

Simply saying 'I want to be more confident' doesn't provide a clear enough goal for us to work towards. More confident when? More confident in what situations? What does more confident look like?

You could use the approaches in Chapter 17 (goal-setting) to do this in a way that really works for you.

Once you have these defined, get quickly into action. I have met many talented people who haven't achieved what they should have done because they didn't take action. Procrastination is the enemy of confidence. Don't hang around, do something! To quote Norman Peale: 'Action is a great restorer and builder of confidence. Inaction is not only the result, but the cause, of fear. Perhaps the action you take will be successful; perhaps different action or adjustments will have to follow. But any action is better than no action at all.'

STRETCH YOURSELF

There are many times in your life when you will have experienced a confident state. This may have been at a particular time, with certain groups of people, completing a set activity or perhaps in a specific environment. But you probably didn't feel confident the very first time you were in this situation.

Consider the analogy of driving a car. The very first time you stepped into a car for your first driving lesson I suspect that you didn't feel particularly confident. The reason for this is that it was a new activity for you, which was probably pushing you into your 'stretch' zone, or perhaps even your 'panic' zone. If it pushed you into your panic zone then you will have struggled to adapt and learn new skills. The reason for this is that it will have activated your primeval 'fight or flight' response deep within a part of the brain called the amygdala. In this heightened state of alert, your brain channels all of its resources towards survival. In doing so, it blocks out all other non-critical thoughts and processes. There will have been absolutely no learning taking place and you will have been in a far from confident state.

Equally, when you're within your comfort zone, very little learning takes place albeit for different reasons. Have you ever been driving along the motorway and suddenly thought to yourself, 'Where did the last ten miles go?'

The reason behind this common occurrence is that your brain is operating within in its comfort zone. Your brain is processing information with very little conscious thought.

KEEP DOING NEW THINGS

My colleague Ben Morton describes beautifully the importance of doing new things to help anchor our confidence:

'We generally tend to feel un-confident undertaking new activities or in new situations because they feel unfamiliar to us. By taking action, by taking small steps towards the very thing that makes us feel uncomfortable we are able to expand our comfort zone to encompass the "new thing". It will not provide us with an instant confidence transformation (although it may for some), but over time by consistently and repeatedly taking small, action-orientated steps we are able to expand our comfort zone.'

The key is to not beat ourselves up about the fact that we don't feel like the world's most confident person. Research by David Rock shows that among other basic human needs we also have a requirement for a sense of certainty and relatedness. Certainty is about knowing what is coming, how an event will turn out and what the outcomes will be. Relatedness is about our social needs, needing to feel connected to and accepted by those around us. Having these needs met activates a primary reward response in our brains and equally, not having them (or perceiving that we may not have them) activates a primary threat response.

DON'T LET UP

Consider for a moment the metaphor of a 'confidence muscle'. To strengthen a muscle we need to exercise it over and over again; in doing so it grows bigger and stronger. It is the same with confidence.

By repeating our small actions over and over again our brains begin to create new connections through a process known as neuro-plasticity, and in doing so, our comfort zone begins to expand.

Once you begin to feel more comfortable with the one action, you simply need to repeat the process. What is the next small action you could take to move you another step along the scale?

Accessing a more confident state is about taking consistent and repeated action. The reason that we can often feel un-confident is as a result of something being new, unfamiliar and outside of our comfort zone. One strategy to enable us to tap into a more confident state is, therefore, to take action. It is about turning towards the very thing that makes us feel un-confident and taking small, deliberate actions that will move us just one step closer to confident. And in doing so, we slowly but surely begin to expand our comfort zone until it completely encompasses the thing that once scared us the most.

Putting it all together

This is perhaps the simplest of all of the principles, but perhaps is the one that should be restated most often. Do something and keep doing things that take you in the direction that you want to go. Even if your action isn't quite on the right track then I strongly believe, as the metaphor goes, that it is easier to change the course of a ship that is moving than it is to get it moving in the first instance.

Stretching yourself out of your comfort zone creates a learning habit and a powerful one at that. A habit of finding new things to do programmes our brains to get certainty in new ways. Certainty for innovators often comes from the knowledge that they won't get it right first time rather than the desire to get it right first time. Once you have started these things then don't let up. Keep going and experimenting constantly. If you aren't naturally action-orientated then help reprogramme your brain to reduce the thinking time and increase the doing time.

30 FINANCIAL CONFIDENCE

All I ask is the chance to prove that money can't make me happy.
Spike Milligan

How connected are confidence and money in your life? Do you have more confidence the more money that you have? Many of us believe that the more wealth we have the happier and more confident we will become. My experience is that this generally isn't true. In this chapter I want to share with you some of the beliefs and strategies that the financially highly confident people I have encountered have about money and wealth. However I want to clearly steer you away from this as a starting point. Wealth and financial comfort comes as a result of mastering the strategies contained throughout the rest of this book. Confidence does not come as a result of a large bank balance.

Several years ago I carried out a study on happiness and found that, other than in the social group that had the lowest financial resources, there was no correlation between wealth and happiness. In addition those with a higher income often had less confidence in their financial position than those in the lower earning brackets. The important message is to ensure that you are anchoring confidence in every area of your life. You can then use these strategies for financial confidence as the icing on the cake.

Every financially confident person that I have worked with or studied shared an additional financial belief, strategy and behaviour. Each of them clearly demonstrated an abundance mentality. They made giving a fundamental part of their approach to money. One of the coaches I worked with would tithe one third of his gross income every month. This would be automatically taken from his account and not be part of his financial calculations. He started this practice when he earned a very modest income and continued through his business career even when he was earning a seven-figure sum. Indeed one of the things he credited to his increased wealth was his abundance mentality.

Before you even continue to the main strategies in this chapter think about how much you could give to those needier than you and how this may help to build your confidence in finance and life.

CHECK YOUR FINANCIAL THERMOMETER

How much would you have to have in order for you to consider yourself rich? £10,000? £100,000? £1,000,000? More importantly how much would you have to have in order to be completely financially free?

For many people the actual amount of money that they need to earn and save in order to be financially free on paper is much less than they think. We rarely think about it because we haven't consciously set our financial thermometer. In other words we aren't consciously aware of the settings on our internal belief system that tells us what too much and too little money is.

Stop for a moment and answer the following questions:

1. How much would you love to earn in a year?
2. If you checked your bank balance tomorrow, what figure would you be overjoyed to see in it?
3. How much do you think you deserve to earn this year?
4. What amount of money would be uncomfortably high to see in your bank account?

Your answers to questions 3 and 4 should be considerably higher than 1 and 2. If not then revisit your beliefs about money and work to increase the amount of money you would be comfortable with earning and having.

If you have a steady income and service any debt that you have, but still regularly worry about money, then take time to review objectively your financial status.

A great question to ask is: 'If you didn't earn another penny from this moment on, how long would it take before you were out on the street?' Most people's initial estimate significantly underestimates the reality. Take into account any savings you have, luxury items you could sell and money you could borrow from family and friends. If the length of time is three months or more, it is highly unlikely that you would ever find yourself in that position. You will have the skills, knowledge experience and network to find another job. With this insight you have the foundations of your financial confidence. Unless you plan to take big risks you are highly unlikely to end up penniless so you can examine your worries with a more objective viewpoint.

SPEND LESS THAN YOU EARN

This could win the prize for the simplest strategy in this book. It might be the easiest to understand, but it doesn't appear to be the easiest for people to implement. Now is a useful point to ask yourself the question: do you know the difference between the amount you earn and the amount you have to pay out each week? A highly successful financial advisor recently told me that very few people know their outgoings versus their income. Even those with higher incomes are prone to get into financial difficulties due to a lack of attention to the basics.

If you have become wrapped up in the current 'buy now pay later' culture, it is time to change the question that you ask yourself. Instead of asking, 'How can I get that outfit/phone/car etc?', the new question you must ask yourself to regain your financial confidence is, 'What is the best lifestyle that I can create on the income that I have?' Taking control of your spending doesn't mean that you don't get any treats; in fact it probably means the opposite. After a short period of time you will find that you are more mindful about spending and buy treats and luxuries that you appreciate most.

(There is a brilliant money saving expert website, with a great page specifically to help you save money, listed at the back under Further reading).

BUILD A MONEY MACHINE

One of the best approaches to increasing your financial confidence is to create a system that you know helps to grow the assets that you have. One of the most commonly touted by personal development experts is the 'three pots' approach to assigning your assets. This approach ensures that you take a balanced approach to saving and investment but one that allows you to grow your assets.

Out of the money that you have to invest you create three pots to allocate that money to.

The security pot

This is where you make investments that are secure by nature. These investments won't give a huge return but over the longer period the return grows. Your first investment must be into your security pot.

Typical security pot investments include:

- Cash (2–6 months' worth)
- Pension
- Life insurance
- Fixed bonds
- Government investments
- Your home

The growth pot

This is where you place your growth investments. These investments provide a much greater rate of return but have a much greater risk that the investment may not be successful. There is no guarantee of return on a growth investment.

The fantasy pot

These are the material things that you want for no other reason than it would be wonderful to have them. It could be a home in the sun, an executive box at your favourite sports venue, a second or third car. Essentially anything that you don't actually need but would love to have.

Typically if you are starting out on your investment journey, you may want to put around 40 per cent of your investment capital in the security pot and then split the rest between the growth and fantasy pots. Remember the more you put into your fantasy pot the less your return will be.

If you are older you may want to play it safe and put more in the security bucket, while if you're younger or more aggressive you might consider dropping the security pot to 30 per cent.

Your next step is to decide what the right balance is for you and, with the advice of an independent financial expert, decide on the right investments for you.

Putting it all together

High salaries and big bank balances do not guarantee confidence. However, as you are developing confidence in all other areas of your life, it is a great opportunity to insure against financial challenges that may make it more difficult to maintain your confidence levels.

The financial services industry is awash with advice and the fundamentals of being confident are not complicated. The crucial factor that is ignored by most financial experts is that your wealth and financial confidence is a direct reflection of your beliefs and relationship with wealth. Let me illustrate this with an example a coach shared with me following a conversation with a client.

He had worked with this client for some time and knew he was a highly successful businessman in Los Angeles. The businessman contacted him for an emergency coaching session. He asked the coach to advise him on how to convince his wife of the importance of a business deal he was about to embark on. He described to the coach how important the deal was and that if he didn't focus on it, it could jeopardize his whole business. His wife didn't understand this and was threatening to leave him if he went through with it. For a moment the coach was caught up in the story but then stopped his client to ask, 'If you didn't earn another cent from this day, how long would it take before you were out on the street?' The client paused thoughtfully before answering, 'Seven years'. When the coach probed a little further he revealed that his assets were in the high tens of millions of dollars.

My coach helped me realize at that point that our financial confidence does not shift with our bank balance. In fact, instead we must build our confidence in order to build our wealth.

31 BECOME THE WORLD'S LEADING EXPERT

You have to have confidence in your ability, and then be tough enough to follow through.
Rosalynn Carter

My early steps into consultancy and coaching were tentative and nervous. My tender age and lack of formal qualifications left me in awe of colleagues and clients and with a consistent feeling of having to fake it until I made it. Few people had a greater role in my development in those early days than Patrick Hare. Not only was he one of the most intelligent and insightful people that I have ever met, he was also one of the most self-confident. He was brilliant and exemplified so much of what real genuine confidence brings. He also developed one of the most valuable confidence strategies that I have ever learned and used, and I am delighted to share it with you.

This strategy is perfect for those moments when you are put on the spot to answer a question that you haven't had the time to formulate an answer for. It will help you to remain calm, appear confident and to answer any question well. As you get comfortable with the process it is best to follow it precisely and in the order described in this chapter. When you are familiar with it you will refine it and find your own format.

I have one final note of caution before I share this strategy. I am aware that some people use this 'world's leading expert' to become a fantastic bluffer. This isn't what the strategy is designed for and, while it will help you to fly by the seat of your pants more convincingly, eventually you will be caught out. In a meeting when you are being challenged on facts, figures or data, if you really don't know then there is more confidence in calmly saying that you will need to confirm the information and come back to them than to completely guess. The world's leading expert strategy is better placed in situations where you are being asked your opinion or when you know the answer but can't bring it to mind.

MAKE EYE CONTACT AND STEP FORWARD

When people are nervous or put on the spot, one of the automatic physiological responses is to take a step back. This is a small socially acceptable version of our flight reaction kicking in. Nervousness also reduces our comfort with eye contact, again triggered by a reptilian response to look for other threats and escape routes. Understanding this makes sense of the first two stages of our strategy. When asked a question that you want to respond to in the way a world's leading expert would is to give full and relaxed eye contact as they ask the question. An old but valuable guide for good eye contact is to rotate your gaze within the triangle formed by the two eyes and mouth of the person you are connecting with.

As they finish asking the question, make a very small subtle movement towards them. For example if I am presenting to a group and one of the members asks a question, I take a small half-step towards them as I prepare to answer. If you are in a meeting where all participants are seated the movement may be a gentle lean forward onto your elbows in their direction.

This movement sends an unconscious message that you are confident in the answer. It is important not to step into the questioner's personal space as this may be perceived as overly assertive.

THANK THEM BECAUSE YOU ARE THE EXPERT

I am sure you have been in a situation where your inner voice's immediate response to a question is a resounding 'oh no' followed by a huge internal diatribe about why you wish you hadn't been asked that question. Of course this is hugely unhelpful when comes to responding and often shows on your face. With this in mind the third strategy for the world's leading expert process is to thank the questioner for the question. This applies no matter how tricky the question is or how negative the intent from the enquirer may be. It is even more powerful to accompany this with a gentle and genuine smile.

It is only right to thank them for the question when they have asked you about something you are a world's leading expert in. And you are, aren't you? Well if you follow this process then it suggests that you are. When we teach this to groups we encourage them to use those words exactly; however, when using the strategy in real life you will probably need to refine it slightly. Telling your finance director that you are the world's leading expert in budgeting may not be the best career move. Instead you might suggest it is an area you have been reviewing lately or that it is a subject you are passionate about. Of course if you are an expert I think it's perfectly acceptable to say so. Highly confident people aren't inappropriately humble.

SHARE THREE THINGS

There are many views on why the number three is such a significant number. Some attribute it to its implicit connection to the holy trinity. Others attach meaning to the long-held view that the brain was made up of three specific parts (a view now considered to be outdated). Whatever the reason, three is a powerful number and when establishing expertise it is the only number you need. From this moment on there are only three things that you need to know about anything.

When answering a question having smiled, taken a small step forward, thanked them for the question because this is an area you are an expert in, you now advise the questioner that there are three things they need to know. Underline this point by holding up three fingers.

It is now time to share your expertise. Answer the question with short, to-the-point answers. If you practise this process, don't prepare the answers in advance. The strategy enables you to tap into your expertise by getting you into a great state to answer the question, so notice how effectively you respond. In real situations you will have done your preparation; the strategy allows you to demonstrate your knowledge effectively.

As you make your three points, mark off your answers on each of the three fingers that you held up. This gives congruence to your answers and keeps you on track with your responses.

One last note, I always advise starting with three. If during the process you think the two points you have made are enough then after two you say, 'Actually I think they are the two most important things,' and stop. Similarly if you want to add one extra point, then do so, and then end but make sure you maintain eye contact and remain in the forward physiology.

Putting it all together

To help recap the process I will use an example from a new client meeting I had recently.

Client: Richard, can you tell us the most important things this senior team need to keep in mind to make this project a success?

Me: [*Keeping eye contact with the person posing the question and taking a small step forward*]. It's great that you've asked that as supporting senior teams is a specialism of mine. There are three things that make the biggest difference [*holding three fingers up*]. First is how well the business projects are connected to the strategy [*tapping one of the held-up fingers*]. Two is to support the groups to stay connected between sessions [*tapping the second finger*]. Third and most importantly is to ensure that of every member of the senior team models the new behaviours in every decision.

These replies led to another really positive conversation about how we support that client. It wasn't a question I was well prepared for, but the process helped me to access the knowledge that I had on the subject.

The examples I have given throughout the chapter have been work related, but the same strategy can be used no matter what environment the tricky question is posed in. From dealing with tough teenage questions to difficult doorstep conversations with neighbours, the world's leading expert process allows you to access your most resourceful self.

32 CONFIDENCE IN CONFRONTATION

Only be you strong, and very courageous, then you will make your way prosperous, and then you will have good success.
Joshua 1:7

Can you define what conflict is for you? It is an interesting and important starting point for developing your confidence in times of conflict. People have very different conflict barometers. For some it is a cross word or raised voice at the family dinner table, while for others a full-volume shouting match across a boardroom is considered clearing the air and still doesn't qualify as real conflict. The importance of checking and potentially adjusting your conflict barometer stretches further than having your own internal strategies for being at your best in those moments of disagreements.

It is also crucial to develop your awareness of others' comfort with conflict. If you are uncomfortable with conflict it is likely that you will encounter robust conversations that only you see as conflict. An ex-colleague of mine used to ring me regularly after team meetings to check if he had been involved in any discussions that I considered conflict. The answer was almost always yes, but his comfort with and confidence during conflict was such that interactions had to be long, loud and highly emotive before he even considered there to be conflict. Until then they were just robust conversations.

Beyond this the confidence required for conflict is a calm one. Even if the moment calls for a raised voice or energetic response, your internal state must be composed. This steady state will help you to think clearly and keep the strategies in this chapter at your fingertips. You will be able to choose to embrace the conflict or walk away from it when the moment is right. Good conflict should result in a change for the better. This may be a different decision, or a change in relationship, or the commitment to a new course of action.

Conflict for conflict's sake is rarely healthy. Whether in work, home life or in other relationships, only engage in conflict where it is possible to have a healthy outcome, even if it doesn't feel good at that moment.

MAKE CONFRONTATION YOUR CHOICE

There are two main reasons that people don't walk away from conflict. The first is that they view walking away from a confrontation or challenge as weak. The second is simply that when you get embroiled in a conflict it is easy to forget that you can choose to remove yourself at any time.

It can take more strength to walk away, especially in arguments or conflicts that you have an emotional stake in or when you are being unfairly attacked, but it is important to recognize that you have options which maintain your integrity and show your strength rather than weakness.

The useful question to ask is, 'Why should I stay involved in this conflict?' Identifying the purpose of the conflict is a pivotal point in building your conflict confidence. For example, if you are in a project meeting at work and a peer is shouting down your ideas and being unfairly critical of your work, before responding ask yourself the question. If the answer is to protect your reputation and that of the team, then respond appropriately. If, however, the drive to respond is just to show the others in the meeting that your confronter is an idiot, then a neutral response such as, 'Of course I believe you are wrong, but I don't intend to get into this now,' is likely to be a more powerful one. If they continue with their attack they are just demonstrating that they are being driven by an unhelpful ego.

ADOPT A WINNING PHYSIOLOGY

The physiology that you adopt during a conflict will send the quickest message to those confronting you about your power and confidence in the situation. It will help to reduce the fight or flight mechanism that is triggered when you feel attacked and will help you to think more clearly. Here are three sub-strategies to maintain the right body posture:

Breathing

Keep your breathing slow and deep. Make sure that you are breathing from deep down in your stomach. The natural reaction to conflict is for our breathing to quicken and become shallower and you must counteract this.

Slowing your breathing down will help you to think clearly and maintain a sense of calm. Inhaling for a count of eight then exhaling for eight can be really useful in levelling your breathing.

Eye contact

Keep your eye contact steady and relaxed. Make sure the muscles around your eyes don't tense up. Avoid staring. The eye contact triangle formed by the other person's eyes and mouth is a great place to look. If you want to look away for a moment then look above or to the side of the person you are confronting. Avoid looking down. Finally don't blink too much. We tend to blink more under stress and this will send an unconscious message that you are feeling the pressure.

Stay centred

Those uncomfortable with conflict or confrontation will be familiar with a slightly dizzy or lightheaded feeling that grows as the tension does. It can feel literally like you are going to lose your balance. In moments of confrontation focus your internal attention on your abdomen. Imagine a heavy weight in the centre of your body which is keeping you steady. It can also be useful to focus for a moment on the feeling of your feet on the floor. These simple ways to keep yourself centred will again help you steady your sense of calm and control even in the most heated disagreements.

SAY LESS

At the exact time you want to rant and hit out verbally it is a great idea to say very little. If you have employed the other strategies in this chapter so far this will be easier. Keep your sentences short and to the point. For example, 'I don't agree' or, 'That isn't true' said firmly doesn't need any qualification.

Always stick to the facts. Your influence is reduced the moment you introduce speculation or assumption into your argument. Don't get derailed if your confronter is bringing up historical issues.

You must avoid insults, even if others are throwing them; they will only inflame the situation. There is nothing more unsettling than being smiled at by someone you are insulting. If those who you are in conflict with are swearing then it can be useful to mirror their language to demonstrate how they sound, but don't go on foul-mouthed rants. In most cases excessive use of bad language will damage your credibility.

All in all the less you are saying the more time and attention you have to listen for the holes in your confronter's case and to formulate the appropriate responses.

Putting it all together

I once encountered an expert on dealing with conflict who suggested we should approach it in the same way that Homer Simpson approaches doughnuts (mmmmm conflict). In theory I agree, but for many of us there is some significant groundwork to be done before we get to that point.

It is fair to say that those who are highly confident around conflict and confrontation embrace it and see the friction involved as energy for getting things done. They also know exactly the right time to walk away from unhealthy and unhelpful confrontation. I have spent a large part of my life avoiding any sort of confrontation at work and home and only recently realized how detrimental this is to getting the best results. I am not advocating seeking out conflict, but if it appears, and there is value in observing or being involved in it, then approach it with calm confidence.

In businesses today there is a growing desire to encourage staff to have courageous or difficult conversations. In the UK I think this is a tremendously healthy step. We have to move on from the culture that results in meetings which produce apparent agreement followed by bitching and sabotage.

In families confrontation will happen. When it does it should be dealt with and moved on from – genuinely – as quickly as possible. Many of the biggest family rifts come from issues that have been allowed to fester.

33 BUILDING A CONFIDENT TEAM

There is no 'i' in team but there is in win.
Michael Jordan

Organizations rely on teams for their success. In sport the stronger team will consistently outperform the group of talented individuals. Even in battle a fighting unit will only achieve its ultimate purpose when functioning as a highly effective team that has confidence in the abilities of the individuals within it.

If you are charged with creating a confident and successful team, the first place to start is defining what a team is.

The most useful definition of a team I have come across is the following:

'A group of people with a full set of complementary skills required to complete a task, job, or project.

Team members operate with a high degree of interdependence, share authority and responsibility for self-management, are accountable for the collective performance, and work toward a common goal and shared rewards(s). A team becomes more than just a collection of people when a strong sense of mutual commitment creates synergy, thus generating performance greater than the sum of the performance of its individual members.

www.businessdictionary.com

This highlights the fact that, in order to be a team, there must be shared goals and rewards. The success of each team member must be reliant to some degree on others and the end result of the team's work together must be greater than would be achieved without that reliance and support.

If any of those elements aren't present, then you may be trying to create a team where one isn't required. For example a group of marketing managers with responsibility for their own business areas or brands may benefit from working together as a group to share ideas but it is unlikely that their success is reliant on the success of their colleagues. They are a workgroup not a team.

It is an important starting point. We often encounter managers whose confidence is being affected by their inability to get a work group to function as a team. Teams by this definition are desirable and effective but not mandatory. Before moving on to the strategies to create a confident team, ensure that the group you are focusing on are and should be a team.

DEVELOP A SHARED PURPOSE AND VISION

The form of shared goals that your team has will have a significant bearing on the sense of confidence and energy the team has. Strategic objectives are important in a business sense but they rarely engage and energize.

The importance of personal clarity of purpose has been highlighted in other parts of this book. Clarity of purpose for a team is equally important. A team that is absolutely clear on core purpose has the foundations for great decision-making and action.

The key question to ask is, 'Why does this team exist and why should anyone care?' Avoid answering the question as if it is a 'what' question. You and your team will know what you do; this question helps to clarify the purpose of having the team or business function in the first place. Get your team clear on purpose first and confidence will naturally increase.

While purpose is why you exist, vision is where you are going. Here is a simple vision question. 'If your team was hugely successful in the next 18 months, how would you and all of your stakeholders know?'

This question should be answered as richly as possible. Too much focus is often placed on the crafting of words that will look good to those outside of the team. A team's vision acts as a guide to give them clarity and energy for their work.

CREATE A POSITIVE TEAM CULTURE

Your team's culture will determine what is acceptable or unacceptable, important or unimportant, right or wrong, workable or unworkable. The culture of a team provides the sense of how we are with each other and how we do things around here.

Your choice as a manager or leader of a team is not whether it has a culture but what form it takes. Your team's culture will be defined by what you demonstrate through your behaviours and by what behaviours you reward and discourage within the This tacit culture building will always be more powerful than any stated cultural preferences if they are in conflict.

Announcing that you want an open and honest culture will be worthless if you make decisions behind closed doors and only share information on a need-to-know basis. Similarly the desire to have an innovative culture will always be killed if you allow team members to ridicule others' off-the-wall ideas.

First clearly define the culture that you want to foster in the team then describe specifically the acceptable and unacceptable behaviours that will nurture that culture. Be ready to lead the way to give others the confidence to co-create the culture.

ALLOW YOUR TEAM FREEDOM TO SUCCEED

How clear are your team on what success looks like? How well do their individual objectives help them to understand what a good job looks like and what a great job looks like? This is the first step in building a team's confidence in their ability to succeed. It is easy to overlook such a fundamental step but I have extensive experience in organizations where whole middle-management communities work on the basis that if they aren't getting their butts kicked by their boss they must be doing OK.

You also must be willing to step back and give your people the opportunity to flourish. Delegation is a challenge for so many managers and the confidence of their team suffers as a result. Make a clear distinction between the delegation of the what (task) and the how (approach). You are only truly delegating when you allow the individuals in the team to find their own approaches to the task. Even if they don't do it exactly as you would this doesn't necessarily make it wrong. You have to trust and support them to find their own way.

Few things will damage the confidence of a team quicker than an over-zealous superior who steps in at the first sign that members are finding their own way to achieve the task. Providing your team is operating with the purpose in mind, they are in service of the vision and, of course, within budget and the law, then be confident enough to let them flourish.

Putting it all together

If you are in the privileged position to lead or manage people in any walk of life it is a great opportunity to share the confidence that you have developed. Having clarified first if you are leading a team or a work group you must set about putting the structures in place that give the best opportunity for the team to flourish and succeed.

Even if the organization that you are part of doesn't promote the development of a core purpose and vision, take the initiative to create them for your team. When you do you will notice the development of very natural confidence within the team. Defining and most importantly demonstrating the culture that you want the team to adopt gives those team members who haven't yet discovered the secret of confidence the courage to make their mark. If you have team members who aren't willing to commit to the culture then you must tackle them appropriately.

Confidence within a team will always support its success. Technical ability and hard work have their place, but without a sense of confidence they will remain short term. Leadership sometimes requires you to do something different. Draw on everything that you have already learned and have the confidence to make a difference to the people work with and for you.

34 BUILDING A CONFIDENT ORGANIZATION

Vision is the art of seeing the invisible.
Jonathan Swift

What is an organization? Organizations get blamed for some of the world's biggest environmental challenges and are credited with some of the greatest achievements. But organizations don't really exist. It is a generalized term for a group of people with a particular purpose. In business sense this will be to provide a product or service and as a result create profit. It is easy to forget that the achievement of the purpose, vision and financial results of any business relies on its people. So when creating a confident organization the leader's focus must be largely people-focused.

Alexis Bowman is a Managing Director at BT Openworld and reflects this brilliantly through her thoughts on building a confident organization:

> When considering building a confident organization a leader must start with some fundamental questions. Does it exist now or are we all striving to create it? Is it a tangible state we can achieve? What is your definition of a 'confident organization'? As leaders, followers and observers do we know how to take our organizations to the next level? We will all have very different ways of viewing and answering some of these questions but it is my belief that wherever you start on that journey and whatever your vision for a 'confident organization' is, there are three fundamental strategies that will assist us all in our own very unique, challenging, yet exciting journey, be that in business, at home or in life generally.

For me, a confident organization is one that can demonstrate a resistance and ability to adapt to volatility, to capitalize on challenges by making them our future opportunity to grow. It has a robust and positive attitude towards risk and ultimately will attract and retain talent. Confidence isn't just about being aggressive in its approach and strategy but it is about having an air of maturity that allows it to take positive challenges in a variety of environments, drives empowerment of its people in order to develop and grow the business. By nature confident organizations are not arrogant. They avoid narcissism and complacency and are clear they must take their stakeholders with them on their corporate journey.

EMPOWER AND GIVE OWNERSHIP

We talk about empowerment a lot in business, but the benefits of achieving real empowerment across an organization has no bounds. The approach to empowering the people in an organization to make decisions and become accountable for their own actions and outputs is critical. Getting the balance between empowering individuals within an organization and achieving hard business results is key.

To really empower individuals I believe we need to take the bold step away from purely driving our discussions via data and performance metrics. Yes we still need to keep an eye on the numbers and use them to complement our decision-making, but restricting decisions and activity to how we interpret results stifles the human view of what may really be happening and where new opportunities may exist.

We can help people to own their performance by shifting away from the classic top-down approach to management. Enabling an individual within their own local team and away from the classic top-down approach means we are not restricting their actions within the bounds of a data set or trying to force them to make decisions that are derived from someone else's view of the world.

In doing this they will feel like they own part of the organization. Coming from a data-driven world, has been quite a big bit of learning for me and a shift in mindset!

The world shouldn't and doesn't revolve around numbers on a spreadsheet and equally I don't believe one size always fits all in approach, so empowering individuals within an organization to think and to be responsible for their own actions breeds creativity, loyalty and ultimately a greater ability to deliver. As individuals, when we feel like we are not only accountable for something but we also own our own destiny, then we really start to excel.

An organization that works as one team, promoting ownership and empowerment will be a more confident and robust organization. Removing the age-old dichotomy between being accountable but not having the power to own and make decisions yourself will lead you to a more confident organization. In my experience rewarding our best people with increased autonomy has been highly successful for both the individual and for the organization.

INVEST IN TALENT

We all accept that people are the foundation of nearly everything we do. People make the world go round! Investing in people and nurturing talent is an absolute must in creating a confident organization. In doing this you create an organization that isn't reliant on any one individual to make it succeed. Considering that almost all business transactions, business change, business growth and development require human interaction there should be no hesitation to invest in and develop the people who will be leading the business now and in the future. Organizations rely on people to change behaviours and create cultures. People are asked to be engaged and deliver outstanding results consistently. This is more than a work-for-money transaction and therefore it is an absolute necessity that you continue to invest in your people.

Look beyond the traditional approach to developing high fliers. Take time to review the strengths across the organization. While developing those people with the drive, passion and integrity to lead your organization is key, if you have individuals who aren't performing ask yourself why before moving them on. Is it just that you have a square peg in a round hole? By investing in them and helping them move into a role that they will excel at may benefit everyone. Don't be bound by a high level view of the world; there are gems to be found in some of the most unexpected places!

Remember too that when it comes to recruiting and forming teams, aim to achieve a balance between the technical capability needed and those who inspire and demonstrate real passion to achieve. Look for the skills that are difficult to train. Some people have a natural talent and can learn the technical aspects of a role but it is very difficult to do it the other way around. Once you have that team, continue to invest in and challenge them to become the best they possibly can. A confident work force breeds a confident organization.

KEEP AN EYE ON THE LONG GAME AND BE PREPARED

How often do you get to the end of the day having worked non-stop, had no lunch breaks and there are still a million emails sitting in your inbox? We tend as a working community to spend the majority of our time firefighting and reacting to the day's biggest story, but we very rarely schedule in that critical pro-active time. We sometimes are so engrossed in the now that tomorrow seems so very far away. If we as leaders model this way of working then naturally it will become the culture.

To become a confident organization you must create a balance between the long and short term. We need to move ourselves away from short-termism and prepare ourselves for what comes next. Where do we want to go? What is the long-term goal? How do we move away from fixing the symptoms of a problem to actually fixing the root cause and developing those blue sky ideas we all have? I believe there is one simple and effective strategy to doing this – create some space to breathe and think.

It sounds too simple to even mention, but the value your organization gains from allowing people time to think and prepare for tomorrow is huge. Giving people the time to think doesn't mean they will have all of the answers but it does mean they will develop a resilience and confidence in their ability to adapt and excel beyond today's view of the world. This in turn will create a more future-proofed and confident organization.

Putting it all together

Alexis Bowman's view of what is required to build a confident organization mirrors that of other forward-thinking business leaders. From LinkedIn's Jeff Weiner to Cougar Automation's Clive Hutchinson, senior people in organizations of all sizes are creating organizational cultures that engender trust and confidence. In a world where the pace of change continues to increase and what was once considered discontinuous change has now become continuous, this is crucial. Organizations in the 21st century are flexible and responsive. They must quickly reshape and refocus as market forces change while continuing to act in service of their core purpose. In order to do this effectively we have to create organizations, and by that I mean the people who are the organizations, that are confident enough to be creative, resilient and solve problems as they occur for the very first time.

35 CONFIDENT JOB APPLICATIONS

Choose a job you love, and you will never have to work a day in your life.

Confucius

Being a participant in any recruitment process is a hugely challenging and stressful situation for most people. Not only do you need to be at your confident best but you have to showcase the skills and experience that you have in a way that your perspective hirer appreciates.

Applying the strategies in Chapter 23 (on using the power pose) will give you a huge advantage. It is the perfect preparation for any job interview. But the selection process starts way before then and as part of my research for this book I interviewed a number of people who are highly confident and successful in these processes. The good news is that there are some patterns which are easier to understand and apply.

Before we get to the strategies specific to getting hired, it is worth observing that each person I interviewed had a medium to high degree of day-to-day confidence. This doesn't mean that you can't get hired if you don't access your confidence in every area of your life. It simply means that you need to apply a range of strategies at the same time. Applying for jobs when your self-esteem is low in all areas of your life can mean failure is a self-fulfilling prophecy. As in any relationship you must value yourself before someone else can truly value you.

There is also the question of being clear on what the right role for you really is. Too many people apply for a job because they think it is right for them rather than being clear on what they really want or what their skills give them the best chance of being hired for. If you aren't currently employed, I appreciate that your net has to be cast wider, but that doesn't mean you should limit your job searches to the most obvious places. Value your skills and experience and ask yourself, 'What role would enable me to best demonstrate these skills?'

On these foundations you can apply the strategies that I have found to be most common in those highly confident in recruitment processes.

FOCUS ON YOUR ACHIEVEMENTS

Take a look at your CV. What does it suggest is most important about you? Your job history? Your address? Your qualifications? Now consider what your prospective employer would most value in their new recruit? I would suggest it is the ability to get the job done.

Restructure your CV and make your achievements its focus. In any previous job, what results did you achieve or what difference did you make? If your previous work experience is limited, focus on your achievements in other areas such as hobbies and interests or voluntary activities. One of the interviewees for this chapter shared that she is still asked more questions in interviews about her time as part of her school council than about her higher education, despite being in her 30s.

Carry this achievement focus through to your interview preparation. As you prepare answers to potential questions ensure that your language highlights achievement rather than process.

For example:

In response to: 'Can you give me an example of when you have led a team well?'

Say: 'When I led the team that delivered the highest customer satisfaction scores over the last three years, I ensured that everyone was clear on the vision and what their roles were in achieving it ...'

Rather than: 'I led the customer service team for three years and ensured that everyone was clear on the vision and what their roles were in achieving it ...'

This is a simple change but a powerful one that will distinguish you from others.

WHAT MAKES YOU DIFFERENT?

Most of your preparation should be focused on matching your skills and experience to the role, exploring how your personal values overlap with the company values, and matching your experiences to the potential questions you may be asked in the interview.

However, the strategy that differentiates the highly confident during hiring processes is that they also focus on what makes them different.

They all ask themselves variations on the following questions:

- What unique blend of skills, abilities and experience do I have that no one else does?
- What do I bring to the role that no other candidate does?
- What could I help my boss/team/organization achieve that they haven't thought of yet?
- How can I contribute beyond the role that I am being recruited for?

One of my interviewees was the least formerly qualified and in one of the most junior roles, yet was absolutely clear what he could add to any role that others couldn't. This more than anything made him fearless in his approach to the selection process.

WHAT WOULD HAVE TO HAPPEN FOR YOU TO HIRE YOU?

Imagine that you were in charge of recruitment for the role that you are applying for. What would have to happen for you to hire you? Consider the question from every angle.

- What would your CV need to look like?
- How would you need to sound during any telephone interactions?
- How would you need to dress?

- What would your demeanour need to be during the interview (remember to power pose beforehand)?
- What else would convince you to hire you if you were in charge?

It is useful to remember that recruitment processes are incredibly costly. The average cost to replace someone who has left an organization is estimated to be somewhere between £5,000 and £28,000 depending on their level in the business. The longer the process takes the greater the cost. Employers want to hire someone but they need it to be the right person. Answering these questions goes further than good preparation. They send a message to your brain that you are important in the context of the process and that you should feel confident about it. This forms the beginning of another confident loop.

Putting it all together

There are few selection procedures where the end result is guaranteed to be a positive one; whether you are in a job and looking for the next step or aiming to get back into employment, a confident approach will help you illuminate your qualities as a candidate. Going through the motions isn't enough. Nor is approaching it as a process. From the recruiter's side and from your side it is an opportunity to showcase yourself and to make new connections.

Approach it with energy and confidence and you will make an impression. You will also start another confidence loop. Triggering your confidence going into the process and giving your best throughout it will leave you feeling more confident even if you don't get the role. Approaching it half-heartedly or even with energy but without confidence will leave you feeling that you didn't do your best and make tapping into your confidence more of a challenge next time.

The strategies that the highly confident people I interviewed shared are not complicated and provide a clear path for preparing in the best way for your next job opportunity.

36 CONFIDENCE AT WORK (PART 1)

*He who has never learned to obey cannot be
a good commander.*

Aristotle

In business, the ability to be confident and to develop others' confidence in you is a premium quality. I would consider it a requirement of leadership. In fact if I look at the four characteristics that followers most desire from leaders (honesty, inspiration, being future-focused and competent), all require the leader to have a genuine confidence in themselves to do them well.

During the course of my work I am fortunate enough to coach, consult with and learn from some great role models in outstanding organizations. What continues to surprise me after over a decade in this field is the humility that the best have. It is easy to forget that even the most senior people in the largest organizations with the biggest budgets have to develop their confidence. They also have to make choices and face events without a feeling of confidence.

While all of the tips and techniques in this book have been modelled on the highly confident, it is hugely important to me to bring you thoughts and ideas directly from the minds of some of those people. I particularly want to allow talented people in business that I experience as leaders to share their thoughts with you unedited. I trust you will find them useful.

Within moments of meeting Martyn Beachamp, International Director from Tesco Bank, I knew he was comfortable in himself and his approach to business. As his strategies demonstrate, this hasn't happened by accident. Beauchamp grew up in the east-end of London and has built a career with some of the leading names in the financial services industry. He has worked around the world, is fluent in several languages and yet he still sees confidence as something to be nurtured. Here are his lessons from a confident leader.

PREPARE THE IMPORTANT THINGS

For me, confidence is a state – my state – and so I own it. Confidence can be acquired and cultivated but it has to be owned first. That my confidence is largely in my own hands has been one of the biggest and simplest revelations of my professional life. Knowing this helps me manage my mind-talk and frees me to focus on the strategy that matters most to my confidence levels: building resilience through continuous preparedness.

Being prepared gives me confidence. I don't think I'm particularly unusual in that sense. Many of us have agonized over the questions we might be asked on a particular line on any page in a hundred-slide presentation. But as I've progressed through my career, I've realized two things about preparing for confidence.

I find that I spend more and more of my preparation time on state management. For instance, I'll prepare carefully for a big presentation to cement my confidence, but I'll now spend as much time thinking about things like knowing my audience and their motives and coalitions, or how to stay composed if I'm tripped by a low-ball question, as I will about the remotest possibility that I might be asked a detailed question on Appendix IX. In preparation, I'll prime myself with confidence by focusing on a moment when I was at my best and viewing it as a spectator. Knowing myself and then the facts – in that order – gives me the confidence I need to be effective in these set-piece events.

HAVE RESILIENT CONFIDENCE

In between these events are dozens of daily interactions in which the right level of confidence can make all the difference to my impact. It's impossible to prepare in the formal sense for these moments. Which brings me to the second thing I've realized about my confidence: it's the resilience of my confidence that matters – the ability to substitute wild swings with a more manageable ebb and flow within the tolerance limits required for me to lead with impact. I do this through a form of continuous preparation.

Here are some examples. I make sure I spend time each week preparing a range of short, punchy elevator speeches on the issues that matter most, just in case I bump into a key stakeholder. I stay alert, externally focused and keep my eyes open for new ideas. I read widely but economically, focusing on a manageable number of trusted sources, and usually at the same time most nights after I've put the kids to bed, so it's locked down into my routine. I study and know my stakeholders. I don't obsess over it, but I keep it simple and make it a process. I find it consistently improves my ability to prosper in conditions of ambiguity, which makes me feel confident and strengthens my impact.

BUILD CONFIDENCE IN DISCOMFORT

'I deliberately work on being confident when uncomfortable. I want to know that when I'm out of my comfort zone, I've got enough about me to draw on. I use preparedness to give me that confidence: throughout my career, I've consciously and consistently sought out opportunities to test myself outside of my comfort zone. And there are tactical measures I take: when I envisage being uncomfortable, I'll often wear a suit. I know it makes me feel more alert and energized. By owning and strategically managing my discomfort, I feel I can approach areas of difficulty or times of crisis with a greater degree of confidence.

I see confidence as a means to an end: I want to be confident because when I am consistently confident, my personal impact is greater. By playing my preparedness long and making it a process, I feel best equipped to lead with confidence and, on those occasions when my confidence takes a knock, to quickly bounce back.

Putting it all together

Martyn Beauchamp's confidence shows a level of thinking that moves beyond the day-to-day practices involved in the development of self-confidence. He outlines the basis of a more strategic and politically savvy approach to maintaining and developing the level of confidence required to deliver in a challenging role in a dynamic organization. The greatest lesson from Martyn's story is to see the preparation of your confidence as at least as important as your preparation of facts, figures and information. His confidence is deep and genuine but it is also nurtured and developed.

Martyn is unusual only in the detailed nature of his preparation. He is not unique in the sense that what he does can be replicated by anyone who is willing to pay attention to the things that they do. In my work with him, I consider him to be one of the most politically astute leaders I have encountered. I believe that much of the skill he operates with comes from the same principles that he shares in this chapter. If you adopt this strategy, I believe the approach will allow the natural talent you have to flourish and to allow others around you to recognize it.

37 CONFIDENCE AT WORK (PART 2)

Strength does not come from winning. Your struggles develop your strengths. When you go through hardships and decide not to surrender, that is strength.

Arnold Schwarzenegger

My interview with Ray Biggs, the Head of Customer Contact at Sainsbury's, brought back into focus the importance of focusing on what you are already good at. Since reading Marcus Buckingham's *Now Discover Your Strengths* I have been an advocate of developing the positive skills and attributes that you have rather than just focusing on the things you aren't yet good at. According to Buckingham's website (www.tmbc.com/), if you find someone who can answer 'yes' to the question, 'At work do you have the opportunity to do what you do best every day?' you will find a business unit with higher productivity, higher customer satisfaction and higher employee retention.

Buckingham argues that we must change the culture of recruiting people, focusing their training and development on their weaknesses. This is a great opportunity to ask yourself, 'Am I building a career that plays to my strengths?' You can expand the question beyond your work: 'Are the things that I spend most time on allowing me to draw on my most positive attributes?'

Ray's approach to leadership and the development of his confidence as a senior leader in the organization may not have been formulaic, but the following are his clear strategies that can be replicated if you want to build your confidence as a leader in your organization.

USE YOUR STRENGTHS AS YOUR FOUNDATION

'Most people don't know that I have a background in
drama. I actually have a degree in it and drama is all about
communication. It is no surprise then that my style is hugely
people-focused. Confidence in communication at a senior level is
self-fulfilling. The more you communicate the more confident you
become in it. The more confident you are the more you do it.

The very best development I have had in my career helped me
to understand why I do what I do and how those things are
successful for me. For example, I am not naturally a structured
person. The realization that I could still be successful was a real
lightbulb moment for me. I need to build my team with this in
mind, but I have enough confidence in my thought process that
if am presented with a problem I let my unconscious work on it
and the answer will pop out.

Self-awareness is crucial. Reflect on success experiences from the
past and identify what has helped you to achieve what you have.
Know what you're good at; recognize what you're not good
at. I really believe there is a much greater benefit in developing
your strengths rather than marginally improving the things you
aren't so good at. If you look at yourself honestly you can create
a career path that allows you to move up the direction of your
strengths not your weaknesses.'

BUILD YOUR NETWORK

'Leadership is interesting for me. The frustration I have is that
you can't prescribe leadership. It is what you do moment by
moment. I don't think leaders' reputations or confidence are
really built at the big events. It is during the conversations at the
coffee machine. It is how you make eye contact with people as
you pass them in the corridor and whether you say good morning
to them no matter how busy your mind is.

Leadership is about being able to get things done and that
relies on building relationships which in turn relies on your
ability to communicate. As I have said before, communication

is self-fulfilling. It relies on self-belief and self-awareness and it builds self-belief and self-awareness.

I believe that when people struggle in a management role it isn't usually the role, it is their relationships or lack of them in the organization that they are struggling with. During my time with Argos I led through the network that I had developed over the course of eight years in the business. When I joined Sainsbury's I was aware that it was such a huge organization I had to trade on my confidence to build a network. Until I had a strong network I wasn't completely effective. The primary goal was to build the network so I could get up to speed as quickly as possible. If I hadn't spent time in the past reflecting on my successes and strengths this process would have been so much more difficult. It also requires an element of hard work. I have a belief that if I work hard I will get on. As I first stepped into that new role I knew the effort that I made would help me through. I knew that I was unlikely to feel completely ready for the new role, but that feeling unsure was OK as long as the network was growing.'

TAKE CALCULATED CHANCES

'When I was a little younger I used to go for jobs that I thought were too big for me. I would often get to interview stage and that was a boost. This is an example of taking a calculated chance. People with more experience than me wouldn't even apply in case they didn't get it. They would be left wondering 'what if?' I would be left with more experience and more confidence. You have to be prepared to take risks and see disappointments for what they are – just disappointments.

If something isn't working stop doing it and do something different instead. When this feels like a risk or that it will be difficult I just ask myself, how hard can this be? If your gut says you can do it then make the change. I don't believe that there is anyone whose gut feeling is wrong more than it's right and my career turned when I began to trust my gut feeling more. It was noticeable that other people began to trust me when I trusted myself more.

Taking calculated chances also means having the confidence to stand up and be counted. Being able to say, 'Sorry, I really don't understand' or, 'No, this is wrong' in a skilled enough way is crucial. If you haven't got the skill to do that yet, then you must develop it. If you don't have a voice that impacts on your confidence much more than having a voice and not being listened to. Have the right conviction and stand up to be counted on the right thing.

While you have to accept that not every decision you make will be right, by being willing to make considered leaps of faith people will think you are the expert. When people tell you you are an expert it helps to bolster your confidence. As your confidence gets stronger you will be more willing to take a leap of faith. It is a great sequence to begin.'

Putting it all together

The strategies that have served Ray so well over almost two decades in the retail sector should give great hope to any aspiring young leader in business today. Nothing that has helped him to a senior role in one of the biggest brands in the UK is impossible to replicate. His confidence in his communication and decision-making comes essentially from taking action, reviewing his successes and doing more of what works.

38 THE CONFIDENCE TO GO IT ALONE

It's fine to celebrate success but it is more important to heed the lessons of failure.

Bill Gates

I can speak with first-hand experience that being an entrepreneur is both hugely rewarding and hugely challenging. Being your own boss is a privilege balanced by the occasional sense that you are at the beck and call of your clients. Creating, maintaining and growing a business has been one of the toughest things I have done in my life, yet I wouldn't change it for the world.

In the recent economic downturn a record number of businesses were created in the UK. This means a record number of entrepreneurs whose core confidence will undoubtedly be tested to its extreme. Around 50 per cent of businesses fail in the first three years and with the houses, family incomes and self-esteem of the entrepreneurs creating these business on the line, it is important to take every opportunity to make confident decisions that work out for the best.

As this chapter implies, I believe that anyone creating a new business must look beyond the immediate challenge of creating one that is financially viable. In order to be a confident and happy business owner you must aim to create an operation that moves you towards the life you want to lead. It is so important to me. I have met too many talented people who have focused too highly on the lifestyle element of the business and ended up with an enterprise where profits were so low they had to work every hour just to keep it solvent. Equally I have met many people who have created hugely profitable businesses that kept them away from their families and allowed them precious little time to enjoy the fruits of their labour.

This chapter doesn't profess to give the answer to every question an entrepreneur will face, but it does present three strategies that I have observed the most genuinely confident business owners use and what they focus on consistently.

IDENTIFY YOUR NICHE

To get straight to the heart of the matter, too many businesses are created to provide too much to too many people. This is driven by the fear of the business owner that they may miss out on a sector of the market.

In almost every business sector you won't create a highly profitable business without identifying a niche. If you are creating a new business it can feel counter-intuitive to exclude some of your market. The reality is that people pay more for expertise or difference so you can make more money for less work or risk. For example if the roof on your house needed to be repaired and you saw the following two vans on your way to work, which of the following would you choose to call?

- The generic white van. A little rusty around the edges with 'Joe Bloggs Repairs – no job too big or too small. Call us now for reliable work for a cheap price'.
- The silver Mercedes van. Clean and well driven with 'Joe Bloggs Specialist Roof Repairs – high quality work from the roofing specialists'.

Around 90 per cent of people will go for the latter despite the expectation that they will pay more than if they contacted the first company. The 10 per cent generally do so because they haven't got the money for the latter company and feel that they have to make do for now.

Which do you want to be in your business sector? How do you want to make money (remembering that turnover is vanity and profit is sanity)?

Ask yourself the following questions to begin the process of identifying your niche:

- What makes my product or service different from the rest?
- Who would I love to do business with (and do they have the right budget to do so)?
- What would I have to change to double my profits with the same turnover?
- How can I position myself differently from the rest of the market?
- What would be so enjoyable that I couldn't help but make a ton of money while still benefiting others?

BE CLEAR ON WHAT YOU DON'T DO

To support the identification of your niche you must get clear on what you don't do and who you don't do business with. This requires real confidence but, as you reap the rewards, it will reinforce your confidence in your decision-making processes. You must be ruthless in your thinking. For example, I coached a former senior Head of Learning and Development who had decided to set up her own development business. When I raised the question of niche, she told me she had considered that already and was going to focus on management, leadership and coaching for middle and senior managers. It took some convincing her that this wasn't a niche as it was including way too many people. This kind of approach will lead you to be seen as a generalist and therefore not allow you to command the fees that a specialist does.

In the retail world, in recent times, those at the very end and very bottom end of the market have thrived. Those who target everyone as their customers have faced the biggest challenges.

Answer the following questions:

- What products or services do I absolutely not provide?
- What kind of customers don't I want to do business with?
- What sectors do I want to avoid?
- Who shouldn't be able to afford what I offer?

BE BRILLIANT AT BALANCE

I once attended a seminar during which the expert speaker on the stage told a rapt audience that in order to become a millionaire entrepreneur you must be willing to sacrifice everything. He shared stories about missing out on time with his family, missing holidays and obsessively working through the night. I decided at that moment that if that was what it took to become a millionaire then I would rather continue with my very happy and comfortable lifestyle. In fact I know that is not what is required. I know many millionaire entrepreneurs who would credit their focus on balance as a key-contributing factor to their success. That is not to say they don't work incredibly hard but they don't do it at all costs.

Christine Riordan, the Provost and Professor of Management at the University of Kentucky, wrote a wonderful article on balance for the *Harvard Business Review* 'Work-life 'balance' isn't the point, 4 June 2013) and suggested three key strategies for finding your balance:

- Strive for worklife effectiveness, not balance.
- Define success in all categories of your life.
- Maintain control.

Integrate this approach into your initial business plan. If your business already exists, challenge your thinking about balance and how present you have to be for your business to be a success. Highly confident entrepreneurs know that they must take time to recharge their batteries to avoid burnout. Make this part of your business strategy.

Putting it all together

Entrepreneurs are likely to be the drivers of the new economy. As the numbers of self-employed and new business owners grows, so does the need for an understanding of the confidence challenges they face. If you are already in this position then you know first-hand what this means. Every day brings decisions that call for you to be brave and certain.

A keen understanding of the foundations of confidence and the applications of techniques throughout this book will help you to stay on course and make good decisions when all around you are falling into doubt and panic. The three strategies in this chapter will help you to lay the foundations of a business which has the opportunity to survive and thrive.

My wish for you is that you create more than a successful business. Frankly, life is too short to just create a successful business. My wish is that you use the opportunity to build the life you want to lead with your business as the fuel for doing so. Doing successful work that makes you come alive is a wonderful way to anchor confidence in your business life and beyond. If that work also makes a positive difference to others then your legacy becomes one that stretches far beyond the simple creation of a business.

*I always try to be myself. Ever since I was an introverted kid,
I'd get on stage and be able to break out of my shell.*
Beyoncé Knowles-Carter

There is a common misconception that an introvert is a person who is shy. In fact being an introvert is quite a different thing. Shyness means feeling apprehension and nervousness around others. An introvert can be shy but many extroverts also feel the apprehension in others' company; they just react to it differently. Put simply, an introvert is someone who is energized by being alone and whose energy, particularly their mental energy, is drained by being around other people.

Introverts are more concerned with their inner world. They enjoy thinking and exploring their thoughts and feelings. They often avoid social situations because of the drain of being around people. This is true even if they have good social skills. After being with people for any length of time, such as at a party, they need time alone to 'recharge'.

When introverts want to be alone and are forced to be with others it can be particularly wearing. They simply want the time to be with their own thoughts and being with people, even people they like and are comfortable with, can prevent them from achieving their desire to be quietly introspective.

Introverts are often strong conversationalists; however those conversations are generally about ideas and concepts, not about what they consider the trivial matters of social small talk.

So why have a specific chapter on confidence for introverts? Well my guess is if you are asking that question you probably aren't introverted and there is great value in reading on to understand more. For those of you who have read this introduction so far and are saying, 'Yes, that is me', then you are likely to have faced the challenges that growing and showing your confidence as an introvert brings.

The myths about introverts are common and unfortunately widely believed, especially in many sections of the business world. You are likely to have been labelled as shy, not liking people, always wanting to be alone and not liking to be in crowds. None of which are true but how do you show your confidence to others when doing so for long periods drains your energy? Many of the introverts I work with feel that it is an extroverted world and to get on you have to somehow be 'fixed'. I hope that in time the power of introversion is more valued by the media and social commentators, but until then here are three simple strategies to help others see your power without your battery running out.

ENLIGHTEN THE EXTROVERTS

I had best come clean now. I am an extrovert. More importantly, my affection and value for introversion came relatively recently. I had been blindsided by the myths too. I thought I should just leave the introverts alone to be quiet together. Remember that introverts and extroverts perceive their worlds quite differently. While this may seem like an obvious statement it needs to be emphasized. It is more than a general difference of opinion. For many extroverts the idea that being alone recharges your mental energy is quite odd. They want to be with others to refresh theirs and make decisions on this basis. If you are working with a group of extroverts take time to explain your introversion to them. Don't wait until your energy is low to do it. Too often introverts are forced to explain why they want to be alone or why they are being quiet at exactly the wrong time. Remember, the extroverts assume there is something wrong with you and will try and be social to perk you up.

A little information is usually enough to stop the extroverts badgering you every time you want a moment with your thoughts, along the lines of, 'I'm a bit of an introvert, so when

I have been in a meeting all day sometimes I just like to spend some time in my own company or I get a little quiet. It's nothing personal and there is nothing wrong, so don't worry if you notice me joining in the conversation a little less' As one extrovert put it, 'If we aren't talking often we aren't thinking. We forget that isn't true of introverts'.

Share your introversion confidently and you are likely to get huge support from fellow introverts in the group.

STAGGER YOUR RECHARGE TIME

This is by no means a time management book, but some extra thought to your planning can go a long way to keeping your introverted confidence up. One particular introvert I work with plans her diary around almost a monthly cycle. For three weeks she will attend meetings, then arrange social activities and even host parties at weekends. She then has a week where she works alone and avoids seeing anyone socially. The challenge for her is week three when her mental energy is so low she struggles to function at anywhere near her full capability. Even her social interactions are less enjoyable and have a forced sense to them.

It is much healthier for introverts to stagger their interactions. If you have a socially busy period at work, then reduce activities outside of work that impact on your energy. If it is possible to leave gaps between meetings then do so and ensure that time is used for activities that recharge.

Be discerning about who you spend time with both in work and beyond. Social circles change over time and as an introvert you can benefit from spending more time with people who demand less from you in social situations.

Overall, plan your time and interactions in such a way that you don't wait until your energy is gone completely before you have time on your own. Doing this will only reinforce the introvert stereotype.

HANG OUT IN BIGGER GROUPS

This may sound a little counter-intuitive at first, but spending time in larger groups can be less draining than in smaller ones. Smaller social groups can be more intense and require more interactions. In larger groups you are likely to be required to contribute to the conversation less and to be left to your thoughts more.

I recently ran a training event for 120 people in an organization where groups are usually limited to 12 participants. One introverted member of the group spoke to me during the lunch break to say that she was enjoying being able to learn without being constantly put on the spot. She could choose to contribute to the conversation when she felt it was valuable and not just for the sake of it.

If your job requires you to attend networking events, I would highly recommend groups attended by larger numbers of people. Smaller networking events with the traditional structured small talk are hugely draining for introverts. Larger events allow you to choose the conversations you get involved in.

Even public speaking can be more palatable when larger numbers are involved. One executive shared that she much preferred speaking to groups of 500 than to groups of 20, as she was more comfortable with the less personal nature of the sessions. She also said she much preferred being on the stage than having to make small talk with her colleagues afterwards.

What opportunities can you create to experiment with spending time in larger groups?

Putting it all together

If you are extroverted and have made it this far through the chapter, I applaud you. Your new insight will not only help the introverts you spend time with, it will also help you to influence more subtly with a wider range of people.

If you are an introvert, I know that there are times when it feels like the world is run by extroverts. From presidents to CEOs, the extroverts are cast as the great trailblazers, influencers and leaders. Be sure that isn't true. Remember, you only see the extroverted behaviours, you don't see the preparation and recovery that some of those in the public eye undertake to be able to perform in this way. Also, there is without doubt great power in introversion.

In her thought-provoking TED Talk, Susan Cain (author of *Quiet: The Power of Introverts in a World That Can't Stop Talking*) has three calls for action for the extroverted world:

'Number one: Stop the madness for constant group work. And I want to be clear about what I'm saying, because I deeply believe our offices should be encouraging casual, chatty cafe-style types of interactions you know, the kind where people come together and serendipitously have an exchange of ideas. That is great. It's great for introverts and it's great for extroverts. But we need much more privacy and much more freedom and much more autonomy at work. School, same thing. We need to be teaching kids to work together, for sure, but we also need to be teaching them how to work on their own. This is especially important for extroverted children too. They need to work on their own because that is where deep thought comes from in part.

Number two: Go to the wilderness. Be like Buddha, have your own revelations. I'm not saying that we all have to now go off and build our own cabins in the woods and never talk to each other again, but I am saying that we could all stand to get inside our own heads a little more often.

Number three: Take a good look at what's inside your own suitcase (her metaphor for what is really important to you) and why you put it there. So extroverts, maybe your suitcases are also full of books. Or maybe they're full of champagne glasses or skydiving equipment. Whatever it is, I hope you take these things out every chance you get and grace us with your energy and your joy. But introverts, you being you, you probably have the impulse to guard very carefully what's inside your own suitcase. And that's okay. But occasionally, just occasionally, I hope you will open up your suitcases for other people to see because the world needs you and it needs the things you carry.'

40 CONFIDENT INFLUENCING

It's easier to win when everyone wants you to win.
Randy Komisar

If you have ever wished that you had the confidence to ask for what you wanted, or if you have avoided a negotiation just in case you didn't get what you wanted, then this is the chapter for you.

Haider Imam is a gently challenging and playful former colleague of mine who also happens to be an expert in the field of influence. He is the author of *Straight To Yes* and is your coach for the next few pages.

… And in the blink of an eye, the dinosaurs were gone and a new world order emerged. 185 million years of rule by brute force and stealth disappeared overnight, paving the way for an increasingly gentle, diverse and interdependent ecosystem. I believe a similar transition is occurring in how we interact, influence and achieve success both at work and at home.

Okay, okay, maybe a little overdramatic but, as Bob Dylan said, the times they are a changin'. Thankfully for those of us with slightly quieter natures, having an impact is no longer about displaying the loudest voice, the biggest shoulder pads or the most creative skulduggery. We know now that these stereotypically 'Wall Street' behaviours are both unsustainable and dangerous to ourselves and the wider system.

So what is the new way? The latest scientific research presents us with some wonderful paradoxes in that, in the game of success, nice guys actually finish first. And last. That rejection is actually a key to success. And that our ideas are far more persuasive when people think they came up with those ideas themselves. So, here are three of my favourite lessons in influence that I am confident will serve you well.

FEED YOUR NETWORK AND DON'T OVEREAT

In today's interconnected, interdependent world, don't we need to look after one another more than ever to realize our ambitions? For many of us, however, our kind and generous behaviours have sometimes led to having figurative sand kicked in our faces, watching the wrong person get promoted or resolving, 'No more Mr Nice Guy!' The trouble is that wearing the mask of Ming the Merciless only lasts a few weeks before we revert to type because masks are notoriously uncomfortable and fiddly to keep in place. If only being a kind, decent person could equate with being a top performer in our field. Well, turns out it can.

Wharton Business School's top professor Adam Grant published a body of research in his 2013 book *Give and Take* outlining just that. In his work, he identified three kinds of behaviours or 'types': 'givers,' 'matchers' and 'takers.' Givers operate from generosity, doing favours for people in their network. Matchers operate from *quid pro quo* – keeping score of favours and demanding the same amount in return. Takers operate from self-interest, looking to see how much value they can extract from the system around them. Grant's research looked at how successful each type is in their organization or field and presented various conclusions:

1. Takers end up near the bottom of the success ladder: the lone wolf attitude of dog-eat-dog, withholding information and self-interest means that, over the long term, takers are despised by those around them, resulting in a fall from grace.
2. Matchers end up in the middle of the success ladder: they reap what they sow.
3. Givers end up at the bottom of the ladder: constantly responding to people's requests for help, empathizing and putting others' interests ahead of their own means they are least productive and successful.
4. Givers end up at the … top of the ladder: wait … what?

Fascinatingly, Grant's research showed that nice guys finish first ... and last. The difference? Quite simple, it seems. While both sets of givers generously feed their network of colleagues, friends, suppliers and even competitors by doing useful things for them, unsuccessful givers overEAT. That means they overindulge in (E) empathy, (A) availability and (T) timidity. Being emotionally over-involved in other people's stuff, giving so much time to others that our own work suffers and being too timid to ask for what we want or need (or ask for help) is a great recipe for last place. Top givers were empathetic enough, asked for what they needed and, while generous with their favours, protective of their time.

- Go through your contacts list or address book every few weeks to remind yourself who is actually in your network.
- Make strides to understand what people in your network want or need: what are their desires, hobbies, interests, challenges, anxieties or opportunities? What do the people who are important to them need?
- Regularly schedule these 'five-minute favours' for an hour or two in your diary each week and do them in one block, not *individually*.

COURT REJECTION

Many people spend their lives nervous of looking incompetent, pushy or greedy. I believe it mostly all comes back to a fear of being rejected. Since we're social creatures, being isolated is a death sentence: biological self-preservation encourages us to stay in good favour with people. We tend to ask for a lot less, a lot less often and with a lot less conviction, just in case we're rejected and fall from grace. And yet successful persuaders collect more rejections than most people because they ask for more, more often and with more conviction than most people.

So, here's a three-level exercise to build your rejection muscle and achieve oneness with being declined – and know that it is a muscle, that grows with practice. The aim is to intentionally seek out small rejections and when you get them, to realize that your internal health and wellbeing remains intact. Feel free to substitute the following examples for your own:

Beginner level: Next time you're eating somewhere that gives diners sachets of ketchup, mustard and mayonnaise, politely ask if you can have one extra sachet for free, regardless of how many you have on your table or plate.

Intermediate level: Next time you're in a restaurant, politely request something that's not written on their menu, simply because you're in the mood for it.

Master level: When you're next buying something in a shop, ask for a particular item for free.

Learn to love rejection because the more often you're being rejected, the more often you're asking; the more often you're asking, the more you'll start hearing 'yes'. And it's perhaps useful to remember that in life, if you ever happen to cross the line, it's generally easier to seek forgiveness than to ask permission!

PULL FIRST, PUSH LATER

Whenever we try to convince, persuade or push someone to accept our ideas, we can inadvertently create resistance and push-back (it's called psychological reactance – a natural defence mechanism). This is particularly the case with people over whom we have no direct authority. And teenagers.

So, rather than purely relying on pitching, suggesting, telling and 'Why-don't-you-ing' we can aim to 'pull', to let the other person have at least some input into the idea, so they feel that it is partly or wholly their own. Once they articulate the idea, they'll feel vastly more committed to following it through.

Here's how: avoid saying, 'Here's what I think we should do ...' or 'Can I share my ideas about (...) with you and why I think it'll be great for us?' or anything that involves you 'selling' your ideas.

Instead, try sharing your desired outcome explicitly (for example, 'I'm really keen to head up a finance project team ...' or 'I'd like to visit the Chicago office to forge links and share practices ...')

and then asking any of the following questions, or your own versions of them:

- 'What are your thoughts on how that might benefit us/you/the department?'
- 'How could you see that working, practically?'
- 'What would have to happen for you to be happy to sign off on that?'
- 'How would you pitch that to your team?'

When you hear answers that support your outcome, express interest and probe more. If you hear a flat refusal, acknowledge their answer and firmly ask the question again, emphasizing words like 'could', 'might' and 'would' to make it safe and hypothetical.

Particularly when we have to influence upwards or persuade big egos, pulling on intrinsic motivations is always a better way to get what you want. And you can always 'pitch' afterwards if you need to.

Putting it all together

Notice how many of Haider's strategies feel comfortable and how many challenge your current influencing boundaries. During a team meeting Haider once challenged me to go to a shop and ask for something for free. I refused on the basis that it was wrong to ask for something for nothing. As the rest of the team returned from the experiment with some pretty cool things that they had picked up for nothing but a human exchange, I realized that I needed to expand my influencing bandwidth.

As your confidence becomes more grounded, challenge yourself to influence in new and more daring ways and enjoy the rewards. Here is a summary of Haider's strategies for influencing with confidence:

1. Your success potential is a function of your network strength.
2. To strengthen your network, proactively feed it, regularly and generously, but never overEAT.
3. Practise collecting rejections of increasing size.
4. Instead of pitching your ideas first, offer your outcome and ask the other person or group how that could be wonderful.

By marrying your goals with the goals of those you're hoping to influence, it's possible to transform both your results and your relationships.

41 CONFIDENT PUBLIC SPEAKING

*To suppress free speech is a double wrong. It violates the
rights of the hearer as well as those of the speaker.*
Frederick Douglass

In October 2013 a poll found that more people feared public
speaking more than they feared being buried alive. One hack
suggested this was 'because being buried alive at least would
be private. No audience to watch you writhe'. These findings
aren't unique. A similar poll in the USA in the nineties put public
speaking at the top of a list of things that those surveyed were
afraid of. Number two on the list was death. The suggestion that
some people would rather die than speak in public is of course
ridiculous, but it shows the power of negative thinking that
people have about presenting to audiences. Indeed even the most
confident sports and business people I have worked with over the
years have found this to be one of the biggest challenges. So in
this chapter I would like to share with you some ways to tap into
your natural charisma and present with confidence.

Before we get on the stage, it is well worth remembering the
power of mental rehearsal as covered in other chapters. If the
pictures and movies that you are playing in your head prior
to the presentation are of it going badly you are increasing the
likelihood of that happening and making yourself feel bad too.
Create a rich mental picture of the whole presentation or speech
going brilliantly and keep it in focus in the lead up to the event.

It is also worth remembering that most of your audience want
you to do well. There are very few situations where those in
attendance want you to fail. Stay positive in your thoughts about
their thoughts as a way to boost your confidence and use these
strategies to keep it high.

HONE YOUR GESTURES

In my earlier days working with large groups I studied some of the most charismatic and confident presenters, trainers and speakers in the world. My quest was to find out what helped them keep their audiences' attention so well. I was surprised to find that the single thing they all had in common was that their gestures were more pronounced than others who were less successful in front of large groups.

This doesn't mean that you have to make wild and extravagant gestures, but when you do, make the movement more pronounced. For example, if you point to something on a visual aid then do so with a quick, definite movement.

To give you more of an idea, place the palms of your hands together then move them out to around a shoulder-width apart slowly and with your hands relaxed. Now place them back together and do the same again but moving your hands quickly and while keeping them tensed. Imagine you were using these gestures while describing the projected growth of your company. Which would be more powerful? Remember it isn't always about making bigger gestures but making them more marked and distinct.

As you become more confident with your gestures, use them to give weight to the key messages in your presentation. The more your gestures accentuate your message the more confident and charismatic you will appear. Of course you aren't miming every word but using your gestures to highlight the most important points.

CONNECT WITH SUPPORTIVE AUDIENCE MEMBERS

One of the most common questions I get from those speaking to larger audiences is how do you connect with a big group? The answer is that you don't; at least not all at once.

As you are speaking connect first with those who are willing to be connected with. Find the smiling faces or those nodding encouragingly. Keep eye contact with them for slightly longer than the others – around three to five seconds will be enough. Then sweep your gaze across the rest of the audience to the next person to connect with. As you continue, the other people in the audience will be drawn into the energy exchange between you and the initial connectors.

It is a simple and powerful technique that you will have experienced many times. If you have ever noticed two people connecting with each other across a crowded bar then you have been drawn into the energy connection between two people. Don't wait until you are presenting to a large group to practise this for the first time. When in meetings try to subtly connect with those who you think are open to it. Soften your focus as you do so and just hold the connection for a moment or two then move your eye contact around the room again for a while before returning. The aim is to become comfortable with the process. When that happens you are certain to draw an audience of any size in to your presentation.

ANSWER THE FOUR QUESTIONS ANY AUDIENCE HAS

In the 1970s Dr Bernice McCarthy developed 4MAT®, a new method for helping learners learn in their preferred style. It has been used in thousands of teaching settings for over 25 years and the four core questions provide a fantastic template upon which to develop a presentation, talk or speech.

When preparing your presentation, work on the basis that your audience has one of the following four questions and set out to answer them in this suggested order:

Why?

Why should they listen? Why are they here? Why is this important and why now? This engages these audience members emotionally. If you miss this question, as many people do in formal presentations, those for whom 'why' is the most important question will tune out.

What?

What is the concept, idea or information? This may also be the detail or structure. The more academic or theoretic members of your audience will need this information.

How?

This covers the practicalities. How will this work? What is the plan? The doers in the audience need this information to be covered. They will be patient enough to wait until you have answered the 'why' and 'what' questions but they will be vociferous if you don't give them enough of the 'how'. If you have ever had a question following a presentation that started with, 'That's all very well in theory but ...', you probably haven't given a strong enough 'how'.

What if?

What are the risks and possibilities of this idea, concept or proposal? Some of your audience will be naturally risk averse and want to know that you have thought about the risks and done something to negate them. Others will be possibility-focused and will have immediate thoughts about how this can be developed, expanded or moved on. Show your audience that you have considered these but try not to be derailed by giving huge amounts of detail to the 'what ifs'.

Highly confident presenters and speakers tend to have a basic structure that they develop their content around. I highly recommend this as yours. You can use it just in the introduction, in the main body or in both. Take time to notice the positive impact of using the structure to anchor your confidence further.

Putting it all together

The biggest barrier standing in the way of most people becoming confident speakers and presenters is the thoughts they have about speaking and presenting. Many people see it as one of the biggest challenges they will face. Seeing the absurdity of these thoughts will create the biggest shift in your confidence in these situations. Enhancing your vocal and physiological skills becomes easy when seeing presenting as easy or even enjoyable.

In other chapters of this book I have shared strategies about the value of simple breathing techniques and using the whole of your vocal power. I would highly recommend marrying these with the strategies in this chapter. Together they will provide the foundation for you to become a highly proficient and confident presenter and speaker.

As you develop your skill and certainty, I would recommend that you take opportunities to speak to as wide a variety of audiences as possible. This will prevent you from falling into the trap of thinking you're confident presenting to some groups and not others. As you already know, confidence is transferable and so are speaking skills. The only thing that impacts your ability to speak to one audience over another is your thinking about the audience.

42 CONFIDENCE IN SPORT

There may be people that have more talent than you, but there's no excuse for anyone to work harder than you do.

Derek Jeter

While this chapter is primarily aimed at those who play competitive sport, the lessons from it are relevant to anyone who has to deliver moments of peak performance in any area of life. By peak performance I mean specific times when you need to be at your best and draw on some specific skills to deliver a result. This could be in a high-challenge meeting or interview, or in a dramatic performance, or any situation that requires you to draw on previous training.

Sport is one of the most obvious environments that confidence and the lack of it is seen and felt. When athletes lose form, quite often it is confidence that isn't present. This prevents the athlete from tapping into their training and allowing their body to do what it has been prepared for. Take professional football as an example. Most players will have been passing the ball since they were five or six years old. Professional players train for three to four hours most days of the week and play at least once a week. Despite this, most players will go through a spell where they misplace passes and struggle to do the basics of the game to the standard they should. It looks like their ability and sometimes even their energy has been sucked from their body. Clearly this isn't the case but we probably all have that sensation that we just aren't able to do things that we know we have the capability to. It is a huge confidence drain.

This chapter will help you to take back control of the mental processes that can lead to these dips in performance. My work in sport has given me access to some talented athletes but also some of the most mentally strong people I have met in any walk of life. The application of their strategies will help anyone who wants to make the most of their potential.

TRUST YOURSELF

Graeme Carrick has a unique view on football. He was a highly rated midfielder and a graduate of West Ham United's acclaimed youth academy. In his early 20s his playing career was ended by injuries. He has continued to work in the game he loves and is currently a highly rated national Grassroots Coach. As well as being a respected coach he has the unique perspective of watching older brother Michael's career blossom with Manchester United and England. Graeme is a student of the game and has just completed a Masters in Sports Coaching.

Carrick is clear that trusting yourself is a crucial part of maintaining your confidence. 'As a player you know what your best routine is. It is important to stick with this even when performances aren't at the level you would want. Everyone is different, everyone knows what their best approach is. Even on match days you will have developed a pattern that is right for you. Minimize the impact that external factors have on this routine. Towards the end of my playing career my confidence was at its lowest when I couldn't trust my body to do what it needed to. That's when I knew I had to retire. As a coach I see it as part of my job to pick up on players' routines and allow them to maintain them as the foundations of their performance.'

I share Graeme's belief that you should trust yourself and the abilities you have developed. Your job is to relax enough that your body can do what it has been trained to do. Over-thinking doesn't help. It can be much more useful to distract your mind than making extravagant changes to your approach.

During a confidential coaching session with a cricketer, he told me that when he broke into the England squad he was told he should change his whole approach to the game. He was asked to tone down the way he spoke to colleagues and even had to change how he warmed up for games. It was made clear that if he didn't he might not remain in the squad. Unfortunately as he made the changes his performance level dipped and he was left out due to a lack of runs.

Following our session he decided to be himself more. He was careful not to upset others and explained why he prepared in the way that he did, but he stuck to his routines and approaches. Naturally his form returned and he had a successful spell on the side. It is always important to trust your approach and not change it at the first downturn in performance.

KEEP THE BIG PICTURE IN MIND

James O'Connor is currently a player coach of successful US soccer team Orlando City. As of 2015 the franchise will be part of the MLS (the top tier for professional soccer in the US) and is one of the most successful teams in the history of the US Soccer League. O'Connor's playing career in the UK saw him make 554 appearances for West Bromwich Albion, Stoke City, Sheffield Wednesday and Burnley. He also holds the highest coaching qualification in Europe, the UEFA Pro Licence.

O'Connor's number one message for sporting confidence is to keep focused on the big picture.

The goals I had for my career remained the same for ten years, yet when I went through spells when my confidence was low it would coincide with getting overly focused on smaller, less important challenges. Always keep the end goal in mind and ask yourself, "Is what I am doing helping me to get closer to my end goal?" This approach helped me to make good choices about my health, fitness and my mental attitude. I didn't achieve everything that I wanted to in my career in England but I can be satisfied that I did everything that I could along the way. I can't imagine how much people must regret not doing everything they can to make the most of their potential.' Graeme Carrick agrees. He believes that keeping the big picture in mind will help you to manage the perceptual challenges: 'If your confidence is low your focus tends to narrow too much. You concentrate too much on the detail and don't see the big picture. Keep the big picture in mind. Focus on the overall job in hand and what you want to achieve.

FRAME MISTAKES USEFULLY

Carrick also believes that framing mistakes usefully is crucial as you build and maintain your confidence. 'One of the differentials of highly confident people I have played with and coached is that they keep mistakes in perspective. They don't dwell on errors for too long. We have to see them as opportunities to learn. No matter what level you play or perform at you will slip-up at some point. Learn what you need to and then move on to the next thing you can do to move you towards your big picture.'

James O'Connor suggests three simple questions to help you to frame mistakes usefully:

1. What do I need to do to make sure the right thing happens next time?
2. What can I learn from this?
3. Can anyone support me in avoiding this mistake in the future?

He suggests asking these simple questions, answering them, then mentally leaving the error behind.

If you watch the top players over the years they make a mistake then are willing to put themselves in the same position again. I have played against some great players and they were all willing to push themselves to be in challenging situations and take risks even if they had made an error. This feeds confidence rather than being a result of it. Dwelling on mistakes makes you fearful and seriously inhibits performance.

Putting it all together

The experiences of Carrick and O'Connor give another layer of strategies to build and maintain confidence in the sporting arena and beyond. Their experiences playing, working and, in Graeme's case, growing up with athletes at the very top of their profession makes them well qualified to give an insight into confidence in sport.

My personal experience has shown me that confidence will increase technical ability significantly. Ability without confidence will never flourish. In order to perform at your best you must also take care of the environmental factors that affect performance. On regular occasions that I am called in to work with a player who is struggling mentally I find someone who isn't sleeping or eating well. These things must be corrected alongside any interventions to increase confidence or any other mental ability.

If you are fortunate enough to have the talent to perform at a good level in any sport, take every advantage you can to make the most of that talent. Confidence is a crucial factor. Alone it will not help you to realize your potential but alongside great technical and physical development it will help you to reach your personal heights.

43 WHAT COMEDY TEACHES YOU ABOUT CONFIDENCE

The intelligent man finds almost everything ridiculous, the sensible man hardly anything.
Johann Wolfgang von Goethe

There are few things that require more confidence than going on stage with the job of making people laugh. Being funny to a roomful of people who are expecting to find you hilarious is daunting to say the least. One of my early teachers in the art of presence and charisma was Kevin Cherry. As well as being an esteemed business consultant, he is a lay preacher and a performer with the He-Ha's improvised comedy troupe. Having come to comedy as a profession late in life, he is well placed to guide us through comedy's lessons on confidence.

The comedian Demetri Martin points out that your true identity as far as others are concerned is the second thing people say to identify you at work or at parties. You know:

'Demitri Martin' (the first thing)

'Who?'

'The geeky one with the bowl haircut' (the second thing).

'Oh, yeah.'

Take a moment to reflect on what the second thing people say about you is.

It doesn't matter what your self-image, USP or elevator pitch is, your social or work circle will have their own 'second thing' to identify you and you have little control over that. I simply can't alter the fact I am 'the short Scottish one' in most situations in which I'm involved.

But what has this to do with confidence?

Well, we don't generally mind that period of incompetence we all experience when learning a new skill until we have to present the fruits of our labour in public (e.g. give a presentation, play a competitive game of golf, start a conversation with a stranger). We might experience frustration, even anger, but these are nothing compared to the heady cocktail of disappointment, awkwardness and downright shame we feel when failing publicly. Consciously or otherwise we are concerned about that 'second thing' we are creating. Here are my experiences and strategies for dealing with this experience in a confident way.

CHANGE YOUR 'SECOND THING'

The unconfident response we have in these situations is a learned response and can therefore be unlearned. In their book *The Improv Handbook*, Deborah Frances-White and Tom Salinsky point out that most children's goal is to have 'as many turns as possible' and often use this to measure their success rather than quality of performance. This approach is by definition childish. And yet it is such a confident approach to learning something new.

As adults, more often than not, we want to sit back and assess whether we'll be any good at something before we even give it a go (certainly in public). This process strikes me as both highly inefficient and geared to promote 'failure'.

Young children do not share our fear of appearing ridiculous or silly. This gives them a great advantage when it comes to confidently learning and practising new skills. Think about it, when in your life did you learn most and when in your life was learning effortless and even fun? Because children apply this process to life in general they are always learning rather than languishing in self-doubt or self-consciousness.

Secondly, this demonstrates it is not the *first thing* (fear, going blank, making a mistake) it's the *second thing*, how we define or name that thing, which undermines our confidence. So the classic adult pattern goes something like:

'Gone blank.'

'Who?'

'You know, the one that makes you blush uncontrollably and dig yourself into an ever deeper pit of self-loathing.'

'Oh, him.'

Sound familiar? Well it is time to change your 'second thing' descriptors because it's not what you feel that's important, it's what you feel about what you feel.

Now it would of course be mischievous of me to suggest that you can trade your terror for excitement simply by changing what you call it, so that is exactly what I'm going to do.

For example:

'Gone blank.'

'Who?'

'You know the one that makes you smile to yourself and get really creative.'

'Oh her, of course.'

Identify your 'second thing' label. Develop some alternative labels and test-run them in a number of mental rehearsals. Whatever works best, take it with you into the live environment and practise, practise, practise.

LEARN TO BE OK WITH NOT BEING OK

If you are human and you interact with other humans, then you are going to mess up. You will find yourself out of your depth. You will miss the point or get the wrong end of the wrong stick at some point. Believe it or not these moments are not your downfall. It's what you do with them that count.

Build your tolerance to these moments by having more of them. To begin with find a safe, non-judgemental environment to do so. I found this initially in Physical Theatre Training (particularly clowning) and subsequently have honed it doing improv (improvised comedy) to paying audiences. It's not that you can't fail (though some improv trainers will say you can't), it's more that your audience love it when (in the words of John Wright in *Why is that so funny*) you are in the shit. It's an expected part of the deal.

Find something you have the capacity to learn but that will stretch, challenge and make you feel awkward (that last one is important) during the learning process. This builds a tolerance and comfort with 'not being OK'.

For me this process has performed a kind of lobotomy in that it has surgically separated confidence and capability. Just because I lack capability in an area doesn't mean I have to relinquish confidence in myself. Perhaps ironically this 'isolated' confidence tends to allow me to develop capability more quickly and less painfully.

STOP TAKING YOURSELF SO DAMN SERIOUSLY

Practise seeing the funny side of every situation (even if you don't share it with your audience, the board or the judge). One way to practise this when the stakes are low is to ask the question, 'What could this mean?' rather than 'What does this mean?' This is what observational comedians do when they find new ways of framing familiar situations to find the fun in them.

Let me give you a personal example. I have recently been suffering from an on-going urological problem which has gone undiagnosed and not really treated effectively. It was really getting me down and affecting my more general health and sense of wellbeing. An Eastern European consultant proved to be my saviour, but not in the way you might think. He conducted the kind of invasive examination that is the stuff of a man's nightmares, inserting a camera where a camera really ought not to go (are your eyes watering yet?). He discovered, nothing.

However his letter to my GP proved a turning point in my attitude to the illness and my general wellbeing. The words 'Mr Cherry's external genitalia are unremarkable' made me laugh out loud for the first time in months. It had the same effect on many of my Facebook friends.

As C.W. Medcalf says 'taking your challenge seriously and yourself lightly' opens up many possibilities for ourselves and invites others unconsciously to join us. Smiling is thought to be one of the few universal languages.

Putting it all together

The word 'silly' has over many centuries taken a fascinating journey through a range of evolving meanings. 'Silly' did not originally refer to the absurd or ridiculous – in fact quite the opposite. The word derives from the old English word 'seely', meaning happy, blissful, lucky or blessed. From there it came to mean innocent, or deserving of compassion, only later mutating this sense of naive childishness into a more critical, mocking term, signifying ignorance, feeble-mindedness, and foolish behaviour – the meaning we know today.

My lessons about confidence from comedy can be summarized in three key points:

- Feel what you feel without judging yourself. It is the 'second thing' that matters.
- Build your 'in the shit' muscle and make tricky business like business as usual.

- Face it we are ridiculous. Most of our social constructs, if we had to explain them to a Martian (or even a child) are made up, arbitrary and frankly ridiculous. Accept that and those awkward moments will lose all of their sting.

Professor A Nalsphinctre (aka Kevin Cherry, Agent Improvocateur)

44 CONFIDENT TEACHING

Education breeds confidence. Confidence breeds hope.
Hope breeds peace.

Confucius

'Teaching is the worst job in the world but the greatest vocation.'

Joanne Nugent is a former head of history in a challenging area of the north-east of England. In her role as Extended Schools Consultant she has coached and enabled hundreds of teachers, parents and vulnerable teenagers to develop their confidence and self-esteem. She is also your coach for this chapter.

As a young and enthusiastic trainee teacher at one the finest educational establishments in England, I was greeted with the above statement during my induction. For me teaching was my destiny. There was nothing I wanted to do more and for someone to suggest that it was a terrible job was baffling to say the least. Yes I was young and very wet behind the ears but I was enthusiastic and determined to be a great teacher. Clearly I had a lot to learn. Teaching isn't all motherhood and apple pie. It challenges you mentally, emotionally and physically. It forces you to question your values, your belief system and your self-worth. The expectations of you as a teacher are high. Your headteacher, head of department, parents, social workers, community police, your pupils and the media all expect teachers to be more than great. Perfection is the requirement and to be void of mistakes.

High expectations are essential to raising standards. However, such expectations in an ever-changing profession can demoralize and chip away at the confidence of any teacher no matter how enthusiastic or experienced they are.

The pressure to perform and to prove that you have added value can make you question your place in the profession.

A number of headteachers have asked me over the years to help, support and coach teachers who they feel lack confidence. As a teacher it is difficult to admit you need help or that you are not this all-singing, all-dancing performer who has every pupil eating out of the palm of your hand! The single most important point to note is that great teachers are not born they are made. So much emphasis is placed upon raising the confidence and self-belief of young people. However, unless we place the same value and importance upon raising the confidence of our teaching staff we will lose great talent and our children will suffer.

BE THE CONFIDENT TEACHER YOUR PUPILS NEED

I have encouraged many teachers to use this technique as the starting point to develop their confidence. It is a great way to hold the mirror up to your own behaviours and their impact on your students' confidence. Write a list of all of the habits and dispositions you want your pupils to have by the end of the year, or whatever time span you will be working with them for.

The list often include such qualities as:

- To be enthusiastic about life.
- To have a hunger for learning.
- To be tenacious.
- To learn from mistakes.
- To learn from others.
- To ask questions about their learning.
- To be happy.
- To feel safe and confident in the classroom.
- To feel successful.
- To believe in themselves.
- To know what they are good at/where their strengths lie.

After reviewing the list, flip it to give you the behaviours you must demonstrate most. It is important to accept that unless you display those qualities your pupils won't. As hard as it may be to accept, you have to be a model for your pupils. That includes modelling enthusiasm, being tenacious and believing in yourself.

Use this as the basis of your personal development planning. If any of these aren't natural to you then what needs to happen for you to make them so?

FOCUS ON BEHAVIOUR MANAGEMENT

How often have you thought 'Year 9 are out of control,' or, 'My Year 11 class will not listen and they are so lazy'. Teachers rarely get the opportunity to just talk about their experiences or what happens in their classroom. If you are having a problem with a particular pupil or class then the chances are so will others. Try to seek out a friend or a colleague whom you trust or at least respect. A number of professions offer their staff supervision. This is not performance management but an informal opportunity to discuss your work and air your worries or concerns without the fear that you are failing or are incapable. I have worked with a number of schools that operate under challenging circumstances and they have implemented such an approach. They have noted several positive outcomes, such as a reduction in staff sickness, higher retention of staff, more purposeful and enthusiastic staff meetings and a happier staffroom.

If your environment doesn't provide this support, I would highly recommend being brave and videoing yourself teaching. Many people fear this, but it is hugely beneficial. Video your favourite class or your favourite subject and watch it through twice. The first time watch and enjoy the lesson. The second time make a note of the atmosphere in the classroom, the relationship between you and the pupils, and how disruptions in the classroom are dealt with. Focus on positives not negatives. Having done this, video yourself with your worst class. Again watch it through twice then compare and contrast their performance in both videos. The results are often very enlightening.

Be ready to notice yourself mirroring the behaviour of the children. For example, I have often coached teachers who noticed that they were primed for bad behaviour so they could pounce on it immediately and as a result they made the situation worse. Focus on rebuilding the rapport between you and the more challenging class. Remember just as 'great' teachers are not born neither are 'great classes'.

PREPARE

Confident teachers plan and prepare their lessons. No matter how qualified you are or how many years you have been teaching, planning and preparation are essential to the success of you and your pupils. If you are teaching a subject that you don't fully understand or enjoy, you have to work harder to make sure that you are comfortable with the subject matter and that your delivery is enthusiastic and effortless. Odd as it seems these are often your most memorable lessons.

If you are given a lesson plan, be sure to make it your own. You will get greater results if you take ownership of it. What would bring the subject to life for you? What would make it easy for you to understand?

Beyond that, be sure to remain consistently prepared for the role. Always keep up with current educational research and theories about learning. Research the internet and be keen to attend training courses. There are many key strategies that thousands of teachers believe have transformed their teaching and the learning of their pupils. Don't ignore or dismiss what others say is working for them. Their strategies could work for you too and you could enjoy yourself in the process. Just because we are teachers does not mean that we are not learners.

This may seem very obvious but over the years some of my most unwilling learners have been teachers. Be a magpie and take from others what you need or want and it will make you feel confident. Surround yourself with successful members of staff, those who enjoy and achieve. Don't be dragged down by negativity or sourness.

Putting it all together

To become a confident teacher you need to consistently keep focused on why you became a teacher in the first place. Headteachers or heads of departments will come and go as quickly as education secretaries, but you must know what your core beliefs and values are. This clarity will impact upon the effectiveness of your teaching and the learning of your pupils more than anything else. You expect high standards from your pupils. Demand the same high standards of yourself. Be the best teacher you can be. Know where your strengths lie. Understand what works for you and what works for your pupils. Do what needs to be done. If something isn't working do something about it, change it. Do something you are proud of. There will be bumps in the road. There will be obstacles that you struggle to climb over. Don't get stuck. Find a new route and get round it.

45 CONFIDENT LEARNING

If we learned how to walk and talk the way we are taught how to read and write – everybody would limp and stutter.

Mark Twain

When you think about learning what image do you conjure up? Is it a classroom with a teacher hosing you with information while you struggle to keep up? Perhaps it is a training course with the trainer practising death by PowerPoint as you strive to stay focused and awake? Or do you think of a joyful and energetic experience where you interact with others and explore information that is relevant and easy to apply?

For all too many people the former examples are true. Education can be an unpleasant requirement of life and because much of our formal education takes place during our most formative years this struggle leads to a long-term impact on our confidence. My younger brother was neither academic in the traditional way nor enjoyed sports or the arts. School was extremely tough for him and building relationships was difficult because he wasn't naturally included in the pursuits of others. He left school having been bullied throughout and with very little in the way of qualifications and even less confidence. Yet now he holds a steady job in financial services involved in rock bands. How can this happen? My experience suggests it is because most approaches to learning and education are hugely out-dated. Our education system is founded on principles that are over a century old and the targets that many teachers and trainers are set lead to an approach that isolates many modern-day learners.

I am incredibly fortunate to have worked with a visionary in the field of learning who changed my view on learning and life forever. Kimberley Hare is the Managing Director of Kaizen Training and has been voted one of the world's most influential people in the field of Accelerated Learning. It is with huge thanks to her that I share three strategies to help build confidence through learning more quickly and elegantly. If you are a teacher, trainer or consultant I would highly recommend her book *The Trainer's Toolkit: Bringing Brain-friendly Learning to Life*. If you are in business, are a parent or just want to keep learning then use these to make your learning journey easier and more enjoyable.

DISCOVER YOUR SMARTS

One of the most profound discoveries that I have made in my years as a trainer was the work of Dr Howard Gardner and his coding of multiple intelligences. Dr Gardner and his colleagues found that the notion of IQ was both limited and out-dated. IQ really focuses only on mathematical and verbal linguistic ability and this is only a fraction of the picture.

After many years of research Dr Gardner asserted that there are eight ways in which we are all intelligent. These are:

- Visual Spatial
- Interpersonal
- Intrapersonal
- Musical Rhythmic
- Verbal Linguistic
- Mathematical Logical
- Bodily Kinaesthetic
- Naturalist

For more of a description of each of these read Dr Gardner's paper 'In a nutshell' (listed in Further reading).

Perhaps even more important than understanding the intelligences in-depth is the appreciation that:

1. We are all intelligent in different ways. The question is not, 'How smart are you?' but instead, 'How are you smart?'
2. Potential is not fixed. All intelligence is developable.
3. You can develop any intelligence through any of the others.

Armed with this knowledge you can naturally and easily become a more confident learner. If I apply this knowledge to my younger brother's experience again, we now know he could use his musical rhythmic intelligence to develop the more traditionally academic verbal linguistic and visual spatial. Which intelligence that you are naturally high in could you use to develop the others?

It is almost impossible to only develop one intelligence at a time. When James joined his first band then the academic intelligences increased as expected but his interpersonal intelligence naturally developed because he was spending more time with more people. As he practised his music more, his musical intelligence grew yet stronger.

Knowing and understanding that you are smart in various ways and that your intelligence can be continually developed is a great first step to becoming a confident learner.

START WITH THE END IN MIND

A major flaw in the traditional approach to education is that much of it seems to be a means to an end. The brilliant Sir Ken Robinson captures this brilliantly in his 2006 TED Talk on how schools kill creativity (see Further reading for details of this).

> If you were to visit education as an alien and say, 'What's it for, public education?', I think you'd have to conclude, if you look at the output, who really succeeds by this, who does everything they should, who gets all the brownie points, who are the winners, I think you'd have to conclude the whole purpose of public education throughout the world is to produce university professors.

The challenge reaches beyond education into corporate training. Most people get their list of training courses that they can attend and choose some because we are told that we should want to develop.

Stepping into becoming a confident learner is to become brilliant at defining your learning outcomes. Specifically this means being able to get absolutely clear on what you want to be able to do differently as a result of the learning you are going to do. How will you know it has been a success? How will the relevant people around you know?

This additional clarity will help you to become much more discerning in the learning that you do but also to help you recognize your progress much more easily. All training courses should be designed with outcomes (not just training objectives) at their heart. If you are able to, challenge any that aren't.

REFLECT ON YOUR LEARNING

In a world where most learning is a means to an end it is completely understandable that we finish a course, pick up a certificate and never think about it again. However the highly confident learner will reflect on learning experiences from the most powerful to the most disappointing. They will do it whether that learning was in a formal setting like a training course, or self-managed learning online or from a book.

Great reflective questions to ask include:

- What worked? Why?
- What didn't work? Why?
- What will this help me to do differently?
- How can I share this experience with others?
- What else do I need to do differently as a result of this experience?

The habit of *reflections* helps to anchor the learning and reinforces a self-perception that you are *learning* and a good one at that? To build this habit will also wire your brain to recognize that you are important because you and others have invested in your learning.

One final recommendation would be to have a specific book for your reflections. This provides a brilliant resource for review in the future and becomes a superb reminder that you are a font of knowledge.

Putting it all together

It is hard to separate learning in its broader sense from confidence, as we understand it. The challenge for many of us is that we have been conditioned into thinking we aren't good at learning. As human beings we are naturally predisposed to learning. Perhaps the two most difficult things that we ever learn to do – walking and talking – happen in the most instinctive way. Sadly the learning systems that have been in place throughout recent history and beyond get in the way of our natural approach.

By applying the three strategies in this chapter you undoubtedly take a more natural approach to learning which in turn will help you to access your confidence more easily. In turn feeling more genuinely confident more of the time will help you to learn more naturally and stay away from experiences that will hold less value.

Learning, when done well, should be stretching and challenging and ultimately rewarding. At times it will also be fun. While enjoyment must be part of the journey it is important to remember that highly confident people will often embark on learning experiences that aren't necessarily fun at the time because these can be the most rewarding. As your confidence grows, be sure to embrace learning that both builds on your strengths and grows the areas you need to develop most.

46 BODY CONFIDENCE

I share the same advice that my mom gave me – stay hydrated and sleep well. And that being a beautiful person on the inside is what really matters.
Jessica Alba

No matter how practised we become at triggering confidence from the inside out it is difficult to ignore the impact of feeling good about your body. I am not talking about the need for defined abs or toned butts but the benefits of genuine confidence in being in our own skin. For the past couple of years I have worked closely with Performance Enhancement Specialist Nick Grantham. Nick's clients include Premiership Football Clubs, international athletes and even Royal Ballet companies. He is one of the UK's top experts on athletic preparation and is your coach for this chapter.

How can you develop body confidence? Confidence is a feeling that we get as a result of what we think, what we do with our body and how we perceive the world around us.

Type 'A Confident Body' into a search engine and you'll be amazed by the number of results you get (within 0.24 seconds I discovered 122,000,000 links). Rather predictably, if the information at the end of a mouse click is to be believed, having a confident body is simply a matter of developing a 'bikini body' and is predominantly a problem faced by women.

First you need to forget what the internet and popular media would have you believe. Throughout my career as a performance enhancement specialist I've helped shape thousands of 'confident bodies' and I've come to realize 'a confident body' means different things to different people.

- The world champion judo player with an injured shoulder who can no longer perform his 'signature move' on opponents.
- The working mum who constantly feels exhausted at the end of the day and is longing to keep her eyes open past nine o'clock in the evening!
- The 65-year-old recreational triathlete returning to fitness following a brain tumour that left him with balance and coordination problems.
- The successful executive living through an endless cycle of corporate hospitality, who is so out of shape that he can't have a game of football with his kids in the park at the weekend.

All real-life clients that I've worked with, all looking to develop 'a confident body', and none of them wanting to walk down the beach in a bikini or pair of speedos! In each case they created structures and habits around the following three key strategies.

KEEP IT CONSISTENT

'Are you 'fit for *purpose*'? The first thing that needs to be established is what you want your body to be capable of doing, physically.

Can you run for the bus without straining a muscle? Can you play with your children in the park without having to sit on the park bench for five minutes while you catch your breath? Can you play five-a-side with the 'Class of 72' every Sunday night without aching for the next five days?

Once you've figured out what you want to be able to do, you can plan how you are going to do it. It may mean a trip to the gym a couple of times a week but it could simply be dusting off the bike in the garage and getting out for some fresh air on a regular basis. Regardless of how you go about becoming 'fit for purpose', continuity is the key to success and will help you to establish a training habit. Habits build confidence. Time-efficient programmes will help you to get the most out of everything you do. Find out what the minimum 'dose' is that delivers the maximum 'effect'.

We all lead busy lives and a 'results by volume' approach to fitness training is inefficient and a bit dull. A 15-minute training session completed four times a week will form a stronger habit than a 60-minute session completed once a week. Continuity and efficiency are fundamental aspects of developing a successful physical preparation programme to enable you to develop a confident body.

EAT WELL AND HYDRATE

What would happen if Lewis Hamilton's pit crew decided to fill up with a few gallons of diesel instead of the sophisticated fuel blend they usually use? He wouldn't get out of the pit lane. Yet this is precisely what we do on a daily basis.

The body is a pretty sophisticated piece of kit that needs the right balance of nutrients to perform optimally. The adaptations that will allow you to develop a confident body can only occur when the body is fuelled appropriately.

Let's take a quick quiz to gauge your nutritional knowledge.

1. What is better for you, a chocolate muffin or an apple?
2. What is better for you, a can of fizzy drink or a glass of water?
3. What is better for you, a side portion of chips or a side portion of seasonal vegetables?
4. What is better for you, a takeaway pizza or a home-cooked meal using fresh ingredients?

You already have all the nutritional knowledge that you need. I'm not about to suggest you go on a 'mung bean superfood milkshake diet'. Establishing nutritional habits to help develop a confident body requires structure. Make appropriate food choices and stick to a plan. Concentrate on getting the basics right:

- Eat regularly.
- Limit sugars, and refined and highly processed food.
- Eat fruits and vegetables.
- Drink more water (2.5 litres a day).
- Consume lean proteins.

MAKE RECOVERY IMPORTANT

Many of the issues related to poor body confidence are linked to chronic fatigue. I wouldn't expect my athletes to train 60–80 hours a week, 50 weeks of the year without a rest, so why are you any different? I've worked with successful executives and stay-at-home mums who have shown all the signs of 'overtraining' yet they've not worked out in years! If the body cannot cope with the physical and mental demands of what life has to throw at it, it will quickly become exhausted.

Sleep is one of the most important forms of recovery and provides time for adaptation and recovery.

Try to establish a regular sleep pattern and aim for eight to ten hours of good-quality sleep each night. If you like to burn the midnight oil, remember that the hours before midnight are far more valuable for recovery and regeneration (every hour of sleep before midnight is equal to two hours of sleep after midnight).

Create an effective sleep environment:

Relax. Use relaxation skills to switch off; turn the TV and electronic devices off.

Quiet. Use ear plugs, place 'do not disturb' signs on doors, switch phones to silent.

Dark. Reduce light in the room 30 minutes before going to sleep, wear an eye mask. Keep the room cool – 18°C/65°F is the optimal temperature.

Comfort. Make sure you've got room to manoeuvre!'

The basis of Nick's advice may be common sense to some, but is it your common practice? As he is at pains to point out, 'A confident body is being secure in the knowledge that whatever it is you want your body to do (run for the bus, play with the grandchildren, complete a charity 5km run or simply make it to 8pm without falling asleep) you can achieve it by sticking to the basics and developing habits around a comprehensive physical preparation programme and sound nutrition strategy, while remembering to take some time out to relax and unwind'.

We have been mutual clients over the years, with him getting me in better physical shape and me working with him to develop his business strategy. In one of our first meetings I asked him the best way to lose weight and his response was to 'burn more energy than you consume'. No shocks there, other than the realization that I had to change my eating and/or exercise habits.

Similarly most of us know that we should drink the 2.5 litres of water a day that Nick recommends, but how many of us actually do it? I have worked with clients whose confidence levels have increased just by getting their water intake to a healthy level. They reported feeling more lucid and having more energy.

Until recently Nick's website (www.nickgrantham.com) displayed the Miles Kington quote: 'Knowledge is knowing that a tomato is a fruit. Wisdom is knowing that a tomato doesn't belong in a fruit salad.' Use the core information in this chapter as part of your confidence platform. Your goal may be to recreate *Baywatch*, but once your are clear on what it is then take simple and consistent steps to achieve it.

47 CONFIDENT DATING

Courting is a much sweeter term than 'dating'. It sounds like it has more intent, more like an agreement that two people enter into with a future in mind.

Kim Cattrall

This chapter is for everyone, not just those who haven't found Mr or Miss Right yet. Imagine how many failing relationships could have been salvaged over the years if those in them were willing to go back and revisit some basic dating principles. Unless you are 100 per cent happy with your relationship, then I would encourage you to read on.

For those of you who are still looking for a great relationship, there should be no surprise in learning that confidence plays a key role. I am sure that you have had the 'how have they ended up with them' conversation in your head many times as someone you watch, someone who is highly attractive, leaves a club or party with someone much less attractive. It is especially infuriating if their date appears to have confidence that outstrips their physical attributes and even their personality. I am not saying confidence is everything, but genuine confidence is unquestionably attractive.

It is also worth deciding before you read further what kind of date you are looking for. If you are younger you might want to read this chapter to help you get the most attractive or cool date that you can. As long as you stay safe that is all good with me! If you are slightly older you might be looking for a life partner. While physical attraction is crucial in any relationship your awareness that beauty is wasted on the young comes to the fore. You want more than the prettiest, best dressed or fittest. You will identify more with the quote: 'More girls need to be infatuated by a man with an education, ambition, faith and goals rather than a dude with 'swag'. In ten years swag won't pay your bills.' While the incredibly hot high school date or holiday romance could turn into the partner you spend your life with, it is quite rare. If you're looking for a good time don't rule out everyone who isn't an intellectual genius and if you are looking for a father for your children don't date gorgeous slobs. Whatever relationship you are looking for here are three strategies that I have observed in the most confident daters I have studied.

PAY FULL ATTENTION

Think about the last date you went on. Think of the person you were with. What were they wearing when you met? What was the most personal thing they told you about themselves? If you were going to date them again what information from your previous time together could you use to start conversations and show that you are interested?

The most significant difference between highly confident daters and the rest is that they pay full attention. Strategies for connecting and really listening are already covered in other areas of the book but when dating there is something extra at play. You are paying attention for what really seems to matter most to the person you are wooing.

This information doesn't come from a single obvious source. It comes from small subtle sources and quiet messages. If you are focused on the self-talk that is chatting inside you or on working out what you are going to say next then you will miss them. Depending where your date is taking place, the environment or your date's friends can be an incredibly useful source of information. Being able to ask a question about something you have noticed and prompting your date to talk about it is the number one way to be seen as interesting. It is a myth that you have to have interesting stories to tell. The secret is to create the opportunity for them to tell interesting stories and then to really pay attention to everything they are saying.

BE YOU … AT YOUR BEST

Having read this book and applied the techniques this should be both easier and more obvious. Let us just assume for a moment that your dating approach and date selection is so successful that you find someone who you want to be with long term. This is doomed to failure if you try to be someone you aren't in the honeymoon stages of the relationship. I have friends who would invent hobbies and interests to impress the opposite sex. I have even more who have deleted hobbies and interests so as not to scare off a potential partner. Many of the friends that I have I have met through playing football. In our younger days so many teammates would complain that their now serious girlfriend was trying to stop them from playing. This was rarely down to an over-controlling girlfriend but much more often down to a lack of honesty by the guy involved in the early part of the relationship.

Being you at your best stretches much further and deeper than being honest about how you spend your time. It includes but isn't limited to:

- Being well dressed and well turned out but in the style you are comfortable in.
- Taking your dates to the best of the places you know. Don't go to wildly extravagant places if you aren't comfortable or try to be a cultural expert if you aren't.
- Talk about things you are really interested in, in moderation (unless you know for sure that they are interested in them too.) Passion about any topic is attractive. Having a date go on endlessly about something you find dull isn't. There is no point trying to hide the things you're interested in altogether though. Unless of course you are prepared to do so forever.

THE BALANCE BETWEEN INTERESTED AND DESPERATE

I am sure at some point in your life you will have had the experience of being pursued by someone you really were not interested in. It can be cute and flattering, unless they seem desperate. In which case it is incredibly unattractive and uncomfortable. If at any point in your dating journey you feel desperate to be with someone you should stop dating and start working on your confidence in other areas of your life. Desperation is repellent to all but to all but the worst potential suitors.

The flipside of that is that most people you date want you to show that you are interested in them. I recall fondly the first time that I met my wife. Her friends were getting ready to move on to the next party and, having been engrossed in conversation for about an hour, it was clear that one of us had to make the big move of asking for the other's number. I took the plunge first. Looking back on that first meeting, I once asked her what she would have done if I hadn't asked. She replied that she would have left it until she was about to walk out the door to ask, 'Don't you want my number?' This is a classic 'check-out' of interest.

One of my best friend's mantras when he was dating was 'play it cool Trigger', a reference to a famous scene from UK sitcom *Only Fools and Horses*. At the moment the lead character is trying to play it cool he loses the chance to impress his potential date. It is a great metaphor and leads to a great question to ask yourself when dating. How would you want to them to show they were keen but not desperately so? What does the right balance look like for you?

Putting it all together

Beginning a new relationship is a challenging and exciting time. Even if your aim is to find Mr or Miss Right Now, rather than the person you will spend the rest of your life with, the road is a bumpy one. That road can be smoothed by applying the foundations of confidence overlaid with some specific strategies that will keep you connected with your potential suitor.

The core principle of being seen as interesting by being interested is crucial in the early stages of dating. 'Watch, listen and remember' should be the mantra. Put your full attention on them and their environment. Find out what interests them, what is important to them and what you have in common. Make this the foundation of any future relationship.

Show up to the early dates – and beyond – as the best, most confident version of you. A date hungover from the night before is unlikely to be attractive unless you are looking for a party animal for a partner. I was once given the fantastic advice: 'Wear yourself well, but wear yourself'. Trying to be someone or something you aren't is tiring and will cause relationships to stutter in the long run.

Don't be the desperate one at 3:30am trying to hook up with anyone who is left in the nightclub. Desperation is one of the most unattractive traits and the only people you are likely to attract are those so insecure in themselves that they want to be with someone else less confident than them. Balance this with the confidence to say, 'Yes, I would like to see you again'. Playing hard to get will drive more good dates away than it attracts.

The final point of this chapter is slightly clichéd but also completely true. You will only find love when you are at peace with yourself. Don't wait for a relationship to validate you and give you confidence. Trigger your confidence and make it the state you hang out in most and the rest will take care of itself.

48 CONFIDENT RELATIONSHIPS

The meeting of two personalities is like the contact of two chemical substances: if there is any reaction, both are transformed.

Carl Jung

If you skipped the previous chapter on confident dating, then congratulations on being in a strong and steady relationship. If it is a fulfilling one for you, or you want it to be, my wish is that this chapter helps you to nurture and maintain it. While not every one of the highly confident people who I have worked with or studied were in a great relationship, I do see a strong relationship as a great foundation upon which to build personal success and confidence.

A loving and intimate relationship should not be a prerequisite of confidence. In fact, that ability to access and live in your confidence before and during your relationship is much more likely to lead to that relationship being successful. However, as a species wired for contact and connection, being in a great relationship can easily be the most satisfying and fulfilling part of our lives.

Modern-day life can place obstacles in the way of these relationships being successful in the long term. Longer and less consistent working hours, the globalization of careers, a media that sets unreasonably high expectations for the physical aspects of relationships are just a few examples of the challenges we all face.

With these challenges in mind we must nurture our relationships to keep them strong. Even at those times when we doubt our relationships or partners, fostering the relationship will give us a sense of confidence. This comes either from the knowledge that we have done what we can to make it a success or from affirming love and affection from a happy and fulfilled partner.

This also seems like the perfect time to remind you that everything else in this book remains valid. Your confidence is an emotional state that you can trigger at any moment. It can be built and anchored through a whole plethora of strategies. Your confidence does not hang on the love of someone else. If you have done what you can in a relationship and your affection or commitment has not been reciprocated this does not need to affect your confidence. If it does it is because of what you are thinking about the end of that relationship.

If you are in a great relationship, here are a few strategies to maintain it.

BE PRESENT

You may be surprised to know that I don't specifically mean that you need to spend the right amount of time with your partner. I am talking quality, not just quantity. One of the attributes that I notice consistently in those people who are really confident in their relationships is that when they are spending time with their partner they are fantastic at being really present.

When spending time with your loved one, avoid distractions and clear your mind of nagging worries. Listen to and focus on what your partner is saying and doing. You will notice things that others don't.

Here are a few things to avoid in order to be present with your partner:

- **Avoid social media.** The likes of Facebook and Twitter are addictive and time consuming. A quick look can lead to a chunk of time disappearing. If you are interested in a conversation that is taking place online your focus will be drawn there even when you aren't on reading your updates.
- **Use the record button.** For many people the routine at the end of the workday culminates in settling on the sofa with your partner and the TV. Unless you are watching programmes that you both enjoy and that promote conversation between

you, be very careful about becoming lost in a programme and losing the opportunity to connect with your loved one.

- **Stay out of your head.** We all get lost in our thoughts at times. We have concerns that need mental attention. We have hobbies or interests that provide a mental release from day-to-day life. Date night is not the time to get lost in your thoughts. If you have something on your mind during the quality time you have with your loved one then let them know that is the case. You don't have to talk about it in-depth. Just let them know and give them permission to help you snap out of your thoughts if necessary.

- **Switch off your telephone.** Many people seem to have forgotten that if they switch their phone off they will still receive their messages when they switch it back on. If you are spending time with your partner, don't take calls unless they are genuinely urgent and ignore your messages until a more appropriate moment.

ASK FOR WHAT YOU WANT AND EXPRESS GRATITUDE

If you ever have a conversation with your partner that includes, 'You should have asked', 'Well you should have just known' then this strategy should act as a reminder that confident relationships require each partner to ask for what they want. Ask your partner to go places with you, ask them to help you make decisions, ask your partner to say or do things that fulfil you. Ask for what you want physically, mentally and emotionally.

This of course doesn't guarantee that you will but those who are confident in themselves and their relationships are completely comfortable with asking and comfortable with not getting everything they want. Relationships are much more likely to be damaged by a partner avoiding making requests and hoping that their companion guesses what they want. Great relationships are built on love and trust not mind-reading.

Showing gratitude is at least as powerful and important. In research supported by the American National Institute of Mental Health grateful couples were found to be more satisfied in their relationships and felt closer to each other. Go beyond showing gratitude for what your partner does. Be grateful for who your partner is. Show appreciation for the attributes that make them unique and especially for those that attracted you in the first place.

Be thankful for them and be overt in the ways you say and show this. Even if this isn't natural to you, create a system to remind you to show your gratitude for them.

FORGIVE FREELY

If you are in a relationship you will screw up and so will your partner. Human nature is to err. How you react to your partner's mistakes will define the relationship and your confidence in it. Highly confident people do not forgive everything but when they do forgive they do so fully and do everything that they can to leave the incident behind.

When I coach clients on challenges in their relationship there is often residue from a partner's past misdemeanour that is becoming a barrier to intimacy or communication. No matter how big or small the fault is, if you decide to move on then you must do so completely.

Bringing up past arguments and errors when your companion makes another mistake is of course damaging for the relationship. It can also have a negative impact on your confidence. By packing together all of the errors your loved one has made you will begin to question your judgement in forgiving the previous misdemeanours or being with them in the first place.

Of course there is a time to see a pattern in behaviour and end a relationship. For example if your partner has an affair then you must choose whether to forgive them. If you do you must work together to move on completely. If your partner has another affair in close succession, despite promises to change, then it is completely within reason to see this as a pattern of behaviour. Whether you forgive again is a choice you have to make, but do so with confidence in the knowledge that your relationship doesn't define you and that you have done everything you can to make it a success.

Putting it all together

Great relationships don't just happen. Even relationships that start great must be cultivated to stand the test of time. We live in times where gender roles are becoming more blurred and even the nature of same-sex relationships is changing. It is becoming easier culturally for relationships to fall apart than to be maintained.

If you want a great relationship that feels like a confident entity in itself as well as helping to foster the confidence of those in it, then you must nurture it. Confident relationships aren't hard work; at least not all the time. They do require attention especially in the midst of demands from children and careers.

If you make time to be present with your partner then you will notice all of the things they need to be emotionally satisfied and you will reap the benefits in return. Asking for what you want shows an attractive self-confidence, and regularly demonstrating gratitude shows a love and humility that will prove irresistible for the right partner. Finally, the ability to genuinely forgive your loved one for their inevitable faults and mistakes strengthens the foundations of love and trust that any long-term relationship must have.

There is no blueprint for a great relationship but a relationship fuelled by genuine confidence has the best chance to flourish and be fulfilling for everyone involved.

49 CONFIDENT PARENTING

The more people have studied different methods of bringing up children, the more they have come to the conclusion that what good mothers and fathers instinctively feel like doing for their babies is the best after all.

Dr Benjamin Spock

Becoming a parent changes your life. Being a parent becomes your life. It is a job that you do not get paid for, the hours are endless, the conditions smelly, there is no annual leave, and no professional development. Being a parent is the toughest thing you will ever do and the most important job you will ever do.

It is also the most rewarding and joyous experience of your life. It is a gift and so many people don't receive that gift but long for it every day. You want to get it right. You want to be a good parent. The pressure to be a good parent is greater now than it has ever been. Parents are told that they are their child's first and greatest teacher. Scientists and educationalists insist that the first five years of a child's life are the most important in terms of the development. They provide the foundations for a child to achieve their key developmental milestones. The brain develops more rapidly in the first three years of life than at any other stage in their life. Ninety per cent of a child's brain develops by the age of five. Does that mean if you don't get it right in the first five years all is lost? No, but it is an example of one of the pressures parents are placed under.

Not only are you raising a happy and healthy child but you have to make sure that you raise a child who has manners, morals and good hygiene. Your child must be independent, literate and an excellent communicator. We are bombarded with stories of child geniuses and world changers yet most of the pressure we feel comes from within. While confidence in our parenting skills may be difficult to maintain we now have a greater understanding of what helps children flourish and what stunts their development. We know what children respond to and how the brain in children and in teenagers develops.

WHEN YOU SAY 'NO', MEAN 'NO'

Being a parent you want to give your child the world. You want them to have anything and everything if it makes them happy. The problem arises when we give our children things to keep them quiet. It is easier to say 'yes' than to say 'no'. Parents often tell their children 'no', but how often do they mean it? The ramifications of not meaning no are huge. In the short term you may feel the consequences but the long-term consequences are on the child.

Children and teenagers know how to get you to change your mind. No matter whether it is a bar of chocolate, to use your iPhone or to be allowed to stay out late, no must mean no. This doesn't mean no until they create such a scene, cry their eyes out or be sufficiently mean to you that you feel guilty and give in. This creates an unhealthy pattern for you and them.

Firstly they will know that your word is not to be trusted. When you want them to do as they are told, such as when you are out and about, they will take no notice of you as they know they can get round you. The child will appear spoilt and you will be embarrassed.

Secondly it is very important that the child or teenager accepts 'no' in terms of their health and safety. They must accept that no they cannot run across the road and no they cannot stay out after 9 pm. If you don't stick to 'no' over the little things, how can you expect them to listen to you when you say 'no' to the big things? They will ignore you and do what they want even though this may compromise their safety. As hard as it is 'no' must always mean 'no'.

BE CONSISTENT

Children need stability and structure. They rely upon their parents to keep them safe and to guide them through life.

Children get confused when the boundaries move. Every day you hear parents threaten their children with consequences for poor behaviour. How many parents are consistent and follow through with these threats? Parents promise to ground their children, they will take them home from an outing or party, or they will take a toy off them. These threats are to encourage the child to do as they are told and to improve their behaviour. I sat in a restaurant once and heard a father threaten his child nine times to be good and to stop running around and shouting. The child did not listen to her father once. If his threats had been realized she would have had no TV, no bedtime story, no milk, and no play date with her friends. The list went on and on. The child realized that these threats were empty and didn't take them seriously.

If you are going to warn, threaten or bribe your child with something you must follow through. As hard as it may be to take your child's beloved soft toy off them at bedtime you have to accept that it is for the best in the long term. Simply doing this once means that the next time they are naughty and you threaten them with taking their bedtime toy off them they will listen and stop because they know you will stand by your word.

DEVELOP ROUTINE

As parents we hear these words from the moment our child is born. Parents are told to establish a good routine. Most adults get up at the same time every morning. Many will have the same breakfast every morning and go to the same place for lunch every day. Most people love the excitement of the Christmas holidays but also enjoy getting back into their normal routine in the New Year. Children and teenagers are no different. A good routine is essential to giving a child security and stability, and to teaching them about organization, which in turn enables them to become more independent.

Many people face their biggest challenges first thing in the morning, at meal times and at bedtime. A routine will take stress out of these busy times and reduce frustration, boredom and poor behaviour.

Decide what you want your meal time routine to be. If using cutlery and eating a variety of foods is important, then focus on it every time you sit down. If you allow children to eat with their hands or watch TV at the table this will become their routine. Stick with the routine that you want until it becomes the norm. Backing off from it will undo all your hard work, confuse your children and impact on your confidence.

A good routine is essential at night. A child needs sleep to develop and grow and parents need their child to sleep so they can have some 'me' time. To be clear, a routine means doing the same thing at the same time every night. If you want your child to sleep by 7pm then bath them at 6:15pm every night without fail until the routine is established. Only when this happens and the child is sleeping for an adequate amount of time should you relax the routine to accommodate family occasions and outings. Check out Dr Tanya Byron's recommendations for the required sleep a child needs each night. Her book *Little Angels* is a great starting point for establishing a bedtime routine.

Putting it all together

We live in a culture where the parenting expert and TV personality mould our family life. The 'naughty step' and the 'reward chart' are part of our daily existence. Names such as Gina Ford, Jo Frost, Tracey Hogg and Dr Tanya Byron are often quoted in the playground as the answer to many a parenting problem. Don't be afraid to learn from the parenting experts as they are sharing their experiences, offering support and help and, certainly in the case of Dr Tanya Byron, decades of professional, clinical findings.

It is vital however, that we don't lose touch with who we are and where our strengths lie. If you feel your child needs a more structured routine, use Gina Ford's methods but don't allow them to take over your life. Use the books and the TV programmes as inspiration for new ideas. If you are going to use a particular technique by a parenting expert, use it as it is prescribed. Remember that one size does not fit all.

Every child is different. Not every child will respond to the 'naughty step', they may prefer the 'time out' technique.

Be positive, focus on and praise your child's good behaviour and spend less time highlighting their poor behaviour. Give them boundaries and structure if their behaviour does need improving. Remember we make mistakes as parents, but children and teenagers make mistakes too. Ultimately a parent who is confident and positive in themselves is likely to develop a confident and positive child.

50 SHARING YOUR CONFIDENCE

Life is a gift, and it offers us the privilege, opportunity, and responsibility to give something back by becoming more.

Tony Robbins

This chapter may appear to be a simple reminder to share your learning with others; however it is included firmly as part of your journey to genuine and deep confidence. The benefit to others is a very positive bonus. One of the most powerful and certain ways to anchor learning in your long-term memory is to teach others the things you most want to remember. The fact that you become a force for good as you anchor your learning is a brilliant by-product.

Confidence, like any other state, is contagious. Living it will affect others but sharing your learning and experience will amplify the impact you have on others dramatically. It is useful to remember that reading this book sets you ahead of most other people in your understanding of confidence. Applying the strategies puts you in a very tiny percentage of people who can manage their confidence in any situation. Some might say that it is incumbent on you to share your knowledge with as many people as possible. If this challenges your confidence management then all the more reason to do it!

Use this chapter to prompt questions about the opportunities you can take and make to share your confidence with others. Some of this sharing will be directly from the techniques in the book but I also hope that you have identified some of your own natural confidence strategies. Be sure to share these too; you can now be considered one of the highly confident people referred to throughout the book.

As you have applied these strategies successfully it is possible that you may be seen as little evangelical to others. I don't think that is necessarily a bad thing but find ways to take people with you on the journey. Make the difference for them that you have made for yourself by putting the strategies into action.

TELL YOUR STORY

In Chapter 41 on confident public speaking I encouraged you to find opportunities to speak to varied audiences. Sharing your journey to discover genuine confidence is a great opportunity to embed your confidence and help others to take their own journey.

Tell others why you felt you needed to find or strengthen your confidence. Share what confidence is for you and what it is like when your confidence is strong. Most importantly tell your audience how you made the differences that you did. How did you make the strategies work for you? Advise them of the risks you took and what you might do differently if you had to take the same journey again. Finally share all the reasons why you think they should take their journey to real confidence.

Tell your story at every opportunity and to anyone who is interested. In informal situations use the world's leading expert technique (Chapter 31) and take the opportunity to practise the strategies for remaining calm as you share the details of your journey.

In addition, I would love to hear your journey. If you have applied the techniques in this book and they have made a real difference to you please drop me an email to richard@ twentyoneleadership.com. One of the most rewarding aspects of writing a book like this is hearing the impact that it has made on its readers. I will send a token of my gratitude to everyone who does this.

TEACH THE STRATEGIES

I love people who are confident enough to learn a strategy, put it into practice and then teach that strategy to others. This approach has formed the basis of my way for the last decade.

I never teach anything that I haven't practised or tested myself. It's a wonderful way to learn and to help others to learn too.

As you experiment with and apply the strategies contained in this book, make a note of those that you find most powerful and valuable. As they become natural to you review what you did to really bring them to life. Doing this gives you a framework to share them with others and I would be happy if you did so. In the wonderful movie *Pay It Forward* teacher Eugene Simonet (played by Kevin Spacey) sets his class the homework to think of an idea that will change the world then put it into action. Trevor McKinney (Haley Joel Osment) creates the 'Pay It Forward' movement. This means the recipient of a favour does a favour for three others rather than paying the favour back. Each of these three people does three favours and so on and the impact quickly becomes widespread.

Imagine your teaching about confidence having the same impact. If each person who learned a confidence strategy from you, taught it to just three people think of the difference that you would have made to others.

BECOME PART OF A NETWORK

So who do you tell your story to? Who would be interested in learning some confidence strategies? I think with just a little attention and the help of Google you could find a myriad of groups and organizations that you could share your message with. Here are just a few ideas:

- Your local school – either for the pupils or teachers
- Youth clubs – for their leaders
- Beavers, Cubs, Scouts, Rainbows, Brownies, Guides etc.
- Local business speaking groups – YES Groups, Toastmasters
- Regional professional development groups – CIPD, CIM
- Personal development networks

Actively find ways to support others by creating networks of your own. A number of personal fitness trainers in my area hold seminars for their clients where they focus on topics such as confidence. Being part of these networks and sharing your learning is another great way to increase your confidence while helping others to increase theirs.

If you are keen to do this but aren't sure how to start the conversation here are a few simple questions to help you to kick things off.

- Would your members/students/staff find a session on how to be confident in any situation useful?
- If I were able to do this how would you know it has been successful?
- What kinds of things would you like them to say after the event?

These questions will help you to establish the desire from a group and also give an initial indication of the strategies and stories to focus on when you get in front of them.

Highly confident people are generally great networkers. If you haven't been up to this point, make your new-found confidence your reason to build and influence new groups of people.

Putting it all together

One of my favourite paragraphs in any book comes from *Finding Flow* by Mihaly Csikzentmihalyi. It applies perfectly to the difference you can make by sharing your confidence with others.

'Whether we like it or not our lives will leave a mark on the universe. Each person's birth makes ripples that expand in the social environment; parents, siblings, relatives and friends are affected by it, and as we grow up our actions leave a myriad of consequences, some intended, most not. Our consumer decisions make a tiny difference in the economy, political decisions affect the future of the community, and each kind or mean act modifies slightly the total quality of human well-being.'

Your choice isn't whether to make a difference but what difference you make. By taking your learning about confidence from this book and life in general, and sharing it with as wide a group of people as possible in work and your personal life, you are making a significant positive difference.

My experience from studying and working with the highly confident has confirmed beyond doubt that confidence leads not just to success and happiness but to more decisions and actions being taken for the common good. Deep and genuine confidence can change the world. Play your part by accessing your confidence and sharing it with others.

FURTHER READING

Achor, Shawn, *The Happiness Advantage* (Crown Business 2011)

Bersin, Jenny, *Style, the Road to Freedom* (Mike Bersin, 2012)

Buckingham, Marcus, *Now Discover Your Strengths* (Pocket Books 2005)

Byron, Tanya, *Little Angels* (BBC Active 2013)

Cain, Susan, *Quiet: The Power of Introverts in a World That Can't Stop Talking* (Crown 2013)

Covey, Stephen, *The 7 Habits of Highly Effective People* (Free Press 2004)

Csikzentmihalyi, Mihaly, *Finding Flow* by (Basic Books 1998)

Frances-White, Deborah, and Salinsky, Tom, *The Improv Handbook* (Continuum International Publishing Group, 2008)

Genpo, Dennis, *Big Mind Big Heart* (Big Mind Publishing 2007)

Grant, Adam, *Give and Take* (Penguin, 2014)

Hare, Kimberley, *The Trainer's Toolkit: Bringing Brain-friendly Learning to Life* (Crown House Publishing 2005)

Hill, Napoleon, *Think and Grow Rich* (Wilder Publications, 2009)

Imam, Haider, *Straight To Yes* (Capstone 2013)

Jeffers, Susan, *Feel The Fear And Do It Anyway: How to Turn Your Fear and Indecision into Confidence and Action* (Vermilion, 2007).

Kouzes, James, and Posner, Barry, *The Leadership Challenge* (Wiley, 2012)

McKergow, Mark, and Jackson, Paul Z., *The Solutions Focus* (Nicholas Brealey 2006).

Neill, Michael, *You Can Have What You Want* (Hay House UK, 2009)

Pert, Candice, *Molecules of Emotion* (Pocket Books, 1999)

Wiseman, Richard, *The Luck Factor* (Randomhouse, 2004).

WEBLINKS

Chapter 30

Money saving expert website: http://www.moneysavingexpert.com/family/stop-spending-budgeting-tool

Chapter 23

Learn more about Dr Cuddy here: http://www.hbs.edu/faculty/Pages/profile.aspx?facId=491042

Listen to Dr Cuddy's TED Talk at: http://www.ted.com/talks/amy_cuddy_your_body_language_shapes_who_you_are.html

Chapter 45

Listen to the brilliant Sir Ken Robinson's 2006 TED Talk 'How schools kill creativity' at: http://www.ted.com/talks/ken_robinson_says_schools_kill_creativity.html

Read Dr Gardner's paper 'In a nutshell' at: http://howardgardner01.files.wordpress.com/2012/06/in-a-nutshell-minh.pdf

NOTES

GOLDILOCKS AND THE WATER BEARS

THE SEARCH FOR LIFE IN THE UNIVERSE

Louisa Preston

BLOOMSBURY
sigma

Bloomsbury Sigma
An imprint of Bloomsbury Publishing Plc

50 Bedford Square
London
WC1B 3DP
UK

1385 Broadway
New York
NY 10018
USA

www.bloomsbury.com

BLOOMSBURY and the Diana logo are trademarks of
Bloomsbury Publishing Plc

First published 2016

British Library Cataloguing-in-Publication Data
A catalogue record for this book is available from the British Library.

Every effort has been made to trace or contact all copyright holders.
The publishers would be pleased to rectify any errors or omissions
brought to their attention at the earliest opportunity.

Library of Congress Cataloguing-in-Publication data has been applied for.

ISBN (hardback) 978-1-4729-2009-6
ISBN (trade paperback) 978-1-4729-2010-2
ISBN (ebook) 978-1-4729-2008-9

2 4 6 8 10 9 7 5 3

Illustrations by Samantha Goodlet

Typeset in Bembo Std by Deanta Global Publishing Services, Chennai, India
Printed and bound in Great Britain by CPI Group (UK) Ltd,
Croydon CR0 4YY

Bloomsbury Sigma, Book Sixteen

To find out more about our authors and books visit www.bloomsbury.com.
Here you will find extracts, author interviews, details of forthcoming
events and the option to sign up for our newsletters.

For Daniel and Renley ...

Contents

Preface

The tale of *Goldilocks and the Three Bears* has charmed generations of children the world over, and has been borrowed and scientifically woven into the title of this book again – hoping to charm, but also challenge, its valued readers, encouraging you to think a little differently about the world and indeed the Universe in which we live.

Parents and teachers alike have used the fictional narrative of a plucky young girl and her cheeky invasion of the home of a family of bears to develop the imagination and story creation skills of children, as well as to convey levels of acceptable behaviour and manners, respect for personal privacy and respect of other peoples' property or belongings. And yet it contains another message that hopefully this book will inspire its readers to consider when imagining life out there in and beyond the *final frontier*: the idea that something has to be *just right* for it to be useful. The chairs tried by Goldilocks were either too big, too small or *just right*, the porridge was too hot, too cold or *just right* and the beds were too hard, too soft or *just right*. Only when each condition was *just right* and therefore acceptable to Goldilocks was the porridge eaten or the chair sat in or the bed used for sleeping. Just as in the search for life in the Universe, Goldilocks was searching for conditions that were *just right* for her and so are we. Hunting across the *right* part of the Galaxy for planets and moons that are the *right* size, orbiting around the *right* type of star at just the *right* distance to be able to keep water as a liquid on their surface. Astrobiologists and Goldilocks have much in common.

In this book we shall take a tour of the biological Universe, exploring what life is made of, what it needs to originate and thrive, how resilient and adaptable it can be and how conditions do not actually have to conform to our ideas of what is or is not *just right* for organisms to survive and prosper. In many areas throughout the Solar System and beyond, conditions cover a multitude of extremes – too hot or too cold, too acidic or too alkaline, too dry or too wet, or too light or too dark – and in each of these on Earth, life has found its own version of *just right* so it can survive. The Goldilocks story of life is warped and stretched as life finds a way, no matter the challenges. If this is the tale on our planet, then why should it not be the same on other planets and moons, in other galaxies, and throughout the Universe? We may not be alone in the darkness of space for much longer.

'What about the Water Bears?' I hear you ask. Well, you'll have to continue reading to see where these little superheroes fit into this cosmic fairy tale …

CHAPTER ONE

A Brave New World

One of the oldest relationships on Earth is that between fact and fiction. It has not always been a happy one but over the centuries it has become apparent that one needs and inspires the other in more ways than we ever believed. The fact-loving subject of science is one of the most exciting disciplines in the world, although its teachings can get bogged down in boring educational texts and hidden behind fear, dogma and confusion. The analytical nature of science gives us the ability to perceive the anatomy of the Universe and every molecule in it, but it is the human imagination that gives it life. Descriptions of the history of the Earth, the stars sparkling across the cosmos, worlds so far away we may never see them and the wonderment of what life forms potentially exist out there, contain more exotic characters and magical realms than any fictional tale. By using storytelling, the walls of science are being broken down and a self-conscious reading public, aware of and excited by its own progress and the rapidly changing world around it, can finally engage with a subject that makes the existence of such entities entirely possible.

An Astrobiologist is Born ...

More than 100 years ago in a leafy countryside town just outside London, a 'gentleman' writes about the attempted destruction of the human race by Martians. A meteor lands on Horsell Common near Woking, Surrey, yet instead of a scorched lump of rock, the object opens – disgorging alien beings from the planet Mars. These Martians have abandoned their dry and dusty home during its last dying gasps and travelled to the living, breathing Earth in the hope of their salvation. With two large, dark-coloured eyes and a lip-less mouth, a big greyish bulk the size of a bear, glistening like wet leather, and brandishing two giant tentacles instead of arms, these monstrous creatures emerge on to the Earth – only to struggle to breathe in the oxygen-rich atmosphere and be forced to retreat quickly into their ships. They build frightening three-legged metallic machines with which to lay waste to the towns and villages west of London while forging their way to the capital. They extinguish everything and everyone in their wake, firing deadly heat-rays, spreading poisonous black smoke and a pervasive red weed. This tale ends well for humanity (spoiler alert!) as after a bitter struggle, and at a point where a Martian victory seems inevitable, a humble terrestrial microbe delivers the final blow. Bacteria, against which it turns out the Martians have no defences, infect and kill the invaders, ultimately saving humanity and the entire Earth.

England's father of science fiction, H.G. Wells, penned this story in 1897. Instead of instilling fear, my first exposure to classic science fiction at a very young age made me curious. Was there actually life on Mars that could one day invade us? How could a tiny microbe like the mould that grows on cheese kill the aliens when the 'great and powerful' humans could not? Add these questions to the fact that the entire story took place in my home county and completely annihilated the town in which I grew up, who wouldn't be hooked? This serial called *The War of the Worlds* saw H.G. Wells write the first alien invasion story and create a legacy of distrust, yet also curiosity, surrounding the possibility of contact with alien life. He was one of a few in the nineteenth century who began to popularise the alien, both negatively and positively, and brought to the public arena the science behind the search for extraterrestrial life and the environments that exist on other worlds. This story and others like it have straddled the boundary between science fact and science fiction, inspiring generations of scientists to pursue space science, including me, and paved the way for a new scientific discipline to be born: Astrobiology.

The Science of Alien Life

How does life begin and evolve from the simplest carbon-rich speck to a fully conscious individual? Is there life beyond Earth and if so, how can we find it? What is the future for life on Earth and its existence in the Universe? Humans have looked up at the night sky for thousands of years and asked these questions. We have gazed at the myriad stars twinkling in the darkness, wondering if somewhere out in the silence of space there was anyone staring back. Everyone has probably at some point pondered where life on our planet came from or if we are alone. Today, astrobiology works tirelessly to address the compelling mysteries surrounding extraterrestrial life, while embracing the study of the origin, evolution, distribution and future of life on this planet. It is an eclectic multidisciplinary field, encompassing a range of subjects including physics, chemistry, astronomy, biology, molecular biology, ecology, planetary science, geography and geology – all working together to investigate the possibility of life on other worlds. Yet Astrobiology is an enigma of a science. Unlike geology, which arose to describe the physical materials and origins of the Earth, or microbiology to explain observations of life under the microscope, astrobiology has yet to prove its subject matter actually exists – alien life is currently still fictional. Instead it is all about the hunt, the discoveries, the dead ends and the challenge to think outside of our habitual comfort zone and dare to imagine other forms of life and where they might be hiding.

It was only 50 years ago that humanity began to extend its presence into space – first with robots, then with animals and finally with humans. This tentative expansion of our species towards other worlds has been made possible by the development of technology, which has finally started to reach a level that can complement and support our imagination and desire for exploration. However, considering the size of the cosmos and the growing number of promising sites on many worlds where life might quite like to snuggle up, the search has barely begun. When we finally find life on another world – and we will – it will be one of the most significant cultural events in human history, having a profound resonance on the question of our origins. It is not surprising, therefore, to find that such possibilities have been discussed by every human civilisation and culture, primitive or advanced, as far back as we have written records. Even before these thoughts were given a name and embraced within a scientific discipline of their own, such extraterrestrial wonderings found their outlet through myths and fairy tales, conversations, cave paintings, lectures, letters, fictional literature, philosophy and religions, music and poetry, then later through films and TV shows and video games. Today, astrobiology also features strongly on social media via personal and group blogs, Twitter, Facebook and YouTube.

Star-crossed Lovers

The marriage between science fiction and science fact is built on truth. For instance, science fiction frequently contains the theme of humans living on an alternative planet (for better or for worse) or escaping from Earth altogether and settling on other planets and moons in the Solar System, and even star systems beyond. Science fact forecasts that by the end of the twenty-first century the Earth's human population is predicted to surpass 11 billion individuals, crowding the biosphere and further depleting the raw materials on which life depends. In this all-too-likely version of the future many questions will surround the sustainability of the global population, the growing pressures on the natural environment, world food supplies, and energy resources. Ally this to the fact that what is available now is being polluted and quite possibly ruined for the next generations, and the future does not look promising. Science fiction may one day need to become science fact.

For the vast majority of people, the idea of extraterrestrial life entered their lives not as science but as fiction. Even scientists, whose reputation implies an innate love of the technicalities of scientific concepts, are commonly influenced by alien literature and film. The concept of alien life forms is deeply felt and firmly ingrained in the human mind, and has culminated in some of the most popular movies of all time, including *2001: A Space Odyssey* (1968), *Close Encounters of the Third Kind* (1977), *Star Wars* (1977 to present), *Alien* (1979, 1986, 1992 and 1997), *E.T. the Extraterrestrial* (1982), *Independence Day* (1996 and 2016), *Contact* (1997), *District 9* (2009), *Avatar* (2009), *Guardians of the Galaxy* (2014) and *The Martian* (2015). In fact, if you search for films that include a theme of extraterrestrial life you find that on average over 10 movies a year are released. A beautiful symbiotic relationship exists between art and science, bringing together creative thought and scientific theory, driving forwards both innovation and exploration. As such a number of astrobiology-rich stories over the years have amassed quite a cult following due to their gripping storylines, relatable characters and faithfulness to the science, inspiring generations of the public and scientists alike.

42

What is the answer to the Ultimate Question of Life, the Universe, and Everything? According to legendary comedy/sci-fi author Douglas Adams (with whom I incidentally share a birthday), the answer is 42. In 1979, he published a novel based on his radio show *The Hitchhiker's Guide to the Galaxy*, the first in a trilogy of five books. Yes, a trilogy of five. *The Hitchhiker's Guide* follows the story of a hapless human called Arthur Dent, who is saved from Earth's destruction with just seconds to spare by his good friend Ford Prefect. Prefect, whom Dent at first believes to be human, actually turns out to be an alien who named himself after the Ford Prefect car in a bid to blend in with what he assumed to be the dominant terrestrial life form. He is working for the Hitchhiker's Guide to the Galaxy – a combination travel guide/Wikipedia for intergalactic travellers roaming the Universe by grabbing rides on passing spacecraft. The planet Earth is actually a computer, just mistaken for a planet because of its size and use of biological components, and is destroyed by the Vogons to make way for a hyperspatial express route. Dent and Prefect end up on a series of perilous adventures aboard a ship stolen by the President of the Galaxy, Zaphod Beeblebrox, along with another human runaway Trillian and a depressed robot, Marvin the Paranoid Android.

The importance of science in this famous story is stated right at the start: 'Far out in the uncharted backwaters of the unfashionable end of the western spiral arm of the Galaxy lies a small unregarded yellow sun. Orbiting this at a distance of roughly ninety-two million miles is an utterly insignificant little blue green planet.' This hypothesises how unimportant we are and how wrong humanity is about the Universe. In that way, this very much fictional story is like science in real life: it forces us to reconsider and challenge what we think we know and makes us feel small and insignificant at the same time. Exploration in *The Hitchhiker's Guide to the*

Galaxy is about moving out into the unknown and experiencing new things. This story opened people's minds to a new way to view the Universe and ignited a wish in many to explore the Galaxy. It gave an insight into the possible types of aliens out there and the role of artificial intelligence – quite possibly the next step in our evolution. All the while, a ribbon of comedy keeps it light and engaging. The idea that the answer to any question is 42, and the positive impact the story has had on so many, is visible throughout today's culture.

Seeking Out New Life and New Civilisations

Ever since the starship *Enterprise* first warped across television screens in 1966, *Star Trek* has continued to inspire audiences with its portrayal of a future space-faring species game to 'boldly go where no [one] has gone before'. Its creator Gene Roddenberry, and his daring writers, started with real-life science and s-t-r-e-t-c-h-e-d it to create amazing imaginative inventions and intricately crafted worlds that could fit within remotely plausible storylines. They stayed true to the map of the Universe and kept the stars realistically far away, but designed the human species with the power to reach them in days or weeks, instead of in lifetimes. To reach the nearest star system today, Alpha Centauri, it would take the Space Shuttle and current technology up to 165,000 years. Needless to say, those who start the journey, and even their great-grandchildren, would never see its end. Generational ships such as the *Enterprise* are something commonly thought about for future space-faring humans. *Star Trek* (and its subsequent spin-off series and films) also gave us magical devices such as the transporter, advanced medical instruments and the holodeck, which were included to showcase the fantastical tools that might be built by human engineers in a future where humanity has technologically progressed into the realms of current science fiction. *Star Trek* gave the public a vision of what may one day be possible, and that's just one reason why the shows have been so popular. The real science lies in an effort to be true to humanity's greatest achievements while making it accessible and entertaining to watch. Obviously it cannot be wholly faithful to science and technology today as it is virtually impossible to create a perfectly accurate science-fiction TV series. Some scientists of course discredit *Star Trek* because of certain scientific errors or impossible events, but this is unfair. Accurate science is seldom exciting and spectacular enough to base a weekly adventure TV show upon. More faithful to science than any other science-fiction series ever shown, *Star Trek* has attracted and excited generations of viewers about advanced science and engineering and it is one of a select few shows that depict scientists and engineers of both genders and all races positively, as role models and people to aspire to.

A huge branch of astrobiology focuses on the future of human civilisation and the design of tools and technologies to allow us to one day live among the stars. Science inspired countless aspects of *Star Trek* and now many of the tools designed for the show are inspiring science. Remember the Replicator – a magical aperture in the bulkhead where you could order anything you desired? Although we cannot materialise food out of thin air (wouldn't that solve a lot of problems), we can create many other useful objects. In December 2014, NASA *emailed* the design plans for a wrench up to an astronaut on the International Space Station (ISS), who was then able to create it physically using a 3D printer. Unlike science-fiction Replicators, which seemingly produce objects on demand and whole ('Tea, Earl Grey, Hot'), this 3D-printed version came out as a 20-piece assembly kit that Astronaut Barry Wilmore then snapped together into a working socket wrench. We can also 3D-print artificial organs tailored to fit individual people, which are meant to replace or even enhance human parts, such as titanium replacement hip joints and made-to-order polymer bones that can be used to reconstruct damaged skulls and fingers. The Replicator is not as far-fetched as you may think.

What about artificial intelligence, the potential next step in evolution? Although there has been a lot of press about a computer program that reportedly passed the Turing Test by fooling judges into thinking it was human (it did not), no one seriously suggests that this particular program is sentient. It is still definitely an *it* instead of a *he* or *she*. Sentient machines remain in the realm of fiction, yet the dream of creating a Lieutenant Commander Data is very real. The ways in which thoughts are encoded and transmitted within the human brain remain only crudely understood, preventing real intelligence from being developed just yet. However, simple brain-to-machine commands can be transmitted and have been created, enabling impaired or paralysed people to control prostheses and machines. Do you recall *Star Trek*'s Universal Translator? Microsoft recently announced Skype Translator, which allows near real-time audio translation from one language to another, utilising advances in speech recognition and machine translation technologies. Currently in its infancy, it isn't a galaxy far far away (a *Star Wars* rather than *Star Trek* reference) from reality. Interestingly, the Apple iPad bears a remarkable resemblance to hand-held touchscreen networked computers called PADDs (Personal Access Display Device) used by some Starfleet Officers in *Star Trek*. And although no medical tricorders have been built yet, we do have handheld sonograms that help to observe a foetus and organs inside the body.

The human imagination can create a wealth of gadgets that future generations may find useful but where it really excels is in creating life itself. Now that we understand biochemistry a little better, most scientists agree that life probably exists somewhere out there in other solar systems. The chemical elements needed for carbon-based life are common in the Universe, so maybe life forms built like us are numerous in the Galaxy, too. Our imagination can conjure up all kinds of creatures with any number of arms, legs, eyes or even heads that are quite often equally or a lot smarter than we are. It seems doubtful that humanoid shapes would be as common as the alien races depicted in science-fiction series such as *Star Trek*. We have to allow the show some concessions here, as there are only so many shapes and sizes actors come in. Yet could half-human/half-alien hybrids such as Spock ever exist? It seems almost impossible, although scientists and nature alike have already created interspecies hybrids from plants, the Killer Bee and Wholphins (false killer whale × bottlenose dolphin). Spock is not totally beyond biochemical reality, but definitely at the fictional edge of science fact.

I See You

Next we come to one of the most scientifically plausible, almost educational, astrobiology-themed films of all time, and it is highly enjoyable to boot. *Avatar* (2009) is set in the year 2154 and humankind has reached out to the stars. The white-yellow glow of Alpha Centauri A – a star very similar to our Sun – illuminates the Saturn-sized gaseous giant planet Polyphemus and its fifth moon, the tropical world of Pandora. On this lush green satellite, great beasts roam the jungles and pterodactyl-like creatures soar through the sky. A sentient, blue-skinned humanoid species known as the Na'vi lives here, in harmony with nature and at war with humanity.

Its creator James Cameron, a physics major himself, created this world using science. He set Pandora and Polyphemus in the real Alpha Centauri system, the closest stellar family to Earth. This system actually has three stars, all revolving around one another. At its heart lies a pair of sun-like stars: the first, Centaurus A, is some 20 per cent larger than the Sun, while the second, Centaurus B, is 15 per cent smaller. A third star, Proxima Centauri, orbits them both and is a red dwarf that is 80 per cent smaller than the Sun. Since both Cen A and B are chemically similar to the Sun, the same general mixture of elements that allowed life to develop on Earth should have been available in the primordial soups of both their planetary broods. While planets in other solar systems make the news on an almost daily basis, one of the most remarkable announcements occurred in 2012 when astronomers claimed the discovery of an Earth-like planet circling Cen B, a mere 4.3 light years away. In astronomical terms, that is almost close enough to touch. This discovery may now prove to be false due to a 'ghost' in the measurements taken, but it hinted that perhaps Cameron had the right idea and a world like Pandora won't exist solely in the realms of science fiction and fantasy for much longer.

Making Pandora a moon is a wonderful acknowledgement of recent science. Astronomers in the first instance are looking for planets like Earth – small and rocky – within the 'Goldilocks zone' of their star: a not-too-hot, not-too-cold orbital band around a sun where life-giving water can be liquid on a planet's surface. Nonetheless, small planets, like the Earth, are hard to locate and scientists have found many more of the larger gas giants such as Saturn in the Goldilocks zone around other stars. Those planets are not habitable by life as we know it – although their moons, should they have them, could be. Icy and rocky moons surround all the gas giants in our Solar System, so it is feasible to suggest that this may be the case around alien Jupiters and Saturns. There may be Earth-sized rocky moons orbiting another gaseous world not too far away. A huge problem for life on one of these moons would be extreme radiation emitted from the gas giant. For instance, the daily radiation engulfing Jupiter's moon Io is 4,000 times the lethal dose for humans. Science allows James Cameron to give Pandora a life-protecting shield in the form of a robust magnetic field created by the moon's superconductive rocks, which deflects this harmful radiation and allows life to thrive on its surface. To highlight this, at one point in the film, a spectacular aurora is seen dancing overhead, as happens around the North and South Poles when solar winds hit Earth's magnetic shield.

Movies such as *Avatar* are challenging as they get us thinking about the possibilities, and especially the physical attributes of life. The moon Pandora is rocky, rich in the fictional mineral Unobtanium (an old in-joke in science fiction for materials with physically impossible qualities). From orbit, it looks a lot like Earth, with vast blue oceans, and continents covered in lush tropical rainforests, suggesting that both it and its mother planet must lie fairly close to their Sun, taking advantage of its light and warmth. Pandora's atmosphere is mainly composed of nitrogen, oxygen, carbon dioxide and xenon, and is 20 per cent denser than the Earth's atmosphere. The carbon dioxide makes it toxic to humans, acknowledged in the film by the use of oxygen masks. The trees on Pandora resemble those on Earth in colour and similarly have trunks, branches and leaves, although owing to Pandora's lower gravity (20 per cent that of Earth), the shapes and proportions have been able to be exaggerated. Also because of this lower gravity, most creatures are hexapods (with six legs) and are often huge. The Na'vi, however, are strikingly reminiscent of humans, which as mentioned before is a common science-fiction theme. Their bodies, however, are larger, allowing them to survive in the lower-gravity conditions, and are built to hunt, being blessed with vision beyond the visible range of that of humans, feline ears, a tail for balance, and a snout. All these adaptations are for greater sensory perception, which aids their survival. The Na'vi's skin is blue, containing a pigment of cyanin, producing colours in the blue, purple and cyan spectrum. Na'vi blood is red, utilising an iron compound similar to haemoglobin to transport oxygen throughout the body. Bioluminescent skin cells emit light when ambient light levels are low.

All this detail may seem extreme when used solely for the creation of a fictional world and species, but it's the detail that gives the story its strength and credibility. Cameron and his team of advisers built this entire world upon the terrestrial laws of physics, biology and chemistry. The characteristics of the moon and the physical adaptations of its inhabitants are based upon detailed observations of other planets and moons, and the adaptations to different conditions seen in Earth-life, and common evolutionary trends. This film has predicted in detail what life, and its environment, might look like on alien planets and moons.

Extraterrestrials in most science-fiction stories may not be depicted as perfect human replicas, but do appear as pseudo-hominids that are eerily familiar. They tend to share our bipedal locomotion; bilateral symmetry; build of head, trunk (body), two arms and two legs; upright posture and forward-facing, stereoscopic eyes. Even robots are designed in our image to an extent. The reason lies in science: designs are commonly inspired by the life that we see around us and, most importantly, can interact with. As such, science fiction also commonly assumes alien life will be complex and intelligent, because an immobile silent blob of wobbling plasma would not exactly make for gripping viewing. However, extraterrestrial simply means 'beyond Earth' and there is nothing that says this beyond-Earth life has to be humanoid in form, especially considering that more than 90 per cent of life on Earth looks nothing like us.

Rock, Paper, Scissors, Lizard, Spock

Television shows such as *The Big Bang Theory* bring together the science, the story and the people. Fictional stories based on fact have communicated science to a wider audience for centuries with both real and fictional scientists themselves proving to have an even stronger impact. *The Big Bang Theory* is a California-based comedy that follows a group of self-professed geeks including a NASA engineer, an astrophysicist and two particle physicists that has made science chic again and is even credited with consolidating the growing appetite among teenagers for the once unfashionable subject of physics. Walking the narrow tightrope between science and sitcom, this show is beloved by critics, audiences and scientists alike for its quick wit, incredibly geeky yet relatable characters, and its science and science-fiction storylines. In more than one episode, there is a nod to astrobiology, most famously when the NASA engineer Howard crashed the Mars Exploration Rover into a crevice while trying to impress a girl. The data that it sent back contained the first clear indications that there may have been life on Mars, but he could not take the credit. The show not only embraces science and cult followings of many science-fiction shows, but also the geeky stereotype of scientists themselves while introducing a multitude of scientific concepts. Sheldon at one point refers to geologists like myself as the 'dirt people' – and it is not a compliment – but I'll let him off this once.

The First Astrobiologists

These twenty-first-century writers and scientists are not the first to wonder about the stars and envisage what alien life might be like (although they shout about it the loudest), and they will not be the last. As far back as 4,000 years ago the ancient Babylonians observed and recorded the position and movements of stars, planets, the Moon, comets and eclipses as seen crossing their night-time desert skies. At around the same time on the other side of the world, the ancient Chinese were also beginning to document the heavenly bodies above them and early Hindu writings in India showed a similar trend. Interest in the existence of life really awakened with the ancient Greeks. Democritus, who lived from 460 to 370 BC, is considered by many to be the father of modern science and potentially has the great honour of being the first astrobiologist. He realised that the

Sun was just a star and that what appeared to be the fog of the Milky Way was in fact innumerable distant stars. In his wisdom, he understood that the planets revolved around the Sun and that the Earth itself is a planet. He even theorised about exoplanets – distant planets and moons spinning around other suns. Democritus said that some planets would be arid and lifeless, while others would bear life similar to, but not necessarily identical to, that on Earth. His teachings, written over 2,000 years ago, actually align with what we think and are starting to observe today. A contemporary of Democritus was Aristotle (460–370 BC), who is much more commonly remembered today (as was his mentor Plato, *c.* 428–327 BC), but who firmly rejected the idea of life existing anywhere other than on the Earth.

Thankfully, by the last century BC, Ancient Roman thinkers such as the poet and philosopher Lucretius (*c.* 99–55 BC), disagreed with Aristotle, and expressed in writings their belief in other inhabited worlds. In the fifteenth century CE, the work of Copernicus, and in the sixteenth century Galileo with his telescope, finally put the Sun where it belongs: at the centre of the Solar System. This coincided with the Renaissance, a rebirth of Western science and culture, and was a precursor to the Enlightenment of the seventeenth and eighteenth centuries, in which rationality was preferred to tradition and untested beliefs. In the early eighteenth century, many gentleman scientists, including Sir Isaac Newton – most famous for his love of apples and ideas about a thing called gravity – speculated on the existence of other worlds.

Despite this new phase of illumination, the belief in 'cosmic pluralism' or the plurality of worlds still existed – a non-science-based faith conceived in Ancient Greece, which held that numerous worlds in addition to Earth may exist and harbour extraterrestrial life. In 1862, Camille Flammarion wrote *La pluralité des mondes habités* (Plurality of Inhabited Worlds), a factual account of the philosophy of the possibility of life on other worlds. The creation of the telescope, instead of helping to dispel this idea, actually appeared to prove to many that a multitude of worlds containing life was a reasonable assumption. As greater scientific scepticism and rigour were applied to the question, it ceased to be simply a matter of philosophy and theology and became influenced and educated by astronomy and biology. Fiction started to be based upon and drawn from fact.

Up to this point, a number of prominent 'gentlemen' have dominated the story of both factual and fictional astrobiology, yet there are some truly epic women who have also driven space science and astrobiology forwards, and I hope you don't mind me highlighting it here. They may not be as well known as Marie Curie or Ada Lovelace, but without them science would not be where it is today. There is a reason when looking back at history, of course, for why we are not as familiar with their efforts – Western women have only been allowed to study science at university since the late 1800s and historically have faced a great struggle to be able to engage with scientific subjects. Even though it was not easy and records are few, there is a number of brilliant and influential females who have had a hugely positive impact on mainstream science, fact and fiction – from classic lecturers and professors to scientific researchers, teachers, authors, TV presenters, science journalists, writers and communicators.

Caroline Herschel (1750–1848), sibling to the famous astronomer Sir William Herschel, assisted her brother in his observations and in the building of telescopes and became a brilliant astronomer in her own right, discovering new nebulae and star clusters. She was the first woman to discover a comet and was the first British woman to be paid for her scientific work. She continued her astronomical studies until her death at age 97, compiling a catalogue of nebulae and increasing the number of known star clusters from 100 to 2,500. Mary Anning (1799–1847) was the first female fossil-hunter, and recovered the first ichthyosaur from a seaside cliff near Lyme Regis, England, when she was around

11 years old. In addition, she found long-necked plesiosaurs, a pterodactyl and hundreds, possibly thousands, of other fossils that helped scientists draw a picture of the marine world 200–140 million years ago. There was also Mary Somerville (1780–1872) who experimented with magnetism and produced a series of writings on astronomy, chemistry, physics and mathematics. Other great women, such as Rosina Zornlin, Daphne Jackson, Jocelyn Bell Burnell, Williamina Flemming, Cecilia Payne-Gaposchkin, Joan Feynman, Lydia Becker, Margaret Gatty, Mary Ward, Agnes Giberne, Agnes Clarke and Eliza Brightwen – to name but a few – pushed science and society forwards, and in turn paved the way for astrobiology to evolve. Today a huge cohort of intelligent, driven, and creative women proudly carry on their legacy.

This brings us up to the present, and the earliest published use of the word 'astrobiology'. This is credited to an article written by Lawrence Lafleur of Brooklyn College in 1941 that quite rightly described it as 'the consideration of life in the Universe elsewhere than Earth'. The science of astrobiology in the twentieth and twenty-first centuries has laid significant groundwork for the understanding of the genesis and evolution of life in the Universe. Exploring the farthest reaches of the Earth has uncovered fossils, organisms, and ecosystems that have all led to significant insight into the early Earth – possible models for life's origins, as well as a huge expansion of the recognised environmental limits of life. Laboratory work, coupled with astronomical observations, has added another significant piece of the puzzle and space missions are finally taking astrobiologists away from Earth and out into the cosmos. Given the timeless fascination with questions of the origins and prevalence of life, the science of astrobiology will surely endure long into the future.

Birth of the Alien

One of the most popular themes at the heart of astrobiology and nearly all space-based science-fiction epics is that of the extraterrestrial, the alien, or the menace from space. It is a topic that has greatly captured the public's imagination. Despite the long history of speculation surrounding life in the cosmos, the image of an alien only entered the realm of public literature in the last third of the nineteenth century, even though the topic had already inflamed the popular imagination back in the seventeenth century. The birth of the modern-day alien seems, therefore, to be intricately linked to advances in astronomy and the rise of the theory of evolution.

The alien, it turns out, was invented independently three separate times: in France, Germany, and England, spurred on by the imaginative science of an American. The people most often hailed as its creators are Jules Verne in France, Kurd Lasswitz in Germany and H.G. Wells in England. The famous novelist Jules Verne first discussed extraterrestrials in his 1870 novel *Autour de la Lune* (Around the Moon), but went no further as he constrained his imagination with science. He never wrote a story focused solely on aliens, as he needed proof of their existence first. In 1897, Kurd Lasswitz, the father of German science fiction, published *Auf Zwei Planeten* (On Two Planets), in which intelligent advanced Martians travelled to Earth, not out of some dire need to escape a dying planet or to colonise and rule the puny Earthlings but simply out of curiosity and a thirst for exploration. He believed that using aliens in his story could help illuminate the important role that science and technology played in society. He was not a scientist himself but a philosopher and historian, who adopted a scientific evolutionary universe in his stories. He once wrote that the natural order of the Universe demands not only that 'living, feeling, thinking creatures' exist on worlds currently inaccessible, but also that there should be 'infinite gradations of intelligent beings inhabiting such worlds'. Also in 1897, H.G. Wells serialised *The War of the Worlds* – a story full of scientific ideas gleaned from evolutionary biology and astronomy, undoubtedly influenced by Wells's mentor, the biologist T.H. Huxley (1825–1895). He devised the look and intelligence of the Martians, explored how they would have evolved beyond us due to Mars' greater age; their ability to travel through space propelled by hydrogen gas, the means by which they coped with Earth's stronger gravity; and finally their demise due to disease. This book launched not only Wells' career and legacy, but also that of the alien itself. Its subject matter created an emotional connection with its readers while exploring many, some may say mundane, scientific facts.

The spread of the ideas of extraterrestrial life has jumped from science to literature to film and back again. Although the subject has always been popular since it first burst onto the literary scene, of all the rich variety of science subjects available it could never have been foreseen that this completely fictional, currently unproven, subject matter would become such a universal theme of popular culture, the poster child for science fiction itself – and no life form is more famous than the Martian.

Civilisations on Mars

Astrobiology is so much more than the search for life on our nearest neighbour. The story of this particular search is one of the oldest and has inspired more science writers than any other world. Mars has been a favoured setting for the alien throughout the millennia, and the leading candidate in the *real-life* search for extraterrestrial beings. Known to exist since ancient Babylon, closer observations of Mars only began in the 1500s, with Danish astronomer Tycho Brahe (1546–1601). It was the Dutchman Christiaan Huygens (1629–1695) who first speculated about life on the planet. Extraterrestrial life, he said, is not ruled out by the Bible, and why create other planets if not to populate them? His ideas got a boost in the eighteenth century by Sir William Herschel (1738–1822), who, believing the dark areas on Mars to be seas, wondered if living Martians might not 'enjoy a situation similar to our own'.

Over the course of the twentieth century, the increasing power of telescopes and their detectors, the development of photography, photometry and spectroscopy, and the ability to send spacecraft to Mars, has further fuelled the search. Twentieth-century science has progressed from a hypothetical question of intelligence in the Solar System, to an exploration into the possible existence of vegetation and water, and finally to searching for organic molecules, fossil life and microorganisms themselves. A central character in this saga is Percival Lowell (1855–1916) and his startling idea that linear 'canal' features he saw on the surface of Mars were proof that the planet was inhabited. He was not the one to discover these – that crown is placed upon the head of the Italian astronomer Giovanni Schiaparelli (1835–1910) in 1877 – but Lowell made it a public sensation in 1894. Schiaparelli fuelled Lowell's theory by describing Mars as a planet of change, with two polar caps composed of snow and ice that through melting produced a temporary sea around the northern cap. He believed this water was distributed over great distances by 'a network of canals, perhaps constituting the principal mechanism (if not the only one) by which water (and with it organic life) may be diffused over the arid surface of the planet.' When Lowell joined the debate about the possibility of life on Mars, the general opinion was that the canals were cracks in the Martian crust made during the formation of the planet, although some argued for their artificiality. Backed by his comfortable financial situation, Lowell's passion for astronomy and interest in the notion that the planet might sustain life drove forwards publication of three major works between 1895 and 1908 and the construction of the Lowell Observatory – the first to be sited at high altitude and remote from urban light pollution. He wrote in 1895 that 'a system of irrigation seems an absolute necessity for Mars if the planet is to support any life upon its great continental areas.' He did not just mean any old life, but intelligent life. Life that had evolved enough to control the usage and distribution of water on a drying planet. He and his staff catalogued 183 canals, basing their artificial nature on their straightness, uniform width, and systematic radiation from specific points. He also proposed that vegetation was growing on Mars, and that he was only able to see the canals as they were lined with strips of fertilised land. By 1895, this was a story fully in the public domain and, although outrageous even to contemplate today, science could not disprove or confirm it for more than 20 years. The instruments of science just were not ready yet and personal bias still reigned, driven by scientists with strong imaginations. We now can prove that Lowell's canals actually correspond to no physical surface features on Mars, except for one – the large canyon of Valles Marineris. Lowell was simply observing an optical illusion. He even noted very broad, streaky canals on Venus, again false. Cloud-shrouded Venus was dubbed the most Earth-like planet and even said to harbour intelligent life, yet the planet quickly fell victim in the extraterrestrial life debate, when in 1940 conditions were considered too harsh to support life in any form. Although Venus was abandoned, Mars has remained as a possible site for life – despite our current understanding of its environment. This in no small part is due to science fiction.

The Future of Astrobiology

The drive to gain knowledge is a fundamental and almost evolutionary characteristic of our species. It is not hard to believe that our exploration of the cosmos and under-standing of the how, why and uniqueness of our existence may well influence the future of humanity. Our current astrobiological voyage across the stars in search for life promises to alter profoundly and to expand our notions of life, its origins and its future. If extraterrestrial life were found to exist, if a second origin of life were discovered on another world, or if life very different from Earth life were found outside the realms of life-as-we-know-it, it would change the very nature of what it means to be human, both scientifically and personally. In the search for life in the Universe we are not only looking for life we recognise, but that which might have evolved to thrive in conditions outside the bounds of Earth environments – the *weird* life only previously seen in our imaginations and in science fiction. Despite the literal meaning of the word, astrobiology is so much more than the search for biology in space. It covers the origins, evolution and future of life in all its guises on every world. As such there is one other form of life to consider, one that does not yet exist but that may be created in the future. The destiny of astrobiology may lie within the ecosystem of the World Wide Web.

Several researchers have put forwards the following premise, originally presented by SETI Senior Astronomer Seth Shostak: 'That once a society creates the technology that could put them in touch with the cosmos, they are only a few hundred years away from changing their paradigm from biology to artificial intelligence.' Many scientists predict a strong artificial intelligence will have been developed here on Earth by 2050 – about a hundred years after the invention of computers, or a hundred and fifty years after the invention of radio communication. The dominant intelligence in the cosmos may one day end up not being biological. Can we replicate our own intelligence, or something similar, and is it actually a good idea? This topic has made it to the mass media multiple times. First there was Stephen Hawking, then Elon Musk, and most recently Bill Gates. All of these visionary people have suggested that artificial intelligence (AI) is something to be watched carefully, 'lest it develops to a point of an existential threat'. What this threat might be has yet to be established. Hawking has suggested that it might be in the capacity of a strong AI to *evolve* much, much faster than biological systems – ultimately gobbling up resources without a care for the likes of us. It will do what it must to survive (Darwin's 'survival of the fittest'), even if this is at the expense of its creators. A system with the complexity of a human brain is almost certainly needed to sustain true intelligence, and today we have to wonder if the Internet itself is capable of achieving this. Estimates suggest that there are about 15 billion active Internet connections today and by 2020 there could be 50 billion. It is a world that's increasingly populated by algorithms whose movements and decisions are in part inspired by biological intelligence, or at least our impression of it. Code talks to code, software talks to hardware. Influencing this ecosystem is the powerful and sometimes irrational human mind, with our likes and dislikes guiding the flow of information, seeking to understand what we might search for next, as individuals or as a population. Could something akin to a strong AI emerge from all of this?

This theme has, of course, been translated into numerous science-fiction blockbusters such as *Metropolis* (1927), *The Day the Earth Stood Still* (1951 and 2008), *2001: A Space Odyssey* (1968), *Blade Runner* (1982), *A.I. Artificial Intelligence* (2001), *I, Robot* (2004), *The Matrix* and *The Terminator* franchises (starting in 1999 and 1984), the plucky quadrilateral robot side-kicks in *Interstellar* (2014) and the incredible *Ex Machina* (2015). Even Pixar's cartoon *WALL-E* (2008) has taught children about AI and the possible future of humanity. Fun fact: WALL-E fell in love with fellow robot EVE, the Extraterrestrial Vegetation Evaluator, who is technically an astrobiologist.

As a subject, astrobiology is tackling one of the most profound questions we can ask about our place in the Universe – is the 4-billion-year-old biological experiment that is life on Earth unique? As Arthur C. Clarke once said, 'Two possibilities exist: either we are alone in the Universe or we are not. Both are equally terrifying.' The prospect and nature of life, both on and beyond Earth, is one of the few topics in science that can grab the attention of any public audience. Science fact and science fiction are working together to drive humanity's exploration of the Universe forwards and to support our quest to find a biological cosmic connection. Those of us who are lucky enough to work in astrobiology are perfectly placed and incredibly excited to tell this story.

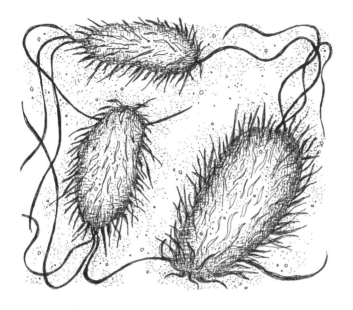

CHAPTER TWO

Life As We Know It

It may seem logical to start the story of the search for life at ... well ... the beginning. Yet it won't make much sense without first knowing what life actually is and what it needs to survive. It isn't pretty and is chemistry heavy, but do not worry – it will prove to be interesting and provide a solid background to what makes life possible. On our planet, living organisms have spread to every nook and cranny that can sustain them – in every direction you look; across land, water and air; from the driest deserts, balmy tropics, and tallest mountains to the coldest Arctic ice; on, within and under rocks and deep within nuclear reactors; there are even living beings inside the bodies of other living beings. Yet even with all this life, we still cannot quite explain it. The question 'What is life?' seems so simple to answer. If something is alive, it is obvious – a chair isn't alive, although the cute little kitten asleep on it is. What distinction causes us to consider one to be living and one not? We only have direct knowledge of one form of life, life on Earth, and have only one data point from which to extrapolate theories about its chemistry and essence. Until life is encountered elsewhere, or aliens finally contact us, we will not have an independent second data set. Even then we may not, if the alien life itself shares an ancestor with life on Earth.

So What is Life?

To truly understand life, we need to explore what it is made of, what it looks like, and what it does. One of the oldest philosophical enigmas ever posed is that of life, and remains to this day a query with no (or quite possibly many) answers. Life on Earth is recognisable; we normally know a living organism when we see it as our brains identify a number of qualities all living organisms display. However, just because an entity presents one or all of these, there is the chance that it is still not technically a living organism. We cannot rely on our gut instinct and say something is alive because we *know* it is such – we need proof.

To start with, we can look at what life is made of. All life that we know about is formed of a close-knit family of units, popularly known as *cells*. Simple life forms are mostly made up of one single lowly but powerful cell (they are called *unicellular*), while advanced life forms, such as humans, are built of a magical mix of many millions and millions of cells working together (unsurprisingly, they are called *multicellular*). Cells do absolutely everything; they provide structure for the body, take in nutrients from food, convert those nutrients into energy, and carry out specialised functions that keep their host bodies working and running smoothly. They can do this because each individual cell is bound by a wall called a membrane that acts as a choosy barrier to the outside environment, sometimes letting in molecules and ions that the cell needs or pushing them out to keep the inside of the cell working properly. Cells are also the librarians of life. They contain the story of the organism they are a part of, holding its hereditary material within *deoxyribonucleic acid* or DNA and storing an instruction manual on how to re-build every aspect of that particular life form. Owing to life's dependence on the cell, materials in living organisms are always seen to exhibit some kind of unit order, and so we believe this order is a necessary condition for life to exist. Since cells and order break down over time, however, death for sure is also an inescapable characteristic of life, but alone does not make something alive in the first place. Besides, we hardly want to wait around for a potential life form to die, just to prove it was once living. As an example, this book has a structural unit order of paper and pages and this order can be broken and destroyed over time, but we would not consider it alive, or in fact dead.

For cells to do their jobs, and run the organisms they are a part of, they need energy and this is a common element always found flowing through living systems. Cells gobble up chemical compounds from the environment, transform them and spew out waste products as residues. In this way, cells obtain the basic materials to build their own body parts, and at the same time gain the energy needed to carry out the thousands of biochemical reactions that must happen every day, such as reproduction, growth, thought and movement. The need for a life form to get around is actually one of the most important uses of its energy. To enable it to survive, an organism must look for food, escape from predators and react to changes in the environment – if it starts to get too hot or cold for survival, then being able to move and find shelter or hunt for more comfortable conditions becomes really rather important. Sometimes an organism does not have to move physically but can interact with its surroundings and actually respond to the changes imposed on it. For example, when it gets hot humans and horses instinctively sweat, dogs pant, and elephants and rabbits send more blood flow to their ears to carry the heat away from their bodies. At a basic level, cells also respond to physical and chemical environmental stimuli and can communicate among themselves about how best to react through small signalling molecules. Using energy, enacting movement and responding to a changing environment are all activities that we have observed in living organisms, but those actions or responses cannot be used as universal indicators or markers to define life. A refrigerator utilises energy to regulate the temperature of its environment and a thermostat in your home increases the heat coming out of the radiators when it senses the room getting colder. Although we appreciate these objects and even in extreme cases rely on them for our own survival, they are most definitely not living beings.

The cellular custodians of life's instruction manual can be reproduced and in doing so pass on this hereditary information to the next generation of cells. *Reproduction* is when cells duplicate their genetic material and divide to produce two new *'daughter'* cells, similar to their mother. All living organisms reproduce or at least are the products of reproduction. One exception to the former statement is mules, which are the hybrid products of reproduction between a horse and a donkey. Mules cannot reproduce themselves: they are sterile. Does this mean they are not alive? We remain reasonably certain that they are. Viruses are tricky; they do reproduce, as the rapid spread of the common cold shows, but they cannot do it alone – they need to hijack the molecular machinery of a host they have infected. Does this mean they are alive or not? Defining life using an entity's ability to reproduce itself is a tough ask, as it means a computer virus could technically be considered a living organism.

Life grows and develops in patterns, yet the final forms, the offspring, are never a completely identical copy of the original. This is the cornerstone of *evolution*. Evolution is the passing on of heritable traits or characteristics, both good and bad, from parent to child and occurs within every generation born. This transfer of information to build a new being is, however, imperfect. In some circumstances, a mutant gene is introduced that imparts either a survival advantage or disadvantage for the newly created life form, making it better equipped to survive in the world it is entering, or possibly cause its untimely death. Evolutionary adaptation over generations is regarded as the most fundamental and unifying of the properties of life mentioned thus far. One of the most famous British scientists, Charles Darwin (1809–1882), has become synonymous with this fascinating skill of life. His research into what he termed 'natural selection' highlighted that those individuals in a population whose traits best enable them to survive and reproduce will go on and produce more offspring, which in turn will survive to reproduce. This is where the phrase 'survival of the fittest' came from. Evolution and an organism's chance of survival is essentially a genetic lottery.

There are many forces found in nature that fulfil nearly all of the above characteristics of life and could theoretically be classed as living organisms but we would still, in the face of all this proof, not say they are alive. Fire is a perfect example – it grows and moves as it encounters material to consume, providing it with more energy. As such it is self-sustaining, as long as the *food* remains available. It *breathes* oxygen and responds to changes in its environment. It excretes waste products of ash, heat and carbon dioxide by some of the same reactions that run the cells in our bodies, and it is even able to reproduce itself and make little fire babies. Like any life form, it can be brought into existence from a parent fire, or born from just striking a match. Even with all this evidence, we still do not say it is alive. Why? Is it because it hasn't demonstrated any intelligence or shown itself to have some kind of spirit or soul?

What if, instead of this list of physical characteristics that we can easily find exceptions to, we try and define life by what it does, rather than from its composition. I like this idea as it can incorporate life forms from the past, those being created now and those that will possibly be designed in the future. Who is to say that a robot or hologram that can think and make decisions, and may even be able to feel emotions or pain, is not alive, just because it is not made up of cells; for growth requires installation of a new part or algorithm instead of growing one itself; is born of a creator instead of a genetic parent; and does not store its blueprints within DNA or is silicon- not carbon-based? The question of what life really is remains by far one of the hardest, but also the most excitingly challenging to answer.

Carbon, Carbon Everywhere!

It is difficult to comprehend, but at the heart of all life is a single element: carbon. Every life form on Earth is built upon a skeleton of carbon and some even need a source of carbon-based food for energy. Since all atoms are essentially put together in the same way – with a nucleus housing a variable number of neutrons and protons, orbited by shells of electrons – what makes the carbon atom so special that life put all of its hopes for survival on it? The answer lies in the *periodic table*, an organised list of all the currently known elements in existence. As you read the table from left to right, both the number of protons within and electrons around the nucleus of each atom of each element increases. The table is also broken into columns, grouping together elements that have a similar number of electrons present in their outer shells. Typically, it is only this outer coating of electrons that gets involved in chemical reactions and is important for this story. Carbon has four electrons out of a possible eight in its outermost shell – it is half full. As the most stable configuration is to have all eight electrons present and accounted for, each atom of carbon has the ability to form up to four *bonds* with electrons orbiting nearby atoms to achieve this stability. The ability to form four bonds is not restricted to carbon – it's a property of every atom with four outer electrons, including those that sit below carbon on the periodic table, such as silicon, germanium, tin and lead. What's special about carbon is that it can form complex molecules built of *double bonds*, sharing more than one electron with other atoms, and these bonds are very strong. The simplest carbon molecules consist of a carbon skeleton bonded only to hydrogen atoms, unsurprisingly called *hydrocarbons*. There are more than a million known carbon compounds, broadly termed *organic* molecules, and it is finding these molecules that drives our current exploration of the Solar System and beyond. These organic building blocks are rife throughout the Galaxy, strengthening the idea of carbon-based life existing outside of the Earth.

The Units of Life

The cell mentioned earlier can be imagined as a membrane-bound miniature chemical reactor containing a library of genetic information, and is the building block of every living thing on Earth. The first known cells are thought to have originated in the oceans of the early Earth about 3.8 billion years ago. These were the *prokaryotes*, organisms made up of one single cell, such as bacteria and archaea. These cells do not have any internal organs, nor do they have a nucleus to house their hereditary material. Instead, their genetic instruction manuals float freely as a twisted closed loop of DNA within a watery cytoplasm inside the cell. For a billion years, the prokaryotes reigned supreme throughout the waters of the Earth. More or less 2.7 billion years ago, however, the Earth and evolution decided their dictatorship was over and introduced *cyanobacteria* to the world – tiny bacteria capable of converting energy from sunlight into food. They not only produced food but also became food themselves. The larger original prokaryotes found these tiny new bacteria highly appetising, and enveloped them in their plasma membranes (mouths had not yet been invented). This resulted in a larger prokaryote with a smaller cyanobacterium inside; instead of the former digesting the latter, a symbiotic relationship developed whereby both organisms mutually benefitted from the new shared living situation. Over generations, these cyanobacteria stopped being a separate organism and became a part of the cell itself.

A second type of cell with internal organs, or more correctly *organelles*, had arisen through evolution and this step changed the course of life on Earth forever. These cells, known as *eukaryotes*, have since been used to build everything from fungi to plants to humans. Most eukaryotic cells, or *animal cells*, are invisible to the naked eye but can do everything from providing structure and stability to creating energy and a means of reproduction for an organism. We could not have evolved without eukaryotic cells, although interestingly in the average human body prokaryotic bacterial cells vastly outnumber eukaryotic human cells – so maybe we are more bacterial than human. Eukaryotes are much more complex than prokaryotes and have a genome that is up to 10,000 times larger, housed in a control centre called a *nucleus*. Eukaryotes evolved thanks to the predatory actions of prokaryotes gobbling up other prokaryotes who, instead of lunch, became a part of the original organism. However, even after their initial inception this eating of other organisms continued, and rather than being digested provided the eukaryotes with even more organelles, enabling them to evolve into ever more sophisticated cells. Inside eukaryotes there are *mitochondria*, which are the powerhouses of the cell, and perform reactions that extract energy from food. Within plant and algae cells there are *chloroplasts*, which perform the light-harvesting reactions of *photosynthesis*. Neither of these organelles is native to eukaryotic cells and chloroplasts are believed to have once been those free-living cyanobacteria that were engulfed by early prokaryotic cells but not digested. Over evolutionary timescales, the symbiotic relationship between the host cell and visiting bacteria developed to a point at which they were inseparable and required each other for survival.

Food for Thought

Every living organism – from the smallest bacterium to the tallest tree and fastest mammal – needs a source of food and an input of energy flowing through its system to survive, driven by an intricate process of chemical reactions within each cell known as its *metabolism*. A strong metabolism allows organisms to grow and reproduce, digest and transport substances into and between different cells, maintain their structures, and respond to their environments. To power this metabolism, humans eat food, plants absorb sunlight, and microorganisms use energy produced from chemical reactions through a process called *chemosynthesis*. To make these reactions take place, a very special molecule called *ATP* (*adenosine triphosphate*) transports the energy created by photosynthesis in plants, by cellular respiration in animals and by chemosynthesis in bacteria and archaea. As such, life cannot only be characterised by what it looks like, what it can do or whether or not its cells have a nucleus, but also by how it uses carbon and energy to metabolise. There are four categories that can be used to describe a life form based on the sources of carbon and energy available to them, and they are extremely helpful for hypothesising how and what type of life might be able to exist on other worlds.

Life can use carbon directly from the environment by drawing it from carbon dioxide found in the atmosphere or dissolved in water. This is how plants find carbon for their energy and so are classified as *autotrophs*. Other life forms derive their essential carbon from consuming pre-existing organic compounds through eating, such as animals and many microscopic organisms and these are called *heterotrophs*. Human beings are heterotrophs. There are also two sources of energy available to life: plants use the power of sunlight through photosynthesis, termed *photo-*; and animals use chemical energy from reactions that happen when organic compounds are eaten, termed *chemo-*. Combining these carbon and energy sources we find *photoautotrophs* – organisms such as plants and microbes that absorb their energy from sunlight and carbon from carbon dioxide in the environment. *Chemoautotrophs* draw their energy from chemical reactions using inorganic chemicals and carbon from environmental carbon dioxide. These organisms need neither food nor sunlight to survive and are found in environments where most other organisms would perish (we will meet a lot of these hardy little life forms later on). *Photoheterotrophs* get their energy from sunlight and carbon from consuming other organisms. This is rare but possible by some bacteria, such as *Chloroflexus*. Finally, *chemoheterotrophs* get both their energy and carbon from food – we humans are chemoheterotrophs. In general, eukaryotes can only feed on certain carbon sources, which can be pretty restrictive, but bacteria and archaea are truly remarkable as they can live off almost any imaginable foodstuff out there.

Molecules of Life

Life on Earth is built from only 24 of the greater than 100 known elements on our planet, each with properties that seem to be essential for a healthy metabolism. With so many elements available it almost seems a pity, and a tad risky, that just four elements – oxygen, carbon, hydrogen and nitrogen – dominate and control 96 per cent of the mass of a typical living cell. Life uses a polymer-based chemistry that includes nucleic acid polymers, DNA and RNA, to store and transmit information; *carbohydrates* for energy; and, when these are scarce or running low, *fats*. Yet the most diverse and multitasking of life's molecules are *proteins*, performing a vast array of functions within living organisms, including catalysing (speeding up or slowing down) metabolic reactions, replicating DNA, responding to stimuli, transporting molecules from one location to another and even building muscle. All proteins within living organisms on Earth are made up of the same 22 *amino acids*, from a selection of more than 500 found in nature. The key elements of every amino acid are the same as those of cells, namely carbon, hydrogen, oxygen and nitrogen. A fascinating quirk of amino acids is that there are two types; they are considered to be asymmetric molecules or *chiral*. To explain this, hold out your hands in front of you. Human hands are perhaps the most universally recognised example of chirality: no matter how you try and orientate both hands it is impossible for all the major features of both hands to match up – a truly opposite mirror image. The same can be said for amino acids. There are, therefore, two possible forms characterised as either *left-handed* (L) or *right-handed* (D). Amino acids occur in both L- and D- chiral forms, but nearly all life on Earth uses the L-form. Sugars are also found in both chiral forms, although terrestrial living cells use the right-handed D-forms exclusively. Why life chooses these particular mirror images over the other is not yet understood. Organic material found in carbon-rich meteorites also seems to have a bias towards a similar handedness. The evidence is mounting that a predisposition to one form over another occurs naturally across all bodies in the Solar System and adds weight to the idea that the precursor molecules for early life are perhaps related to those in space or may even have come to Earth from the cosmos.

Could alien life have the same left-handed L-form amino acids as we do or would they use right-handed D-form instead? Perhaps they use left-handed L-form sugars instead of right? If all life in the Universe, both terrestrial and alien, spawned from the same pool of early molecules, then theoretically every molecule in the Universe would have the same chirality as is found on Earth. It would therefore be quite hard to tell if the life were truly alien, or just a very, very distant relative. The universe of chemical possibilities is huge. For example, the number of different proteins that can be built from combinations of just the naturally occurring 22 amino acids is larger than all the number of atoms in the cosmos. Life on Earth certainly did not have time to sample and test all possible sequences and combinations to find the best. What exists in modern terrestrial life must therefore reflect some chance events in history that led to one choice winning over another, whether or not the choice was ideal. Perhaps some features of Earth's biochemistry emerged because of some now – unknown selective pressures on early life that no longer exist. Today's protein make-up and handedness may therefore not represent the finest design for survival in the modern world, but rather be a vestige of optimisation in an ancient one, such as is the case with the human appendix – once possibly needed in early humans for digesting leaves, today it is just a leftover of an ancient organ that has lost most or all of its original function. Who is to say, therefore, that life in the Universe may, or may not, have followed a similar pattern?

All life forms contain some form of DNA – the vessel containing all of the information-storing genes – life's genetic blueprint. It also has *RNA* (*ribonucleic acid*), which transfers information from the genes to enable the production of the cells' proteins. DNA is shaped like a long ladder twisted into a spiral – a double helix (RNA looks like one half of this ladder). Each strand of DNA's ladder has a carbon backbone of sugar molecules and phosphate groups and attached to it, making up the rungs, are chemical subunits known as *bases*. DNA is composed of four bases: Adenine (A), Thymine (T), Cytosine (C) and Guanine (G). These letters represent the code for building amino acids, that themselves make up proteins. The bases bind the two DNA strands together, with an A always bonding to a T on the opposite strand (and vice versa), and C and G doing likewise. A big question asked by biochemists is why DNA uses these precise bases, in particular adenine, when there are better alternatives? Maybe it was chosen over other available candidates by a freak accident, and was kept because later on it was thought too difficult to replace without losing fitness of the existing life forms. Potentially it was because adenine can be made prebiotically (chemically and before the formation of the first life forms) from ammonium cyanide, and had a much greater availability during the earliest eras in Earth history, making it a better choice in those times for starting life – even though a different contender might now be preferable. Fun fact: if the entire DNA in just one of your cells were unpacked and stretched out straight, it would be nearly 2m (7ft) long. Since you have about five trillion (5,000,000,000,000) cells in your body and just over 2m (7ft) of DNA in every cell, the total length of DNA packed into our bodies would stretch from here to the Moon and back 1,500 times.

No experiments can presently test all of the theories as to why life is built the way it is and uses certain molecules over others in its construction. Trying to understand the possible reasons for such choices allows us to appreciate how easy alternative explanations are, and therefore the number of alien life forms imaginable.

Is Carbon Really the Only Option?

If for some now hidden reason life chose this amino acid over that one, left-handed over right, DNA over RNA, then what if it had not chosen carbon? For years, scientists and science-fiction writers alike have dreamed about the possibility of life based on some other element. To replace life's dependency on carbon would require a carefully chosen competitor. This challenger would have to be an element that is found in abundance across the known

Universe and behave in a similar way to carbon, if life as we know it is still to function. *Silicon* is the first entertaining possibility. It sits nestled directly below carbon on the periodic table so has a similar personality. It has the same four electrons in its outer shell, meaning that it has four electron spaces available, giving it the ability to make four single bonds with other atoms, just as carbon does. It can bind readily to itself to make Si-Si bonds much like carbon can to other carbons, and it also bonds easily to hydrogen and oxygen given the right conditions. On Earth, silicon is more abundant than carbon. It bonded with two oxygen atoms and formed SiO_2 or quartz, the primary constituent of the rocks that make up the planet. The Earth is actually a silicon-rich, carbon-poor world with silicon unlikely ever to be in short supply.

So why on Earth did life choose carbon over silicon? One obvious answer is that outside the Earth and throughout the Universe there is much more carbon available than there is silicon, as fewer of the larger silicon atoms are formed within the cores of stars (we will explore how this happens in the next chapter). Silicon is used by life such as that found in the seashells abandoned along the beach but it is not the basis for any polymeric or metabolic chemistry. If complex silicon chemistry were possible on Earth, surely it ought to have resulted in life based on silicon, rather than its rarer chemical cousin, carbon. The answer may lie in the bonds that silicon makes with other elements, and how these may or may not be useful for life. For starters, it's a larger atom so the bonds it makes with other atoms under the conditions found on Earth are weaker than those made by carbon. There is also a huge difference between what happens when silicon and carbon bond with all the oxygen floating around the planet. Under the conditions found on the Earth, the molecule carbon dioxide (one carbon and two oxygen atoms) is a gas at most temperatures, is very soluble in water (and is therefore available in liquid solutions for life), and can be broken down into its constituent elements of carbon and oxygen – both of which are incredibly useful for life. In contrast, silicon dioxide (one silicon and two oxygen atoms) does not exist as a gas, except at extremely high temperatures over 2,000°C (3,632°F). As can probably be anticipated by the fact that it is the constituent of many rocks on Earth, silicon dioxide is almost completely immune to being dissolved; it's pretty solid. Finally, because silicon really loves to be bonded to oxygen, it is very difficult to break silicon dioxide into its constituent atoms. With respect to living organisms, silicon dioxide can be considered a very inert molecule and therefore somewhat useless for life processes. Consequently, carbon and carbon dioxide win the competition for being more useful to life, both as a molecule and split into individual elements.

Does this really matter when searching for alien life in the cosmos? Do the rules of chemistry work in the same way throughout the Universe? Would we observe silicon behaving differently on another planet if it had an environment unlike that of the Earth? Based on observations made by astronomers, the answer is probably no. Across the cosmic environment of the interstellar medium – interstellar clouds, meteorites, comets and stars – carbon molecules run rampant; not just simple ones, but also some of the more complex organic molecules as well. Oxidised silicon, such as silicon dioxide, is quite common in the cosmic environment although silicon molecules such as silane and silicones that we would consider as silicon-based life molecules are seldom identified.

Perhaps counter-intuitive elements such as *arsenic* might be capable of supporting life under the right conditions? On Earth, some marine algae incorporate arsenic into complex organic molecules, such as arsenosugars and arsenobetaines. Several other small life forms use arsenic to generate energy and facilitate growth. It has even been speculated that the earliest life forms on Earth may have used arsenic in place of phosphorus in the structure of DNA itself. Nonetheless, at no point has it been proposed as a possible replacement for carbon as the key to life. *Titanium, aluminium, magnesium* and *iron* are all more abundant in the rocks of the Earth's crust than carbon; so metal-oxide-based life could even be a possibility under some very non-Earth-like conditions found on a different rocky world. *Boranes* may also be an option. They are dangerously explosive in Earth's oxygen-rich atmosphere, but would be more stable in a reducing environment, one with little oxygen. However, boron's low cosmic abundance in comparison to carbon makes it rather unlikely as a base for life. What about *chlorine* and *sulphur*? Although purely hypothetical, sulphur could replace carbon, as it is capable of forming long-chain molecules just as carbon does. Some terrestrial bacteria have already been discovered to survive on sulphur rather than oxygen but have not as yet been found to replace carbon. *Nitrogen* and *phosphorus* could also potentially form biochemical molecules since phosphorus behaves like carbon in that it can form long-chain molecules on its own and, when combined with nitrogen, can create quite a wide range of useful molecules. Thus far, with no examples of any of these alternative life forms currently in existence, we only have one form to study: that of carbon-based life. In our quiet corner of the Galaxy, the organic building blocks of life are rife and are thought to have rained down upon all primordial worlds. It seems, at least for now, that searching for life built from carbon is the only truly sensible way to go.

Living is Thirsty Work

Carl Sagan famously dubbed Earth the 'pale blue dot' for its ubiquitous liquid. Water occurs naturally across the Earth's surface in all three phases – as a solid at the poles, a liquid in the oceans, and a gas in the atmosphere. Tasteless, odourless and virtually invisible as water vapour, it covers 70 per cent of our planet. The total liquid water on Earth is somewhere in the range of 1,260 million trillion litres

(326 million trillion gallons), although 97 per cent of this is undrinkable salt water filling the oceans and seas of the planet. Only two-and-a-half per cent of all the water on Earth is fresh water and all life living on dry land is reliant on this tiny percentage. Human life can use only a fraction of this, less than one per cent, and of that, about 70–90 per cent is used for agriculture. That does not sound like a great deal is left for us to drink, does it? But actually it is! Given the enduring presence of water on Earth's surface, it is not surprising that early life, and all subsequent life forms, were and are based upon and reliant on water. All life exists in an environment of water, whether it lives within it or uses it to form part of cell structures or as the main solvent in its metabolism.

It Came from Space ... Or did it?

Where this life-giving fluid came from, however, is hotly debated. The infant terrestrial planets were completely devoid of both water and carbon; they were simply too hot, what with being newly formed and recently molten. This means that the water required to allow life must have risen to the surface of the Earth somehow or come from somewhere. We know it showed up after the Earth's formation but probably only within the first billion years or so, either from deep within the cooling planet or from the reaches of space on board comets and water-rich meteoroids. Although the population of comets and asteroids passing through the inner Solar System is, thankfully for us, sparse today, it was a much busier time when the planets and Sun were young. Because our planet is in the Solar System's *Goldilocks Zone*, a region encircling the Sun where water has the opportunity to remain stable as a liquid, once the water molecules had surfaced they remained, and quite possibly played a key role in the development of life.

Until recently, it was believed that collisions with icy bodies from the outer Solar System likely brought much of the Earth's water. However, this theory was dealt a hard blow in 2014 as incredible results emerged from Europe's Rosetta mission (of which we will learn more in Chapter 5). This groundbreaking venture made history by landing on Comet 67P/Churyumov-Gerasimenko in November 2014, and revealed that the water on the icy body is unlike any found on our planet. While the vast majority of water on our planet is made up of hydrogen and oxygen atoms, very occasionally we find a hydrogen atom has been replaced with a deuterium atom. Deuterium is an *isotope* of hydrogen, but holds two neutrons rather than just one in its nucleus, so is heavier. On Earth, for every 10,000 water molecules, three deuterium atoms can be found. This water has the same physical properties, but owing to the addition of deuterium is heavier. Comet 67P was found to contain water that was 3 times heavier than water currently present on the Earth, which means that this variety of comet could not have brought water to our planet. This discovery adds to other studies that have analysed water on different types of comet, such as those that originated in the *Oort Cloud* – a region of space that makes up the outer reaches of our Solar System – which also has a different signature to water found on Earth.

Many scientists now believe that Earth may have had water from the start, inheriting it directly from the swirling nebula that gave birth to the Solar System. The conventional story followed the journey of *carbonaceous chondrites* (water-rich varieties of asteroid) that would have delivered water during the late stages of Earth's formation, possibly around 4.6 billion years ago, and meteorites do provide some of the answers we are looking for. Carbonaceous chondrite meteorites have been dated as some of the oldest rocks in the Solar System, formed around the same time as the Sun, before the first planets, and they have isotopic signatures of hydrogen similar to Earth's seawater. However, it is now thought that the signatures of seawater have changed over geological time, gradually getting heavier.

The original seawater on Earth does not match that found within asteroids but has a hydrogen isotopic ratio closer to that of Jupiter and the solar wind. These are both thought to preserve the original isotopic signature of the solar nebula. As such, water may have snuck into our own growing planet, despite its scorching temperatures, by sticking to dust particles. Some of it may well also have arrived from space, although only around 10 per cent appears to have originated from comets from the *Kuiper Belt* and the Uranus–Neptune region of the Solar System. From the perspective of life, however, the source of the water is relatively unimportant – that it is there is all that matters.

Although the exact mechanisms are poorly understood, it is clear that liquid water, was present on the surface of the Earth only a short time after its formation. Earth is not unique in containing liquid water, however. Jupiter's moon Europa is covered with a sheet of ice that probably sits on top of a global salt-water ocean, and Saturn's moon Enceladus shows evidence of sub-surface water as well. Mars, meanwhile, was once a relatively warm and wet world that apparently harboured large amounts of liquid water in the ancient past – it is the persistence of it in liquid form on the surface of the Earth that is unique and that allowed for the gradual evolution of life.

A Special Liquid

The Earth is a wet and watery world so it should not come as much of a shock to hear that life makes good use of this abundant liquid. All life exists in an environment of water and the earliest life on Earth is believed to have arisen in it. Despite its commonality, water is an extremely unusual molecule in its chemical and physical properties, and life has adapted to become entirely dependent on some of its unique characteristics.

Water as the molecule H_2O is made up of two hydrogen atoms attached to one oxygen atom. Water molecules are greatly attracted to each other and this stickiness is what gives water its high surface tension (imagine insects walking across a lake on what looks like a *film*). Water is the *universal solvent*, a powerful medium that surrounds and dissolves more substances than any other liquid currently known. Salts, sugars, acids, alkalis and some gases – especially oxygen and carbon dioxide – are *hydrophilic* (water-loving) substances. This is a very useful quality for biological processes. All of the components in cells (proteins, DNA and polysaccharides) are found within water, although not actually dissolved, instead deriving their structure and activity from their interactions with it. Other substances, however, are *hydrophobic* (water-fearing), such as fats and oils, and so are *immiscible* in water and will not mix, instead forming individual layers. Water dissolves more substances in greater quantities than any other common liquid and allows them to interact with each other at speeds faster than those obtainable in a solid, and slower than in a gas. Chemical reactions can take place in these other phases as well, of course, but organic life is impossible as a solid or gas. Having molecules available in a dissolved liquid phase also helps cells in gathering essential nutrients and expelling waste products.

One of the incredible abilities of water is its response to changes in temperature. It remains liquid at a range of temperatures and pressures and is transparent in the visible electromagnetic spectrum. This matters because it allowed the rise of early photosynthetic bacterial and plant life, as sunlight was able to reach them through the overlying waters. Today, plants and bacteria have colonised bodies of water across the world, and in every environment. The boiling point of water is 100°C (212°F) and the freezing point 0°C (32°F). This is of utmost importance to the continuity and evolution of life as throughout the last 3.7 billion years of life's history the temperature at the surface of the Earth has remained within this range at least somewhere on the planet. Water, as with all other liquids, boils into steam at different temperatures depending on the air pressure. For example, at the top of Mount Everest water boils at 68°C (154.4°F), compared to 100°C (212°F) at sea level, regardless of latitude. Conversely, water deep in the ocean near geothermal vents can reach temperatures of hundreds of degrees and still remain liquid owing to the overlying pressures created by such a huge body of water. Most known pure substances become heavier as they cool; water, however, has the anomalous property of becoming lighter when it cools to form ice. It expands to occupy a nine per cent greater volume, which is why ice floats on liquid water, as evidenced by icebergs, and as an additional bonus insulates the water beneath from freezing. Water acts as a good temperature buffer as it can absorb a great deal of heat energy without a big rise in its own temperature. This skill benefits all life on Earth – on a global scale by helping the planet to steady its climate through stabilising the temperature of Earth's oceans, and at a cellular level by protecting an individual cell from wild temperature extremes that could disrupt and destroy metabolic enzymes.

Water is vital both as a solvent in which many substances within the body of an organism can dissolve and as an essential part of many metabolic processes; it is fundamental both to photosynthesis in plants and respiration in animals. Photosynthetic cells use the Sun's energy to split off water's hydrogen from its oxygen. Hydrogen is combined with carbon dioxide (absorbed from air or water) to form glucose (energy) and releases the oxygen. Many living cells use such fuels and oxidise the hydrogen and carbon to capture the Sun's energy and reform water and carbon dioxide in the process (cellular respiration). Virtually every environment on Earth that has been examined seems to hold life that has evolved from the water-loving universal ancestor of all life on Earth. As long as water is available, life finds a way to exploit whatever thermodynamic disequilibrium exists.

What If There Were No Water?

Everything we know about life and its relationship with water suggests that Terran life (life on Earth) cannot exist without it. Yet, we can still ask the question as to whether water is specifically needed for life or if life is simply designed for a watery-type environment and any form of liquid solvent could be used? Perhaps terrestrial life evolved to exploit water simply because it was the only option to hand, so could life emerge in other, more widely available solvents on other worlds?

Ammonia, for example, shares many properties with water, and is actually quite analogous to it. It is liquid over a wide range of temperatures (−78°C to −33°C/−108.4°F to −27.4°F, at surface pressure on Earth) and an even greater range at higher pressures. It dissolves many organic compounds owing to the formation of hydrogen bonds, just as water does, and is abundant in the Solar System – it exists as liquid droplets in the clouds of Jupiter and within the dust of outer space. An ammonia or ammonia–water mixture stays liquid at much colder temperatures than plain water alone, so for the planetary bodies further away from their stars this could be a lucrative characteristic. Ammonia would not support the chemistry found in terrestrial life, however, although alternate biochemistries could be formed and may one day be found right here in our own Solar System, perhaps on Saturn's largest moon Titan.

Another alternative to water is *sulphuric acid*. It's seen in the cloud layers above Venus and there are those who think life is possible, floating within these acidic aerosols. Perhaps *Formamide* is a solvent life might be able to use. Formed by the reaction of hydrogen cyanide and water, it is liquid across a wide range of temperatures, dissolves salts, and persists in a relatively dry environment, such as a desert. *Hydrogen fluoride* has also been proposed, as in theory it is a good solvent for both inorganics and organics vital to carbon-based life and has a larger liquidity range than water. The major difficulty is its extreme cosmic scarcity; but this is not a deal-breaker. Liquid *hydrogen cyanide* is another possibility and, unlike hydrogen fluoride, has a reasonably high cosmic abundance.

If a high cosmic abundance of a solvent is an important factor for life, then the most abundant compound in the Solar System is surely worth considering: *dihydrogen*. It is the principal component (86 per cent) of the upper regions of the gas giants Jupiter, Saturn, Uranus and Neptune. So, is dihydrogen a liquid? Well, not exactly. Throughout most of the volume of gas giant planets where molecular dihydrogen is stable, it is a *supercritical* fluid – a substance that can effuse through solids like a gas (but isn't one) and dissolves materials like a liquid (but also isn't one). Little is known about the behaviour of organic molecules using supercritical dihydrogen as a solvent – one thing for certain is that the temperature at which dihydrogen goes supercritical is too high for stable organic molecules.

There is actually no need to focus strictly on polar solvents such as water when considering possible liquid habitats for life. *Hydrocarbons* such as methane, ethane, propane, butane, pentane and hexane are abundant throughout the Solar System and have boiling points up to 75.8°C (168.4°F) at standard pressures. Oceans of liquid ethane and methane have been observed to cover the surface of Titan. Perhaps if there were water droplets within hydrocarbon solvents on Titan, these bodies of liquid could be convenient cellular compartments for evolution. Pure hydrocarbon liquids may actually prove to be better than water for managing complex organic chemical reactivity. Methane could in theory support organic biochemistry although its low liquidity temperatures of –160°C (–256°F) may be too cold for biochemical reactions to run at the fast rates used by life as we know it to thrive. Perhaps life with slower metabolic processes could be possible?

All of these water replacements have pros and cons when considered in respect to our terrestrial environment. What needs to be considered is that with a radically different environment come radically different reactions. Life as we know it is built around a carbon scaffold using a water solvent; this has therefore become the standard chemical model for life. Weird extreme environments may contain weird extreme life forms, so in time we may find that water and carbon are not needed to support life in the far-flung corners of the Solar System, although it is incredibly hard to imagine and design experiments to test for this today.

Everything that goes into creating a life form must come from somewhere. The basic elements that form the backbone of everything around us were created many billions of years ago in the hearts of the first stars. Some people say we come from stardust – let's see how true that really is.

CHAPTER THREE

How to Create a Planet Fit for Life

What is it that allows for the formation of a gas giant versus a rocky moon, a comet versus an asteroid, a planet perfectly suited for the origins and evolution of life versus a barren, lifeless world? Life is resilient but also extremely fragile. It needs to find a delicate balance of complementary conditions and some may say serendipitous events for it to originate, persist and thrive. To create a recipe for life, we need to cook up the perfect world for it to live in. The Earth is such a place, but its journey to becoming host to the only intelligent life in the Universe – as far as we know – has not been a smooth one, and several advantageous events have occurred to help it on its way. All life on Earth owes its existence to a single star that burst into light billions of years ago. In fact, it actually owes its gratitude to the star's death, not its birth. All the elements in existence, apart from hydrogen, helium and tiny amounts of lithium, descend from those cooked inside the fiery hearts of the first long-vanished stars – from the oxygen we breathe, to the carbon in our cells and the silicon in the rocks that built our planet.

A Cosmic Kitchen

Everyone knows the story of the creation of the Universe: there was a *Big Bang* and from nothing came everything. Okay, there is a little more to it than that, of course, but in terms of life, this multi-billion-year-long event can be summarised into a few key moments. The Universe is roughly 13.8 billion years old, a number hard to wrap the mind around with the sense of the hours we live every day. So instead of billions of years, let's imagine just one. If the entire creation of the cosmos were squashed into a single year, there would be 438 years per second, 1.58 million years per hour, and 37.8 million years per day – *the cosmic calendar*. In terms of the Big Bang, we need not bother with an entire year, just the first 15 minutes.

There might not have been an actual physical bang – especially if there was no one in existence to hear it go *pop*. But this is as good a description as any of a process where one moment there was literally nothing in existence, and then suddenly the entire mass and energy of the Universe was ignited from a single extremely dense and hot spot called *a singularity*. At this moment, time officially started, the Universe began to expand and grow, the cosmic kitchen was open for business. There is no life without cells, no cells without carbon, no carbon without matter and all of this is created from three basic particles – protons, electrons and neutrons. A millionth of a second after the greatest cosmic event ever *not* witnessed, a single lowly proton was formed as the newborn Universe began to *cool* to a sweltering trillion °C (around 1.8 trillion °F). The proton's partner in crime, the electron, followed a second later, emerging from a broth of particles and antiparticles simmering at just 1 billion °C (a little over 1.8 billion °F).

After this initial birth by searing fire, the cosmos cooled further and grew increasingly menacing; the *dark ages* of the Universe had begun and lasted for the next 200 million years. During this time the Universe was a smooth soup of energy, its temperature hovering around 10,000°C (just over 18,000°F). The newly crafted protons, neutrons and electrons started to combine and the first atoms began to form. They initially assembled themselves into a single hydrogen atom, the most basic yet most abundant element in the Universe today. From hydrogen came helium and smatterings of lithium and beryllium. The basic ingredients for the recipe of life had been created but in this period the Universe was still completely sterile.

The newly created atoms effectively neutralised the Universe; it was no longer dominated by negatively or positively charged particles, which allowed matter to start to congeal owing to gravity, creating nodules or balls of concentrated matter that threaded across the still growing Universe. This is the birthplace of galaxies. Flurries of proto-dwarf galaxies formed – visually more akin to nebulae than the grand spiral and elliptical galaxies of today. These were the site for the creation of something without which life would not exist. They were the birthplace of the very first stars.

Star Light, Star Bright

Light came to the Universe some 200 million years after the Big Bang. These first illuminating stars were made when a small parcel of gas within one of the newly birthed dwarf galaxies started to *feel* its own gravity and began a slow but accelerating inward collapse. The earliest stars were simple, formed only of hydrogen and helium as this was the only matter in the Universe to have been created so far. They grew within tremendously hot blobs of gas and were enormous. These first stars illuminated with an extraordinary brilliance but their life was fleeting, and they died in glorious supernova explosions that seeded the surrounding gas with their remains. Through these eruptions, nebulae of dust and gas were created that grew to become the stellar nurseries of the Universe. They provided the starting materials for each new brood of stars, which themselves died and flung even more elements, gas and dust into the Universe to be used to build generation after generation of stars – the stellar circle of life.

Without stars there would be no elements of the periodic table, and without elements there would be no Earth and no life. Stars are like giant nuclear reactors, constantly churning, creating and destroying elements. This deep *nuclear fusion* is what makes them shine. When their core reaches a high-enough temperature (a few million degrees) atoms are subject to tremendously violent collisions that release an enormous amount of energy; their nuclei begin to fuse together creating an entirely new element. In the early stages of a star's life, this reaction involves the nuclei of two hydrogen atoms combining to make helium – a process called *nucleosynthesis*. A star slowly converts its hydrogen into helium but there is not an everlasting supply. As the hydrogen fuelling the star's very existence is exhausted, nuclear reactions can no longer continue and the core begins to collapse under its own gravity. These higher temperatures cause the star to shine up to 10,000 times more brightly than before. The outer layers of the star then expand outwards, decrease in temperature, and the star becomes a *red giant* – technically more orange than red, but a giant nonetheless. What happens to the star after this bloating and blushing phase depends upon how large it is.

The smallest stars only convert hydrogen into helium, and that is the end of their life. Medium–sized stars (such as our

Sun and those up to two times the mass of our Sun) will start to convert the newly formed helium atoms in the core into carbon and oxygen as temperatures reach 100 million degrees. Three helium nuclei fuse together to create carbon, and then an addition of another helium to this carbon molecule creates oxygen. The stars now have a core of carbon-oxygen. The largest or most *massive* stars (greater than five times the mass of the Sun) will convert hydrogen to helium, then helium to carbon and oxygen, followed by fusion of carbon and oxygen to form neon, sodium, magnesium, sulphur and silicon. Further reactions can take place, transforming the core into calcium, nickel, chromium, copper and finally iron. A needlessly confusing side note: most of the physical matter in the Universe is in the form of hydrogen and helium, so astronomers conveniently use the blanket term 'metal' to describe all other elements. So when the phrase *metal-rich star* pops up, the elements described are non-metals as far as chemistry is concerned, but considered metals in astrophysics. As I said, confusing. Through all these stages of nucleosynthesis, each new *metallic* element created forms in the fiery soul of the star and is surrounded by a shell of the elements that came before it. If a slice were taken through one of these stars, it would display multiple layers of a giant elemental onion. Finally, we know what makes life possible and where the basic ingredients for life came from: stars. These blazing engines are the creators of carbon, the third most abundant element in the Universe, and by far the most important ingredient in our own creation.

But we have to ask – how do all these elements get from inside a star to our bodies? We mentioned before that the earliest stars that lit up the new Universe 200 million years after the Big Bang exploded in what we call a *supernova*. But what actually is a supernova? Does every star die in this way? And what does that mean for life? The very low mass stars finish nucleosynthesis with a core of helium and a shell of hydrogen but do not go supernova. They have a quiet, dignified death. They simply start to become less luminous, ending their lives as a cool helium *white dwarf.* When stars of great mass (8–25 times that of the Sun), however, have reached the stage at which they contain a fiery heart of iron, and no more reactions can take place, their elemental factory shuts down and the iron core collapses under the force of the star's gravity and implodes. This collapse releases a catastrophic wave of gravitational potential energy, causing an explosion that very briefly can outshine an entire galaxy – the star has gone supernova. This explosion spews nearly all of the star's matter and energy into space at up to 30,000km/s (around 18,640 miles per second, or 10 per cent the speed of light).

Supernovae are essential for the creation of life as they are a vital source of elements heavier than oxygen. Nuclear fusion within the cores of stars creates elements lighter than iron and, although this is where the story ends for the star, it is not the end of nucleosynthesis. The power of the supernova explosion itself causes further chemical reactions that create even more elements, including plutonium and uranium. The Big Bang produced hydrogen, helium and lithium, while stars and supernovae synthesised the rest, enriching the interstellar medium and molecular clouds with metals.

What is left after a supernova is a compact object and a rapidly expanding shock wave of material heading into, and mixing with, the interstellar medium. This process, as brutal and destructive as it sounds, is actually good for life. These death throes of stars created and then seeded the CHNOPS elements (carbon, hydrogen, nitrogen, oxygen, phosphorus and sulphur) throughout the Universe – the elements that are needed to build life (and everything life needs).

The Gauntlet of Galaxies

Around 2.5 billion years after the Big Bang, and 2.3 billion years after the first stars sparked into life, gravity began to pull all the generations of stars thus far created into groups or clusters, commonly known as galaxies. A *galaxy* at its most basic level is a gravitationally bound system of stars and their remains – an interstellar medium of gas, dust and dark matter, all orbiting around a central point. There may be anything from a few hundred thousand stars to many hundreds of billions within a single galactic neighbourhood. Even within the small patch of Universe observable from the Earth there are hundreds of billions of galaxies and thanks to the work of famous astronomer, Edwin Hubble (1889–1953), we know that they will have one of four different shapes: spiral, elliptical, lenticular or irregular – but each as unique as a fingerprint.

One of the most familiar and intricately beautiful galaxy shapes is the spiral galaxy. In fact, when imagining a galaxy, this is what first comes to mind. This is because the Milky Way, the most famous of all galaxies, its neighbour Andromeda, and 77 per cent of all the galaxies so far seen, are winding, flat, disc-shaped spiral galaxies that loosely resemble an octopus. They basically consist of a central bulge (the head) with a number of different *arms* (the tentacles) spiralling outwards. Unlike those of an octopus, however, these arms are not restricted to eight in number. These twisted galaxies can be tightly wound coils of dust, gas and stars or loosely splayed tendrils, with all degrees in between. The oldest observed spiral galaxy, BX442, is around 10.7 billion years old yet these coiled galaxies are believed to be much younger than the less glamorous elliptical varieties. Since the Earth is currently orbiting within a spiral galaxy itself, it would be easy to think that spiral galaxies may be better suited for life. Our continued existence in this rotating mass of stars and dust, however, is the result of so many more factors than just its image, but the way its stars are able to move in well-defined orbits does make it a safer and more stable design of galaxy for the long-term prospects of life.

Elliptical galaxies are the most massive of galaxies with few or no dust lanes, being all central bulge and no disc. They are largely composed of older mature stars and have little to no rotation, so the stars display a variety of orbits, haphazardly moving around like a swarm of flies. These galaxy types seldom have stellar nurseries or new star–forming regions. Owing to stars orbiting in any manner of directions they commonly find themselves heading on a collision course with each other and the centre of the galaxy. As they draw closer, the increasing proximity and density of other stars produces an environment of high radiation and gravitational instability. If that were not chaotic enough, the statistical chance of these stars coming into close contact with more than one ancient star about to go supernova is much higher. These galaxies are therefore believed to be incredibly unfavourable for the emergence of worlds suitable for and capable of sustaining life.

A Galactic Goldilocks Zone

Planets qualified to support life are much more likely to exist around stars that reside in certain parts of a galaxy. The *galactic habitable zone* (GHZ) is a galaxy-wide Goldilocks zone, a theoretical ring threaded through a galaxy, where conditions exist that are favourable for supporting life should it happen to arise in any orbiting solar system. It covers a region lying in the plane of the Galactic disc that possesses enough of the heavy metallic elements that would be needed to build terrestrial planets like the Earth or Mars. As mentioned before, supernova explosions were responsible for the creation of interstellar dust clouds. These became increasingly more metal-rich with every additional stellar deposit and formed a nest filled with new baby stars. With more metal-rich material available, these younger stars were more likely to be able to grow planets to orbit around them. Where there are planets, there may be life. Galaxies, therefore, effectively have a *Goldilocks zone of metallicity*, a belt stretching across their waist whereby the amount of metals is *just right* to go into the formation of planets and where a planet fit for life can exist.

Within the GHZ, the cosmic environment needs to be sufficiently accommodating over several billion years to allow for the biological evolution of complex multicellular life, *i.e.* us. A major threat to this is the, up until now, very helpful supernova explosion. The blast waves created during the detonation, despite sending biologically useful elements into space, also release deadly cosmic rays, gamma rays and X-rays that can be fatal to any life form watching wide-eyed on a nearby planet or moon. This supernova fear factor is greatest in areas with the most stars and the largest amount of star formation. Keeping out of the way of the Galaxy's spiral arms is another requirement of a GHZ. The sheer density of gases and interstellar matter in the spiral arms leads to the birth of new stars. Although this is a good thing and can lead to the creation of planets and ultimately life, it would be dangerous for an already inhabited solar system to cross paths with one of them. The intense radiation and gravitational chaos of entering a spiral arm would cause catastrophic and life-threatening disruptions in our Solar System.

So to build an ideal planet suitable for life, we would start with a spiral galaxy and a metal-rich young star. This star would be orbiting around the core of the galaxy within a ring-shaped Goldilocks region at *just the right* distance from the galactic centre so that it has the minimum metallicity needed to form some rocky life-friendly planets, but is far enough away from the centre so that its solar system would not be continually plagued by swarms of exploding stars.

More Than Just Chocolate

After the chaos of the Big Bang, stellar births and deaths, and the formation of the first galaxies, there is really only one spiralling neighbourhood we are personally invested in: *the*

Milky Way. It is home to the only example of life that we know of, and therefore rather an interesting place. It measures between 100,000 and 120,000 light years in diameter – a light year actually being a measure of distance, not time; it represents the distance that light can travel in a year, a cosmic speed limit, if you like. To put this expanse in perspective, light travels 9,460,528,398,225km (5,878,499,810,000 miles) over the course of one year, so multiply that by 100,000 years and the size of the galaxy is almost unfathomable.

The Milky Way is almost as old as the Universe itself. Recent estimates put the age of the Universe at 13.7 billion years, and our Milky Way has been around for up to 13.6 billion of those, give or take 800 million years. This is measured based on the age of the oldest stars in the Galaxy, so the Galaxy must be older than they are. It is part of a larger family of at least 100 galaxy groups, each made up of 50 individual *Local Group* galaxies that include our neighbour Andromeda, forming a team known as the *Virgo Supercluster.* Within this family of galaxies, the Milky Way is moving through the Universe at a speed of 600km/s (over 370 miles per second). It contains between 200–400 billion stars but when you look up at the night sky with the naked eye, the most you can see from any one point on the globe is about 2,500 stars. The number of stars in the Milky Way changes yearly owing to deaths and births; about seven new stars are born every year. Although this stellar headcount sounds impressive, the Galaxy is only a middleweight. The largest galaxy we know of is IC 1101 which has more than 100 trillion stars. Despite all this stellar illumination you cannot actually see 90 per cent of the Milky Way as most of its mass consists of dark matter that creates an invisible veil. In fact, every picture ever published of the Milky Way in its entirety is in fact not the Milky Way at all but another galaxy or an artist's interpretation. Currently, we cannot actually take a picture of the Milky Way from above because we are buried inside the galactic disc, about 28,000 light years from the galactic centre. It would be like trying to photograph your own house from the inside. But we do know that although incredibly beautiful and perfect for us, it is actually imperfect and warped. Neighbouring dwarf galaxies of the Large and Small Magellanic Clouds which are made up of a mere 10 billion stars are playing a game of tug-of-war with the Milky Way, pulling on its halo of dark matter and distorting the vast quantities of hydrogen gas. The result is a disc that resembles the profile of a sombrero.

The Milky Way is structured like billions of other spiral galaxies; it is not particularly special in that regard. Strong emissions of infrared radiation and X-rays leaking from its galactic centre have strongly hinted that clouds of ionised gas are rapidly moving around some sort of dark object – a black hole, and a supermassive one at that, called *Sagittarius A**, believed to measure about 22,530,816km across (14 million miles), or about the extent of Mercury's orbit around the Sun.

Around this black hole we find the highest density of stars in the galaxy and they are some of the oldest. Surrounding this *'nuclear bulge'* is the galactic disc containing a lot of interstellar matter (dust and gas), as well as young and intermediate or middle-aged stars. Extending beyond this disc is a swollen *'galactic halo'* where very old star populations are clustered. The high volume of stars in the central bulge influences the metallicity gradient spanning the Milky Way from highest in the galactic centre and decreasing outwards. More stars also means more supernova explosions and more metals returned to the interstellar medium to go into making yet more stars. Larger galaxies with a greater number of stars therefore tend to have a higher metallicity than their smaller counterparts. The Milky Way is by no means the largest galaxy out there, but it isn't the smallest either. Some 80 per cent of galaxies are less luminous than the Milky Way, but this is not vanity talking. A galaxy's brilliance is positively affected by its metallicity; the more metals present, the brighter a galaxy shines, and the more metals it has, the greater the likelihood of life arising. This statement depressingly puts 80 per cent of the Universe in a category in which life is far less probable.

The vast Milky Way halo and also the thick inner disc region are dominated by the older stars with low metallicity, so any planets that may arise around such stars are not predicted to have the materials needed for life. Some of the inner regions of the Galaxy, however, have the high metallicity required for the formation of terrestrial planets, but they are also unlikely to be suitable for life as they would be much more prone to suffering from extremes of radiation, being violently thrown around by gravitational fluctuations and hit by supernova shockwaves. The main region of the Milky Way that would be amenable for life is the thin disc where, coincidently, our Sun is found. The Sun's metallicity is used as a baseline (as we know it is good for life). Our Sun is exceptional in being both long-lived – currently 4.5 billion years young – and having a 40 per cent greater metallicity than most stars of the same age. Stars having between 60 per cent and 200 per cent of this level of metals are found in a region encircling the galactic centre at a distance between 15,000–38,000 light years – the Milky Way's GHZ. Unfortunately, for the possibility of other life-bearing worlds in the Milky Way, however, this area contains only about 20 per cent of the total stars in the Galaxy. Also, just because a star falls within this 20 per cent, does not automatically mean it has the potential to sustain life.

The Milky Way is not only moving but growing; it is a cannibalistic galaxy currently gobbling up hydrogen from those same Magellanic Clouds that are causing it to warp. They are currently only 80,000 light years away from the centre of our Galaxy, technically already within the embrace of the Milky Way. They will probably be entirely absorbed into our Galaxy in about one billion years. The Andromeda Galaxy also seems set on a collision course with the Milky Way, a convergence that may begin about three billion years from now. The two galaxies will collide head-on and fly through one another, leaving gassy, starry trails, and scrambling stars to create new constellations. This may prove disastrous for any and all life forms, should they have remained in the area.

A Solar Family

The Solar System lies on the edge of the Orion–Cygnus spiral arm of the Milky Way, a nice secure distance away from the galactic centre, around halfway out, in a relatively uncrowded part of the Galaxy. Its orbit is remarkably circular around the galactic centre, which as a consequence keeps the Solar System safely away from the supermassive and super-destructive black hole, Sagittarius A⋆, at its core. A location in this suburban region also protects our solar family from the huge gravitational tug of stars clustered near the centre, keeping other planetary bodies such as planets, moons, asteroids and comets in their orbits and out of our way. The threat of any nearby stars going supernova and wiping us out is also reduced.

The Milky Way revolves around Sagittarius A⋆ once every 250 million years but not uniformly, with the inner regions moving faster than the outer, and stars constantly overtaking each other. The four spiral arms do not rotate as a rigid structure either, so the orbit of the Solar System will inevitably pass through one of these spiral arms one day; every 100 million years to be exact, and it will take a further 10 million years to make it through, hopefully unscathed! As it takes this daring manoeuvre it will have to avoid increased supernova risks as the concentration of stars grows greater, and dodge the large dusty stellar nurseries, whose dust could infiltrate the Solar System and block out sunlight to any planets and moons. This has the potential to cause life reliant on sunshine to shut down and cool a planetary surface enough to cause an ice age. Luckily, however, the Solar System moves at nearly the same rate as the Galaxy's spiral-arm rotation. This synchronisation or *'co-rotation cycle'* prevents our Solar System from crossing a spiral arm too often.

The Heart and Soul

The Sun is the source of all life on Earth and only its continued presence allows life to exist. A ball of gas held together by its own gravity, it is composed of hydrogen (92.1 per cent), helium (7.8 per cent), and less than 0.1 per cent metallic elements. The diameter of the Sun is about 109 times that of Earth (we could fit some 1.3 million Earths inside it) and is an almost perfect sphere, with a difference of just 10km (6.2 miles) in diameter between the poles and the equator. It is actually the closest thing to a perfect sphere that has ever been observed in nature. The Sun is a G-type main-sequence star (G2V), informally designated as a *yellow dwarf*, with a surface temperature of 5,500°C (9,932°F). The temperature in its core however is about 15 million °C (27 million °F) – it is a nuclear reactor after all.

But where did our Sun and its planet suitable for life come from? Well, about 4.6 billion years ago in a nebulous cloud of gas dust and stars far, far away, a grandparent star exploded in an incredible supernova event. It sent a powerful shockwave through the nebula, compressing regions sufficiently so that they began to collapse under their own gravity. The contracting gas started to move and rotate, whirling faster and faster, until it became a violently swirling storm that eventually broke apart into smaller vortices – each with the potential to form a solar system. The death throes of this single star gave birth to a whole brood of new stars and solar systems. One of these galactic tornadoes began to collapse and flatten into a rotating *accretion disc* swirling around a region that would become the point of origin for a single central star, the Sun. Of the entire disc, 99.86 per cent of its mass, which itself is 99 per cent gas, made its way into the Sun, but even the seemingly tiny amount of mass left was more than enough to make a family of planets, moons, asteroids and comets. The disc was enormous, stretching ten times the distance Pluto currently orbits from the Sun, and apart from gas was formed of tiny grains of dust – the seeds used to grow our planet.

The Rocky Worlds

As the Sun began to shine out across this foetal landscape, dust grains were drawn to each other, sticking and clumping together, growing into larger and larger lumps of rocky material. Once they became large enough, gravity caused them to be pulled towards each other. These rocky embryos became rounded because gravity pulls equally towards the centre of large masses, so anything jutting out was pulled back to form a ball. Within about one million years the accretion disc had become a rock garden, with several hundred rounded planetary pebbles orbiting around the infant Sun. This was not a calm period. The Solar System resembled a cosmic pinball machine with planetary embryos thrown in all directions by gravity, crashing into each other, breaking apart and recombining into larger bodies, or sent hurtling towards the Sun or even flung out of the Solar System entirely. These colliding embryos became the building blocks for the rocky inner planets of the Solar System, including the Earth. The heat of these impacts and the decay of radioactive elements within the rocks themselves melted the interior of the growing planets causing the heavier elements such as iron to sink to the centre, forming a core. These embryos took 100 million years to become fully grown planets but at this stage remained barren rocky worlds, lacking water, carbon and life.

The Gassy Worlds

A stream of charged particles heading straight out from the Sun, called the *solar wind*, swept away the lighter elements such as hydrogen and helium, from the Solar System's inner regions, leaving only heavy rocky materials to create the smaller terrestrial worlds such as Earth. Further away, the solar winds had much less strength, allowing hydrogen and helium to remain and be included into the building of the outermost worlds.

Just as when climbing a mountain an elevation is reached at which the ground begins to be covered in snow, at a certain point within the solar nebula an imaginary snow line forms, where falling temperatures freeze water and other volatile chemical compounds such as methane, carbon dioxide and carbon monoxide, and cluster them together. During the formation of our Solar System the water snow line was found around five times the distance from the Earth to the Sun, more or less where the asteroid belt is found today. Inside this boundary was a zone too warm for volatile compounds to be incorporated into the growing dust grains, so they became a gas and were lost. Beyond it, they condensed into solid ice grains and were built into the growing worlds. Not all chemical compounds have the same freezing point as water, however, so different molecules will freeze at different distances from a central star and may be the reason of why there are specific types of planet. For example, the carbon monoxide line in our system corresponds to the orbit of Neptune, and could also mark the starting point from where smaller icy bodies such as comets and dwarf planets like Pluto began to form.

The temperatures in the outer Solar nebula during this phase were well below $-120°C$ ($-184°F$), creating many more solid grains available for incorporation into planets – and so the large gas giants were born. Of the mass not taken up by the growth of the Sun, the remaining 90 per cent went into Jupiter and Saturn. The cores of these larger planets are rocky and icy but still more than 30 times bigger than the Earth. This means that their gravitational attraction was strong enough to draw in large amounts of hydrogen and helium-rich nebula gas, making the planets even more massive, which in turn pulled in even more gas and dust – the ultimate snowball effect. At the furthest reaches of the Solar System there was little material left to make whole planets, so smaller icy bodies formed, like Pluto and the comets.

So there we have it – from a swirling nebula of gas and dust we have a solar system family of inner rocky terrestrial planets and outer gas giants orbiting around a middle-aged yellow dwarf star. In actual fact, the Sun is encircled by eight planets, at least five dwarf planets, tens of thousands of asteroids, and up to three trillion comets and icy bodies. Yet, within this extended family there is only a single known planet that supports one of the most precious commodities in existence: life.

Building a Home in the Goldilocks Zone

Planets, unlike stars, do not run a nuclear reactor in their cores and so are relatively cool, grateful for the warmth provided by their suns. In a star system such as ours, consisting of multiple planetary bodies, there is a special region that is uniquely suitable for planets to grow and nurture the conditions amenable to life; we call it the Goldilocks Zone, or more officially the *circumstellar habitable zone* or *CHZ*. In this imaginary region that encircles the Sun, surface temperatures on planets and moons have the potential to be able to sustain liquid water – they are wet. If worlds were to exist inside this zone and closer to the Sun, such as where Venus and Mercury reside, they would be too hot on their surface and any liquid water would boil away. They would be dry and desiccated. Planets and moons further out past the CHZ would be colder and any water present would freeze, as it has beneath the surface of Mars or on the surface of Europa. They would be frozen worlds (and incidentally dry worlds, too). Estimates of the CHZ boundaries in our Solar System are 0.75–0.95 astronomical units (AU) for the inner boundary and 1.37–1.90AU for the outermost, with the Earth positioned comfortably in the middle at 1AU (an AU being a unit of length roughly the distance between the

Earth and the Sun). This positioning of the CHZ, however, is quite a simplistic view as for each individual solar system there are many variables to consider that might move or stretch its boundaries, such as the size and radiation of the central star, and the dimensions, mass and atmosphere-holding abilities of its individual planets and moons. Present CHZ models also do not include secondary regions where life not reliant on the Sun as a source of heat and energy could exist.

A Family Affair

Is it solely the distance a planet or moon sits from its sun that determines whether life arises or not? Although a critical dimension, there are many other factors, particularly in our Solar System, that have allowed Earth to hold this unique and privileged position. The first is, perhaps, the protection Jupiter offers the Earth. The comet Shoemaker-Levy 9, discovered in 1993 by astronomers Carolyn and Eugene Shoemaker and David Levy, was observed in July 1994 from hundreds of observatories around the world as more than 20 fragments of it crashed into Jupiter's southern hemisphere. In July 2009, a second comet or asteroid this time ripped a Pacific Ocean-sized hole in its surface. This gives the impression that Jupiter is acting as a protective big brother for planet Earth – a celestial shield if you will, sacrificing itself and deflecting asteroids and comets away from the inner Solar System. The planet's enormous mass – more than 300 times that of the Earth – is enough to catapult comets that might hit Earth out of the Solar System. It is also thought that Jupiter's gravitational pull could thin the crowd of dangerous asteroids and other objects, making Earth less impact-prone. Models of the formation of the Solar System suggest that the presence of a planet as massive as Jupiter also helped to conserve the Sun's angular momentum and stabilised the entire planetary system, especially the motions of the inner terrestrial planets. Three cheers for Jupiter ...

Next, it is perhaps the presence of the Earth's unusually large Moon that may have helped the Earth become stable enough to be a home for life. There is some dispute as to the origins of the Moon, but today the most commonly accepted theory is that about 30–50 million years after the initial formation of the Earth, a huge object with a similar mass and size to Mars smashed into it. As a result of this collision a significant part of the proto-Earth was ejected into space. This debris and that of the impactor coalesced into what became the Moon, one of the largest planetary satellites in the Solar System, with a diameter 25 per cent that of the Earth.

Earth's only satellite, it settled into orbit at a relatively close distance of about 30,000km (some 18,600 miles) but is gradually receding from us by about 3.8cm (1.5in) a year. Our Moon is also slowly *braking* the rotation of the Earth to the tune of about 1 second roughly every 67,000 years. These are both effects of tidal forces occurring between the Moon and the Earth. The Earth's rotation is slowing down due to rotational energy transfer to the Moon through the tides and because of this the Moon is very slowly increasing its orbital radius – and moving away from us.

The Moon has played a number of roles in the evolution and continued presence of life on Earth, although how necessary these have been is not entirely clear. The most familiar effect the Moon has is on the liquid envelope of the Earth, driving the tides, but should we lose it for some terrible (and unimaginable) reason, the Sun could in theory take over. Life wouldn't suddenly be extinguished because of this. The chief role the Moon plays pertains to the stabilisation of the Earth's axis over time. The tilt of the Earth is the main driver of the seasons, and this varies from 22.1 degrees to 24.5 degrees and back (known as the change in *obliquity*) over a span of 41,000 years, currently at a value of 23.4 degrees and decreasing. Without the large Moon to dampen this change in tilt, much wider and life-threateningly unpredictable swings would occur. This stability of Earth's seasons and climate has allowed for even the most complex multicellular organisms to evolve and thrive.

From the Inside Out

We know with some certainty the internal structure of the Earth – it looks a bit like the inside of a gigantic plum or peach. The Earth's innermost part, its inner core, is extremely dense and mostly made up of iron and nickel. It is unbelievably hot with a temperature of around 7,000°C (12,632°F) but instead of melting to form a liquid, it is completely solid. This is because of the tremendous pressures weighing on it, measured in gigapascals (GPa), as the mass of the entire planet pushes down exerting in the order of 360GPa. The source of these soaring temperatures this far underground cannot be due to the Sun. They are partly caused by left over heat produced during formation of the Earth and partly due to the decay of radioactive isotopes of potassium, uranium and thorium, whose half-lives are in excess of a billion years. This heat diffuses outwards, and makes a small contribution to the temperature balance of the Earth's surface. Interestingly, it also provides the heat and energy used by microbes that inhabit the outermost 3km- (1.86-mile-) thick layer of the planet.

The outer core is liquid and this 2,253km- (1,400-mile-) thick layer of iron and nickel moves or *convects*. This flow of metallic liquid is believed to create a geodynamo that influences the Earth's *magnetic field*, a shield that extends from the Earth's interior through the planet and several tens of thousands of kilometres out into space where it does battle with the solar wind. The *magnetosphere* deflects the Sun's charged particles and cosmic rays away from the Earth, protecting the atmosphere, which would otherwise get stripped away, thus protecting life on the Earth from exposure to deadly ultraviolet radiation.

Above the outer core lies the *mantle*, composed of hot but not quite solid rock. Its topmost layer, the *asthenosphere*, flows like a liquid but moves extremely slowly. This upper mantle layer and the outer crust together make up the *lithosphere*, the rigid outermost shell of the Earth, which is broken up into *plates*. The movements of these lithospheric plates over the mantle are known as the process of *plate tectonics*, and are the source of numerous phenomena that strongly affect life.

Earth's Recycling Plant

The seven major and many minor plates of the Earth's lithosphere ride atop the asthenosphere, travelling from only a few millimetres to up to 15cm (6in) a year. Each lithospheric plate can be topped by up to two types of crust – *oceanic crust* and *continental crust*. As their names suggest, one is created under the seas of the Earth and the other builds the land. The plates topped with continental crust can be up to 200km (124 miles) thick when they are carrying mountains, whereas those shifting oceanic crust are only 80–100km (50–62 miles) thick. There are no gaps between the plates; they all touch, forming a fractured but continuous rocky skin around the Earth. Where each plate meets another, however, their relative movements create different types of boundary: *divergent*, where the plates are slowly pulling away from each other; *convergent*, where the plates are colliding with each other; and *transform*, where the plates are slowly rumbling past one another in opposite directions.

As the lithospheric plates ride over the convecting mantle, new oceanic crust is formed along mid-ocean ridges, pushing the plates along and forcing the older oceanic crust back inside the Earth – a process called *subduction*. As such, these undersea rocks are relatively young (less than 180 million years old). Continental rocks, however, can be as old as 4 billion years – almost as old as the Earth itself. When two continental plates converge neither sinks and the plates buckle and crumple together, rising up to form massive mountain ranges. The Himalayas formed as a result of the Indian and Eurasian plates running into each other. Many of the characteristic features of the Earth, such as earthquakes, tsunamis, volcanoes, black smokers and mountain ranges, can be explained by these plate tectonics and the types of boundary between them – as such the consequences of plate movements are of great importance to the evolution and continuation of life.

The surface environment of the Earth shows long-term relative stability because by using plate tectonics it can regulate its own temperature through a process called *the carbon cycle*. It works like this: carbon dioxide from deep within the Earth is constantly pumped into the atmosphere via volcanoes and deep-sea hydrothermal vents, which in turn are made possible by plate tectonics. But the carbon dioxide from volcanoes does not stay in the atmosphere indefinitely. It is actively removed by a process called *chemical weathering* whereby it reacts and combines with the rocks on the Earth's surface, and is then returned to the inside of the planet through plate subduction, preventing any life-threatening accumulations of carbon dioxide from occurring in the atmosphere. This process is, of course, as everything else, temperature sensitive and works faster at higher temperatures. By this mechanism, the Earth regulates its temperature and keeps it habitable for life: if the planet's atmosphere starts to get too hot, the weathering rate will increase and more carbon dioxide will be drawn down and chemically captured within the rocks of the Earth. The concentration in the atmosphere will then decrease, reducing the greenhouse warming caused by too much carbon dioxide, and the temperature of the planet will drop. It is a delicate balance though. If the temperature of the planet drops too much and it starts to freeze, tectonic processes will work to ensure that carbon dioxide is pumped back into the atmosphere to help it warm up again. But without liquid water (as it would all be frozen) there would be no carbon dioxide removal by weathering, so the carbon dioxide concentration will build up in the atmosphere until the temperature rises to the point at which the ice melts, and weathering commences again. During weathering, carbon dioxide is converted to a soluble ion known as *bicarbonate* (HCO_3^-), which precipitates in the oceans as minerals such as calcite and dolomite that go into making seashells, coral reefs and the white cliffs of Dover. These minerals are decomposed when subducted and drawn back into the Earth, releasing their load of carbon dioxide into the mantle, ready to be erupted again by volcanoes. The cycle is complete and the Earth, through plate tectonics, maintains a warm, water-rich environment suitable for both simple and advanced life.

What would happen to life if the tectonic plates stopped drifting? Well, the Earth would be a very different place. The volcanoes of the Pacific Ring of Fire, in South and North America, Japan, the Philippines and New Zealand, for example, would shut down, and there would be far fewer earthquakes. Erosion would continue to wear down the mountains, but with no tectonic activity to refresh them, over a few million years the whole planet would be a great deal flatter. The level of the seas would rise as the polar caps melted, and most of today's dry land would be submerged. Only a small number of isolated dry islands would survive. Would intelligent life have arisen on Earth if it were a mostly aquatic planet? What would happen to all the land-based life? We don't know. If the plates stopped moving, the planet would need to find a new way to regulate its temperature if life were to survive. It is not clear what that mechanism might be, or even if one exists. Perhaps the Earth's crust would appear like the single plate crust of Venus and fall victim to catastrophic volcanic episodes? What is clear to us is that for a world to be habitable for life it needs a way to regulate its temperature so as to keep it suitable for its indigenous life forms. As far as we know, plate tectonics is the perfect mechanism to achieve this.

Lucky Quirks

Part of the handicap we face when designing the perfect world for life to thrive is that there is only one planet in the Solar System where we can currently observe processes such as plate tectonics – any evidence for it on Venus and Mars is at best very tenuous. Life on Earth is adapted to the effects of plate tectonics, but until we find another example somewhere nobody can say if tectonics are crucial for life to exist. There are, however, three factors that we know with complete certainty are essential for life: carbon to build cells, water as described in Chapter 2, and energy; and the availability of each of these is linked to special properties of planet Earth.

The where and why of how we think the Earth obtained its water has also been discussed in Chapter 2, but the most important aspect for life is the fact that we have it and it is wet. Most of the planet is at the perfect temperature, fluctuating within the boiling and freezing points of water, so for the most part water stays liquid. Apart from the role plate tectonics plays in this, where the Earth sits in our Solar System, in the Goldilocks Zone, is the main cause. The amount of solar warmth that envelops the Earth is dependent upon the Suns' brightness as dictated by its dimensions and chemical composition. All planets and moons in the Solar System receive some degree of warmth from the Sun, but their distance from it is key to whether they receive too little, too much, or just enough. As luck would have it, the Earth sits at the perfect distance, where the warmth it receives is *just right* to allow water to be a liquid on its surface.

Distance from the Sun is only one lucky factor that makes our planet nice and cosy for life. The Earth also has an atmosphere full of greenhouse gases, in particular carbon dioxide, which help to warm the surface of the planet below. Without any greenhouse gases and their warming effects, and with the Earth's surface reflecting sunlight away back into space (an effect called its *albedo*), Earth would be frozen and hover around −15°C (5°F). It is not as simple as Earth sitting at the right distance from the Sun therefore: the Earth *itself* promotes life. It can be easily imagined that higher or lower carbon dioxide levels would be necessary to maintain a habitat on a planet whose distance from its Sun is lesser or greater, in response to the volumes of solar radiation it receives. The outer reaches of a habitable Goldilocks zone are achieved when the levels of carbon dioxide in an atmosphere become so high that it forms clouds, blocking incoming solar radiation from reaching the surface and causing an increase in the planetary albedo ... the end result is a frozen world.

The radiation-absorbing talent of Earth's atmosphere also supports this ideal surface temperature for water and consequently life. Our atmosphere has a window; it allows some infrared radiation from the cloud tops and surface to pass through it directly to space without intermediate absorption and re-emission, and thus without heating the atmosphere. Without this infrared atmospheric window, the Earth would become much too warm to support life, and possibly so warm that it would lose its water and come to resemble the planetary greenhouse that is Venus.

A third atmospheric quirk is that it is thick enough to exert a pressure on the surface of the Earth, which suppresses the rapid evaporation of liquid water. Atmospheric pressure is the force per unit area exerted on a surface by the weight of air above. On Earth, the atmosphere around us is filled with air molecules that collectively weigh on our bodies. Although you cannot feel it, Earth's atmosphere presses down with the force of 1kg/cm^2 (or some 14.7lb/in^2) and terrestrial biology has evolved to operate quite easily under it.

The final special property of the Earth is its gravity. Gravity allows the planet to hold on to its all important atmosphere, allowing only a little to escape into space, which is quickly replaced by outgassing volcanoes. At the same time, the Earth's gravity is not so strong as to attract a denser atmosphere, which would over-insulate the surface and produce increased surface temperatures unacceptable to life.

The Earth has proven itself physically fit and highly adaptable which enables it to support and nurture life. Luckily it arose within the Goldilocks Zone of the Solar System, which itself formed and sits nicely within the Goldilocks Zone of the Milky Way. The next step is for life to arise and take advantage of this perfectly situated and uniquely designed world.

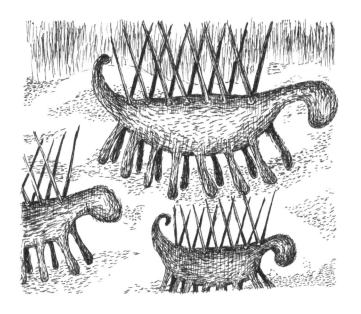

CHAPTER FOUR

The Story of Life

Once a planet has been prepped for life, the time hopefully comes to populate it. Of all the stages that happened during the Big Bang and beyond, stellar nucleosynthesis is by far the most important for this. Remember that nuclear fusion within the cores of the early stars created the heavy elements, such as the biologically useful carbon, nitrogen, oxygen, phosphorus and sulphur, with iron the end of the road. The outer layers then detonated violently as a supernova, hurling all these biologically crucial elements out into the cosmos. These bonded over millennia thanks to UV radiation to create simple compounds such as water, formaldehyde, ammonia, hydrogen cyanide and hydroxyl. Astronomers have so far identified 130 different organic carbon-based molecules in space, the most common being *polycyclic aromatic hydrocarbons (PAHs)* – precursors that are central to the development of life on Earth. The Galaxy is very encouraging for life; the building blocks of terrestrial biochemistry are widespread. So how did all these raw ingredients end up in the cauldron of the early Earth and how did a few simple elements grow into fully fledged living organisms?

Hell on Earth

Let us go back to when time began on the newly created planet Earth. We like to give names to the time periods and events that occurred in the past to help us organise and understand how and when things happened. The first stretch of time, starting from the instant the Solar System began to form, is termed *the Hadean eon*. This covers the events during which the Earth metamorphosed from a gaseous cloud into a solid body of rock. Because collisions between the early large *planetesimals* (gatherings of rock, dust and other debris) released a great deal of heat, the Earth and other newly formed planets would have been molten, only starting to harden as they cooled down. The traditional view of conditions on the Earth during this time is what led to the time period's name: Hadean, from Hades, the Greek mythological underworld. It was seen as a steaming, lava-filled *Hellish* period in history. If we were able to travel back to visit the Earth at that time, it would probably not remotely resemble the planet we know and love today. Opinions about what it was really like on Earth, especially for life, are mixed, as there is very little evidence to work with. But what *do* we know?

In the beginning the Earth was an almost perfect sphere of molten rock, a burning landscape pelted by rocky leftovers from the formation of the Solar System. The common perception is that the young Earth was a hot, deserted world peppered with pools of simmering magma and with an environment that was inhospitable for life. Impacts caused the Earth's surface to be submerged again and again under large volumes of lava – enough to cover the globe several times over in a molten layer of scum. The heavy elements, such as iron, began to sink through this gloopy shell towards the centre of the Earth while the lighter ones, particularly the silica-rich minerals, formed an incandescent ocean covering the surface. Approximately 500 million years after the birth of the Earth, this sweltering panorama started to cool off and rocks began to form on its surface in regions that were in contact with the cold surrounding envelope of space. However, this delicate rind was forced to melt and re-form numerous times as gigantic magma currents erupted from the depths of the planet, while colossal rocks from space came soaring in to tear the new crust apart. Once evidence for hard rock forming on the surface was observed, the geological history of the Earth officially started; the Hadean eon ended and the *Archean* one began.

We recognise that life needs an atmosphere to allow it to arise and take hold on the surface of a newly formed planet, but during the earliest millennia on Earth, even though it did have a primordial atmosphere, it was very different to that which surrounds the Earth in our times. It was probably a reducing atmosphere, meaning it was lacking oxygen, and would have been toxic to nearly all life that exists on the planet today. The combination of exceptionally high temperatures and extreme volcanic outgassing of water, methane, ammonia, hydrogen, nitrogen and carbon dioxide had created this atmosphere. Interestingly, early Earth's atmosphere is quite similar to the current atmosphere of Saturn's moon Titan. The primitive Earth was wrapped inside a blanket of dense burning clouds and remained shrouded in darkness. When temperatures finally cooled sufficiently, the clouds began to drip; the first water droplets started to rain down and the Earth was assaulted by extreme weather events of enormous proportions. At first falling on flaming rock, the rain instantly evaporated, but over time it gradually cooled the crust enough to enable water to collect in the depressed regions of the Earth's surface, forming the first oceans.

Given this picture of a tumultuous and dangerous infant planet, if some hardy organism had somehow popped into existence, surely it would quickly have been extinguished, perhaps by one of the giant meteorites that slammed into the Earth. However, computer simulations conducted in 2014 suggest that the early Earth may not have been as hellish as was previously thought. The common thinking until recently was that life could not have emerged on Earth until the bombardment of projectiles from space eased and the surface was able to solidify to some degree. However, it is now thought possible that between these impacts there were tranquil times when oases of water could have existed and even have supported the early evolution of life. It is not known whether life emerged and was then snuffed out by each later impact, or if it never had the chance to take hold in the first place.

Over the last decade, small hardy crystals known as zircons have been found embedded in ancient – we are talking billions of years old – Australian rocks, and have painted a picture of the Hadean period completely inconsistent with the myth. Zircons up to 4.4 billion years old suggest there was liquid water on the surface of the Earth soon after it formed and that plate tectonics had already started. Analysis of the relative amounts of different isotopes of oxygen inside the crystals show that the ratio was skewed toward *heavy* oxygen-18, as opposed to the more common *light* oxygen-16. When a geologist sees a heavy oxygen signature in rocks, it is commonly understood to be a sign that the rocks formed in cool, wet, sedimentary processes at the Earth's surface.

We now almost universally agree that by at least 4.2 billion years ago, the Earth was actually a reasonably placid place with land, oceans and an atmosphere – representing relatively suitable conditions for the origin of life. An understanding of how, why and where life first arose, however, still mostly eludes us.

It's Raining Rocks

Whether or not you believe that the early planet was a real-life *Hell on Earth*, it nevertheless was a treacherous place for life to arise and be sustained, and this life would have had to be extremely resilient and incredibly tough (we will explore what this life might have looked like in Chapter 6). Sadly, however, any geological evidence that could help us solve this mystery is missing. The oldest meteorites and lunar rocks are about 4.5 billion years old, whereas the oldest Earth rocks currently found are only 3.8 billion years old. Why? During the first billion years after its formation, the inner Solar System was crowded with debris and the newly born planets underwent a lengthy bout of cosmic bumper cars with comets and asteroids. Astronomers believe that about 600 million years after the Solar System was formed (or some 4 billion years ago), a vast expanse of space beyond the orbit of Neptune, the Kuiper Belt, was shaken up by the migration of the gas giants Jupiter and Saturn. This gravitational disruption scattered comets and other icy bodies, flinging many into interstellar space but also throwing some on to orbital paths that wreaked havoc on the inner planets of the Solar System. This period is affectionately known as *the Late Heavy Bombardment* and lasted hundreds of millions of years. Around 3.85 billion years ago this cosmic assault of the Earth finally ceased and the surface was able to solidify. These impacts, along with erosion and plate tectonics, destroyed or buried nearly all of the rocks older than 3.8 billion years, concealing this period of time from us forever. Although no rocks from that time exist on Earth today, we have another source of information – the Moon. Many of the numerous craters and lava flows decorating the Moon's pristine surface provide a record of the Late Heavy Bombardment, and judging by their diameters of hundreds of kilometres, this was a violent and destructive period in the history of the Solar System. An upside to the Earth being blasted by space rocks (yes, there is one) was that this blizzard of comets and asteroids from beyond the Snow Line delivered enormous amounts of crucial volatiles – substances that boil and evaporate at relatively low temperatures – to the Earth's surface, such as additional water, carbon dioxide and simple organic molecules.

We are Aliens

Could the carbon within these asteroids, comets and the dust arriving on the early Earth be the same carbon used to kick-start life? It is easy to imagine these cosmic deliveries of prebiotic organic compounds having played a part in the story. Hundreds of tonnes of organic carbon, the third most abundant element in the Universe, are still delivered to Earth every year, and the rate could only have been higher in the chaotic young Solar System. Today, carbon is transported to the Earth inside meteorites – such as within the carbonaceous chondrite Murchison, named after Murchison, Victoria, Australia where it was seen falling from the sky in 1969. It is one of the most studied meteorites in the world, simply because there is so much of it: more than 100kg (220lb) of space rock. The story goes that on 28th September at 10.58p.m. a bright fireball was observed to separate into three fragments before disappearing in a cloud of smoke. About 30 seconds later, a tremor was felt. Many fragments were found over an area larger than 13km^2 (5 square miles), with individual fragments weighing up to 7kg (15lb); one even broke through a roof, falling into a pile of hay. Regardless of this obvious terrestrial contamination upon landing (even though the pieces were quickly found and collected), these meteorites are extremely carbon-rich, hence the name *carbonaceous*. They carry the signature of the Solar System from the time the Sun was born 4.6 billion years ago, freezing snippets of billion-year-old chemistry in time. Within this single rock the diversity of prebiotic organic molecules is truly staggering. It contains amino acids, carboxylic acids, polycyclic aromatic hydrocarbons (PAHs), nucleobases, alcohols, aldehydes and ketones. Excitingly, over 70 amino acids have been found, even though life on Earth only uses 20 and only six of these 20 needed for life were found in Murchison. The rest are completely alien to life on Earth.

Some comets may have transported water to the early Earth but they also brought organic compounds, the building blocks of life. These dirty snowballs, or in fact snowy dirtballs, are leftovers from the dawn of the Solar System and contain dust, ice, carbon dioxide, ammonia, methane and much besides, preserving evidence of chemical processes that were at work billions of years ago. The nuclei of most comets, which are coated by a dark layer of organic material, are thought to measure up to 16km (10 miles) across. This represents an enormous store of carbon-rich goodness. An early result from the *Philae Lander*'s first suite of scientific observations of Comet 67P/Churyumov-Gerasimenko in 2014 revealed that it supported 16 carbon- and nitrogen-rich compounds. The significance is that some of these compounds play a key role in the prebiotic synthesis of amino acids, sugars and nucleobases: the ingredients for life. Carbon within organic molecules is also delivered to Earth within *Interplanetary Dust Particles* (*IDPs*). These are extraterrestrial grains known as *cosmic dust*, which have been collected in the stratosphere by high-altitude aircraft. These particles comprise different minerals, mainly silicates and, importantly, a carbon-rich material containing hydrocarbons (CH_2 and CH_3) and carbonyl ($C=O$) that can be used by life.

Scientists have long debated the possibility that the seeds of life did not originate on Earth. However, instead of the deliverance of prebiotic compounds onboard space rocks, it has also been suggested that microbial life may have travelled here fully grown from Mars or even another star system, and then evolved into the plethora of species seen today. This idea is called *panspermia*, a highly controversial concept that microbial life is everywhere in the Universe and can spread between planets on board comets, meteorites and dust. In essence we may all be Martians, or even Europans (originating from Europa, one of Jupiter's moons). Although an explanation favoured by few scientists for the origins of life on Earth, there are aspects to it that are intriguing. To get here, simple life forms would have had to endure a litany of harsh cosmic conditions, including ejection into space from their home world on board a rock; the freezing temperatures, radiation and vacuum of space; the million-year timescales involved with the journey to Earth; a fiery re-entry through our thick atmosphere; and finally a high-speed impact into the solid rocky crust. It is proposed that as long as any organism is buried deep enough within a rock of reasonable size and is able to remain in a dormant state over geological time, it might be able to survive the ride to Earth. To transfer a rock between Mars and Earth could take up to 15 million years, since it is necessary to wait for its orbit to cross that of the Earth. That is an extremely long time for life to remain dormant and to survive, and currently we have no idea if it is possible. We know that planets and moons have exchanged rocks before, as evidenced by 132 meteorites arriving on Earth from Mars and 180 from the Moon, and from the photos of meteorites sitting within the surface dust on Mars. There is therefore a chance, albeit slim, that life rode in on one of these rocks and made itself a new home.

From Soup to Cells

Aside from microbes riding in upon a meteoritic chariot, what are the possible routes that life might have taken to arise on the Earth? Where might this miraculous event have taken place? And most importantly ... how quickly after the planet had coalesced from primordial dust and gas did chemicals manage to organise themselves into life? Some astrobiologists approach it from the present, moving backwards in time from complex multicellular life today to its simpler unicellular ancestors. Others march forwards from the formation of Earth 4.55 billion years ago, exploring how lifeless chemicals might have built living beings.

How? Where?

Let's admit this up front – we do not know exactly how life got started, but we do know that all life on Earth is related. Living things (even ancient supposedly *simple* organisms such as bacteria and archaea) are enormously complex. However, all this complexity did not leap fully formed on to the Earth's surface from just a combination of a few simple elements. Instead, life almost certainly originated in a series of small steps, each building upon the complexity that evolved from the last. Humans and chimpanzees share a common ancestor from at least 7 million years ago; humans are related to the first mammal that lived some 220 million years ago, and together with bacteria have evolved from a shared family member who lived billions of years ago. The oldest evidence of life on Earth turns up about 3.9 billion years ago. But what was there before that? Simple organic molecules composed of carbon, hydrogen, nitrogen, oxygen and phosphorus are the scaffolding of life and must have been involved in its origin.

We suspect that ancient organisms shared the same basic traits found in all free-living organisms today – encoding genetic information in DNA and running a metabolism via proteins. DNA and proteins, however, are a paradox – they depend on one another for their survival – so it is hard to imagine one of them having evolved first without the other; although it is just as implausible for them to have emerged together. Chicken and egg! We now think earlier forms of life may have been based on a third kind of molecule found in today's organisms: RNA. Overlooked for many years, RNA turns out to be astonishingly versatile, not only encoding genetic information like DNA but also acting like a protein, carrying out the functions required to keep a primitive cell alive. This *RNA world* may have spurred life into being, although hardier molecules were required to take it further. Once proteins emerged, they would have been favoured by natural selection, as they are thousands of times more efficient as a catalyst. Likewise, genetic information can be replicated from DNA with far fewer errors than it can from RNA.

Just where on Earth these building blocks came together as primitive life forms is a subject of debate. Life started in water – this is probably the only aspect universally agreed upon. In 1871, Charles Darwin speculated that it may have begun in a *warm little pond* and in the 1920s this became known as the *primordial soup*. Based on a theory of a chemically reducing atmosphere and energy from intense episodes of lightning, simple organic compounds may have been created in the atmosphere. The theory suggests that these rained down on to the Earth and accumulated in a liquid pool within which further transformations occurred, creating more complex organic compounds and ultimately life. This idea has fallen by the wayside somewhat, not least because it has been realised that Earth's atmosphere would not have been as reducing as previously thought, owing to the immense volumes of carbon dioxide being pumped into it by volcanoes, and this makes the production of organic molecules in this fashion slightly more challenging, although not impossible.

Starting in the 1980s, many scientists argued that life started in the scalding, mineral-rich waters streaming out of deep-sea hydrothermal vents (fissures in the Earth's surface from which geothermally heated water spews). Here there would have been heat, chemical energy and minerals such as pyrite, or clays that would have provided reactive surfaces to stabilise the organic molecular building blocks of life. Evidence for a hot start included studies on the tree of life, which suggested that the most recent common ancestor of all life seen today was an aquatic microorganism that lived in extremely high temperatures – a reasonably good candidate for the inhabitant of a hydrothermal vent! Nowadays, the hot-start hypothesis has cooled off a bit. If life did appear at hydrothermal vents, the temperatures would have needed to be below 80°C (176°F), or organic macromolecules would not have been able to survive.

Over the last few years, a slightly different picture has emerged of life beginning inside warm, gentle springs on the sea floor that bubbled billions of years ago when Earth's oceans took over the whole planet. These springs – as opposed to the scalding hot acidic hydrothermal vents – would have been cooler and alkaline. Early Earth's oceans were rich in carbon dioxide, as was its atmosphere. When carbon dioxide from the ocean met with hydrogen and methane from the springs over the chimney wall of a vent, electrons may have been transferred, producing reactions that created more complex carbon-containing compounds – essential ingredients for life as we know it.

What is most likely, however, is that life did not kick off from a single spot on the Earth at a single moment, but that the very early cells appeared multiple times in multiple localities. The successful early cells would have colonised all available habitable sites, transported by ocean currents. It is quite possible that the first organic substances arose from a combination of sources as well – from reactions in the atmosphere, rocky reaction chambers on the ocean floor, and even via delivery from space. Over time, life would have run out of available resources in its local environment and have had to adapt to take advantage of other potentially habitable locations, or face extinction. The investigation continues ...

Chemistry Becomes Biology

We still do not know at what point we might consider an early organic molecule to have been *alive* and how this might have happened, which presents us with just one more 4-billion-year-old mystery to solve. We can, however, speculate as to what this first *living* microorganism might have looked like and how it might have lived. This first microbe is commonly called the *last universal common ancestor (LUCA)* as it is the most recent common ancestor of all current life on Earth. Unfortunately, it would have been far too fragile to be preserved within the fossil record for us to find today (or at least no evidence of it has been dug up so far). Nonetheless, we have a few ideas about what it might have been like. It would have been a small, single-cell organism with a cell wall and a freely floating ring-shaped coil of DNA – a little similar to modern bacteria. While its appearance and anatomy are slightly uncertain, the internal mechanisms can be understood based on the properties currently shared by all independently living organisms on Earth. For example, all life today uses a DNA/RNA genetic system and proteins to power its metabolism so the LUCA must have possessed these before it evolved into the two most ancient kingdoms of life: Bacteria and Archaea.

A cell membrane is fundamental to life as it is needed to contain and hold in all of a cell's chemical reactions, but they are very different within archaea and bacteria. Recent studies suggest LUCA had a leaky cell membrane (which modern life could not survive with), which allowed small hydrogen ions to pass through it while keeping the cell contents inside. It could have lived in ancient seawater where liquid dense with protons or hydrogen ions mixed with warm alkaline fluid from hydrothermal vents, which had fewer protons. The difference in concentrations of protons between the seawater and hydrothermal fluids allowed these hydrogen ions to flow into the cell, which led to the production of adenosine triphosphate (*ATP*). This energetic molecule transfers energy through a cell, powering its growth. Life is now technically alive. Now, of course, although living, the LUCA was still stranded at the bottom of the ocean. To spread to new localities and even risk a journey to the surface it would need to evolve less leaky, stronger membranes to survive the less favourable environments. This is when bacteria and archaea would have started going their separate ways, each tweaking its membranes to make them less leaky, allowing them to set sail and colonise the Earth. And, of course, eventually to combine and evolve to become us!

When?

Does the first evidence of life date to 3.85 billion years or 3.45 billion, or even earlier? A 400-million-year discrepancy may seem trivial when discussing an event that happened almost 4 billion years ago yet scientists continue to argue about whether some of the oldest life-hosting rocks ever found date to 4.1, 3.85, 3.65 or only 3.45 billion years ago. The discrepancy matters because the rocks, however old they are, indicate that life already existed at the time they formed. So yes, as with everything else surrounding the origins of life – no one knows exactly when life began. Everything we *do* know is based on educated theories, carbon chemistry and some reasonably convincing wiggly-looking microfossils (fossils too small to be seen without the aid of a microscope).

As mentioned before, very few rocks exist from the early Earth period and even if they did, prebiotic chemistry most likely would not have been recorded in them. As such, the oldest evidence that hints at life we have, that most scientists agree upon at least, is chemical. The ratio between the isotopes of carbon-12 and carbon-13 within graphite contained in the Isua metamorphosed sediments of Greenland is interpreted to represent traces of early life that flourished in Earth's oceans at least 3.7 billion years ago. If correct, this suggests that microorganisms were already well established on Earth by 3.7 billion years ago and so life must have started even earlier.

Actual microfossils found in Pilbara, Western Australia and Barberton, South Africa are suggestive of bacteria and even show enough variety to have been put into 11 different species. They are found in volcanic rocks dating back at least 3.45 billion years. Also, 3.5-billion-year-old dome-shaped rock structures, again found in South Africa and Australia, are suggestive of a microbial presence by this time. This is based on more than just fossils, since these *stromatolites* look remarkably similar to those that are forming today. Right now, communities of microbes, mainly photosynthesising cyanobacteria and heterotrophic (eats food for energy) bacteria that live in shallow, warm waters are producing stromatolites by forming thin microbial films that trap mud. Sheets of these mud/microbe mats build up into a layered sedimentary rock – a stromatolite. Scientists believe this is a similar process to how they would have formed billions of years ago, and to do it they needed some comparatively evolved microbial life.

Harnessing the Power of Sunlight

Although the exact timing of the origin of life is uncertain, what is clear is that by 3 billion years ago there was life on Earth, and plenty of it! Prokaryotes (single-celled organisms) were widespread across the aquatic habitats of the Earth but were reliant upon and trapped within the environment in which they grew up, such as a single hydrothermal spring or black smoker in the depths of the ocean. The advent of the ability to utilise light from the Sun as an energy source to drive the synthesis of carbohydrates (sugars) from carbon dioxide and water – the process of photosynthesis – liberated life from these dark hidden recesses of the world and allowed it to visit the rest of the planet.

There is fossil evidence of the first photosynthetic bacteria 3.5 billion years ago, but because the Earth's atmosphere contained almost no oxygen during this time, many scientists believe that they did not generate oxygen as a waste gas in the way that photosynthesis does today, nor did they use visible light from the young Sun, instead using ultraviolet (UV) light. Early photosynthetic systems, such as those from green and purple bacteria, employed various molecules such as hydrogen sulphide as electron donors to obtain energy. This, however, required a steady supply of electrons from the surrounding environment, which limited their ability to move too far from the electron source. To become a fully mobile cell, life had to cut this umbilical cord and find a more renewable energy source. Life chose light. This allowed cells to be able to rebuild themselves using only carbon dioxide, water and sunlight: simple building blocks that are likely to be found on other terrestrial planets. As such, photosynthesis is quite possibly a universal process.

The Great Oxygen Predicament

On Earth, all atmospheric oxygen is produced through oxygenic photosynthesis; however, the only organisms capable of splitting water to do this are cyanobacteria. These first took hold in isolated marine and freshwater basins, producing only local oxygen oases, but hundreds of millions of years later, some 2.5 billion years ago, the first evidence of rising oxygen levels in the atmosphere and oceans was seen. This is called *the Great Oxidation Event (GOE)*. Iron minerals dissolved in the oceans acted as a sponge, initially soaking up the first free oxygen released by cyanobacteria. They formed red iron oxides that settled to the floor and over time hardened into sedimentary rocks that we now call *banded iron formations*. The surface of the Earth both above and below the waves was rusting. Once the Earth's crust had soaked up as much oxygen as it possibly could, the gas had nowhere left to go but up and the level of oxygen in the atmosphere rose rapidly. Apart from paving the way for oxygen-breathing life on Earth, the rising atmospheric oxygen levels had another important effect on life, especially that destined to live upon the surface. UV light from the Sun split apart oxygen molecules high in the atmosphere producing the molecule *ozone*, thereby creating the ozone layer. Ozone is a strong absorber of UV, so as long as there is oxygen in our atmosphere, sunlight will react with it to create a powerful shield against its own harmful radiation.

The Great Oxidation Event changed Earth's surface environment and made possible the evolution of large and complex life forms, including us. Yet, this event was also a *Great Oxygen Crisis*. The free oxygen produced can be a highly poisonous and toxic gas, especially for those anaerobic organisms that until this point were the dominant forms of life on the planet. The rising concentrations are actually believed to have wiped out most of Earth's inhabitants. Cyanobacteria were therefore responsible for one of the most significant extinction events in Earth's history. If that weren't problem enough, the free oxygen was also busy reacting with the greenhouse gas methane in the atmosphere, greatly reducing its concentration. Without this insulating greenhouse gas, the surface temperature of the Earth began to drop. The world was about to get really ... really ... cold.

Snowball Earth

Primitive humans clad in animal skins trekking across vast expanses of ice in a desperate search to find food – that's the image that comes to mind when most of us think about an ice age. In fact there have been several ice ages, most of them long before humans made their first appearance on the Earth. Our planet seems to have three main settings: *greenhouse*, when tropical temperatures extend to the poles and there are no ice sheets at all; *icehouse*, when there is some permanent ice, although its extent varies greatly; and *snowball*, when the planet's entire surface is frozen over. Between 2.2 and 2.3 billion years ago the Earth plunged into its first ever snowball event, during which the average surface temperature dropped and the ice advanced from the poles towards the Equator. Known as *the Huronian glaciation*, it is the oldest ice age we know about and is thought to have come about with the rise of oxygen and the negative effect this had on the planet-warming greenhouse gases. We do not know how far the ice grew around the Earth, but some liquid water must have remained as the unicellular water-dwelling life inhabiting the Earth was not completely extinguished. Perhaps the Earth was more of a slush ball than a snowball, with a thin equatorial band of open (or seasonally open) water.

Skipping ahead, there have been a number of big-freeze events that have engulfed the planet, not least between 750 and 600 million years ago in a time known as the Pre-Cambrian. They varied in duration and extent, but while in the grip of a full-on snowball event, life could only survive in ice-free refuges, or where sunlight managed to penetrate through the ice to allow photosynthesis to continue. It was a vicious cycle. Once cooling started, the growing regions of white ice reflected more and more of the Sun's warmth away from the planet, which created even colder conditions. As the ice encroached towards the Equator the seas sealed over, and thick ice blocked sunlight from reaching the photosynthesising aquatic organisms. Deprived of its source of oxygen, the seas turned anoxic and the Earth began to suffocate.

Each of these ice ages ended, thanks to the enduring hard work of the Earth and its volcanoes that, throughout it all, kept pumping their gases into the atmosphere. The CO_2 cycle described in Chapter 3 was in trouble. Not only were the rocks that once trapped carbon dioxide hidden beneath the ice but the rate of photosynthesis dropped as well, so this greenhouse gas began to accumulate in the atmosphere up to 350 times its current level, with no way for it to be removed. However, the powerful insulating effect this created started to warm the planet and after several million years it began to thaw. The climate of the Earth slowly settled back into an equilibrium and life returned to its previous niches. It is thought in fact that the release from such an inhospitable period actually provided the evolutionary jump-start for the seemingly sudden appearance of multicellular life on the Earth. Apart from the Andean-Saharan ice age from 460 to 430 million years ago, and the Karoo between 360 and 260 million years ago, Earth has been relatively free of frozen episodes from the Pre-Cambrian to today. This is quite possibly an important factor in worldwide evolution and the spread of life.

An Explosion of Life

About 600 million years ago the *Ediacaran* fauna arose and have now been found on all continents except Antarctica. The earliest known complex multicellular organisms, these were strange tubular or frond-shaped organisms, most of them *sessile* (not able to move from their position). They flourished until the cusp of the Cambrian 542 million years ago, when the characteristic communities of fossils vanish from the geological record. This is almost certainly because around half a billion years ago the Earth witnessed an evolutionary flare when in a short period of time almost every major animal group that has ever existed came into being. Before 580 million years ago, most life on Earth was simple, but in less than 80 million years (a mere blink of a geological eye) the diversity of life came to resemble that of today. This dramatic biological bonanza of evolutionary changes is known as the *Cambrian explosion*. Cambria was the Roman name for Wales, since this region was the original study location for sedimentary rock formed during this interval of Earth history. The lower boundary of the period is widely agreed to be at 543 million years with the first appearance in the fossil record of worms that made horizontal burrows. The end of the Cambrian Period is marked by evidence of a mass extinction event about 490 million years ago.

During the Cambrian Period, the hypothetical single supercontinent *Rodinia* broke apart and by the early to mid-Cambrian there were two: *Gondwana*, near the South Pole, was a supercontinent that was the ancestor of much of the land area of modern Africa, Australia, South America, Antarctica and parts of Asia; *Laurasia*, nearer the Equator, was composed of landmasses that currently make up much of North America and the northernmost part of Europe. There were no continents located at the poles. In the early Cambrian, Earth was generally cold but was gradually warming as the glaciers of the many Snowball Earth episodes receded. The global climate ultimately became warmer than it is today and there were essentially no polar or high-altitude glaciers. Oxygen levels were only some 10 per cent of what they are today but, significantly, there *was* oxygen. The environment was becoming more hospitable for complex life and sea levels were rising due to glacial melting, flooding low-lying coastal areas and creating shallow marine habitats ideal for spawning new life forms.

At this point, no life yet existed on land; all life was still aquatic. The sea floor was covered with oozing mats of microbial life living on top of a thick layer of oxygen-free mud. The first multicellular life forms evolved to graze on these microbes and were themselves only near-microscopic worms that burrowed into the ocean floor, mixing and oxygenating the mud. They were also the first organisms to show evidence of a bilateral body plan that we still use today. The transition of pre-Cambrian life (mainly soft-body impressions in rock) to Cambrian life (shell-bearing fossils and other fossils with hard parts) was revolutionary. Among the animals that evolved during this period were the hard-bodied brachiopods, which resemble clams and cockles; arthropods with jointed external skeletons, the ancestors of spiders, insects and crustaceans; and the chordates, to which vertebrates (animals with backbones) including human beings belong. These toughened-up creatures represented a crucial innovation: hard bodies offered animals both a defence against attack and a framework for supporting greater body sizes. As such, many weird and wonderful forms of life came into existence during this time, although few have survived through to today.

How can we possibly know about the menagerie of alien creatures birthed during the Cambrian when nearly all of them have long become extinct? We turn to rocks, the record keepers of Earth's history, and although rare and hard to find, the oldest rocks and minerals can provide a wealth of information about the past. However, there is a problem: most animals from the Cambrian had no hard parts such as bones or teeth and their soft gloopy bodies rarely left a fossil trace within rocks – the majority of fossil mammals are known only from their teeth, since enamel is far more durable than flesh or bone. Soft parts of bodies can only be preserved by a stroke of luck and commonly in an unusual serendipitous geological situation, such as amber leaking from trees that traps the fleshy bodies of insects before they get the chance to decay and disintegrate. Luckily Pre-Cambrian and Cambrian sediments found in key areas of the world – such as Canada, Greenland, China and the UK – have yielded a fantastic treasure trove of soft-bodied creatures. In fact, the first ever recorded discovery of *Charnia masoni*, the earliest known large, complex fossilised species on record, lay within the rocks of Charnwood Forest in Leicestershire, UK, and remains the only place in Western Europe where these ancient fossils have been found. These rarely located *Lagerstätten* or storage sites of squidgy life are possible thanks to a quick burial within sediments that were free of oxygen, which halted decay; provided protection from oxygen-breathing scavengers that would have consumed them; and kept them safe from the later ravages of the Earth, such as heat, erosion, tectonics and pressure.

The most famous fossil mother lode is found in Yoho National Park, British Columbia, Canada – a place more commonly known as *the Burgess Shale*. Found at around 2,500m (8,000ft) high on a mountain face above Emerald Lake in the Canadian Rockies this site, called Walcott Quarry, occupies one of the most majestic fieldwork spots I have ever been lucky enough to visit. In a lens-shaped bed of shale (the Phyllopod Bed) no more than 3m (10ft) thick and 60m (200ft) long, we have learned more about life during the Cambrian than from anywhere else in the world. The animals here probably lived on mudbanks built up at the base of a massive reef of calcareous algae (the reef-building corals we see today had not yet evolved). Mudslides could have dragged these ecosystems down into nearby basins that were deprived of oxygen, killing these organisms instantly. How do we know they died quickly? First, in the presence of an anaerobic, oxygen-free environment, marine invertebrates normally curl up upon dying. Fossils of the Burgess Shale do not exhibit this coiling; there was not enough time and so their death was quick. Second, there is no evidence of any attempt by these organisms to try to burrow out of their mud prison. If they had survived the fall, then surely they would have tried to escape.

The fossils of the Burgess Shale are spectacular, and many of them preserve exoskeletons, limbs and even guts. In some rare examples, there is actually 500-million-year-old evidence of stomach contents and muscle. In these rocks, the earliest known chordate (spinal cord-bearing animal) *Pikaia* was first found. Other marine creatures of Cambrian seas included the archaeocyathids and stromatoporoids (two extinct sponge-like organisms that formed reefs); primitive sponges and corals; simple pelecypods (ancestors of modern bivalves such as clams, oysters and mussels) and brachiopods; other simple molluscs; primitive echinoderms and jawless fish; nautiloids; and a diverse group of early arthropods. The iconic arthropods of the Cambrian were the *trilobites*, of which there is a huge number of fossils (there is one on my desk, in fact). Trilobites had flattened, segmented and plated bodies that helped protect them in seas that were increasingly filled with predators. With many varieties and sizes – they ranged from a millimetre to more than 50cm (20in) in length – trilobites proved to be among the most successful and enduring of all prehistoric animals. Some species of trilobite were the first organisms to develop complex eye structures. More than 17,000 species are known to have survived until 251 million years ago.

Many species we observe from this time could have been stolen straight from science fiction. An example is *Opabinia*, a slim segmented animal with gills, five stalked eyes, and a long, flexible, hose-like structure extending out from under its head, ending in a claw fringed with spines. Another is the infamous *Anomalocaris*, which resembled the rear end of a shrimp. This gigantic predator was segmented with two large grasping appendages, a mouth with rings of razor-sharp teeth and was up to 2m (6.6ft) long. A personal favourite is *Hallucigenia*, so named because it looked so bizarre. It was a worm-like animal that walked on a set of 14 long rigid spines and had a row of tentacles along its back ... or ... did it walk on the tentacles and use the spines along its back for armour? This creature is so alien to us today that we cannot even determine which way up it goes.

Out of the Sea and on to the Land

One of the most important evolutionary steps for life was the *greening* of the Earth, but adapting to life on its rocky surface was an incredible challenge. Organisms needed to avoid drying out, having always been wet, and anything above microscopic size needed to create special structures to withstand the effects of gravity (which was previously stemmed by the buoyancy of the seas). Their respiration and gas-exchange systems also needed to change and even reproduction could no longer depend on water to carry eggs and sperm towards each other ... sex had to be re-invented.

When plants and animals began to transfer from the water to the land, the first organisms to lead the way were algal mats that dotted themselves along the edges of seas and lakes. This is because until this point, soil – a blend of mineral particles and decomposed organic matter – did not exist either. Land surfaces would have been either bare rock or unstable sand produced by weathering of the rock, and very dry. Microbial mats of photosynthesising cyanobacteria may have been the only organisms capable of survival, since today they are found in areas of modern deserts that are home to little else. True land plants are thought to have evolved from a group of branched, filamentous green algae dwelling in shallow fresh water, perhaps at the edge of seasonally desiccating pools, more than 470 million years ago. Soil-dwelling fungi were probably involved and formed mutually beneficial, symbiotic relationships with early land plants to assist them in their initial colonisation of terrestrial environments. Spores of land vegetation from non-vascular plants that lacked deep roots, just like mosses and liverworts today, have been found in Middle Ordovician rocks dated to some 476 million years ago. The terrestrial world offered these primitive plants mineral resources and plenty more exposure to sunlight than could be found in the crowded seas.

To survive on the land, plants had to become internally more complex and specialised. They needed to photosynthesise to provide food for the entire plant body and this was most efficiently conducted from the top; roots were used to extract water from the ground and the parts in between became support and transport systems for water and nutrients. The Middle Silurian rocks of around 430 million years of age contain fossils of actual plants, including mosses, but most were less than 10cm (4in) high. By the Late Devonian around 370 million years ago, ferns and trees such as *Archaeopteris* were abundant. The establishment of a photosynthesising land-based flora caused oxygen levels in the atmosphere to rise even further, and once it got above 13 per cent there was enough oxygen around to stoke wildfires. This is first recorded as charcoalified plant fossils. Apart from a controversial gap in the Late Devonian, charcoal has been found throughout the geological record ever since.

As the once barren continents became lush green land masses, a hospitable environment – and tasty food source – was finally available to support the first terrestrial animals. Various types of arthropod, the ancestors of millipedes and centipedes, the earliest arachnids, and the ancestors of insects came first. These ate the early plants and each other. Arthropods were pre-adapted to colonise land, because their jointed exoskeletons provided protection against drying out, support against gravity and a means of locomotion that was not dependent on water. Animals had to change both their feeding and excretory systems for life on the surface, and most land animals developed internal fertilisation of their eggs. If that wasn't enough the difference in refractive index between water and air also required big changes in their eyes. On the other hand, in some ways movement and breathing became easier, and the better transmission of high-frequency sounds in air encouraged the development of hearing. The oldest known air-breathing animal is *Pneumodesmus*, an archipolypodan millipede from

about 428 million years ago, but in general the fossil record
of major invertebrate groups on land is poor. It is thought
that insects developed the ability to fly in the Early
Carboniferous, giving them a wider range of ecological
niches for feeding and breeding, and a means of escape from
predators. Finally, we arrive at the *tetrapods* – vertebrates
with four limbs – who evolved from lobe-finned fish over
a relatively short timespan during the Late Devonian, 370–
360 million years ago. As the continents continued to
rearrange themselves into the continental land masses we
recognise today, plants grew taller and evolved wooden
stems, flowers and fruit. At the same time, vertebrates
diversified from fish to amphibians, reptiles such as
dinosaurs, birds and mammals, and finally nature made
way for conscious intelligence.

The Stressors of Life

A sad fact of life on Earth is that without extinction events
there would not be any life as we know it. Death is a
necessity of life. We derive the history of life on Earth from
the study of fossils and the rocks that contain them –
significant events marked by an organism's first appearance
and also its last. As mentioned above, multicellular life
might only have been made possible by the release of
the Earth from a freezing slush-ball period. In the last
million years, throughout the *Quaternary* period, the Earth
has undergone cycles of ice ages, each lasting about 100,000
years, yet the temperature difference has been less than
10°C (50°F). Earth is only now emerging from the last ice
age that ended about 11,000 years ago and this coincidentally
marks the cultural development of humans, which started
only 10,000 years ago. The Earth's climate obviously had
a huge impact on life and today we are still very much
aware of its power over us. This is just one stressor that
life has to contend with. The fossil record tells us that since
the Cambrian explosion there have been five major and

almost catastrophic extinctions, but they had nothing to do with ice …

The major extinctions of the last 500 million years bear witness to the repetitive reboot of Earth's biosphere. The greatest is the Permian catastrophe 252 million years ago, whereby within one million years 70 per cent of all land species and 85 per cent of all marine species were erased from existence, but the jury is still out on what caused it, with both terrestrial and extraterrestrial culprits proposed. The most iconic mass extinction occurred 65 million years ago and is commonly accompanied by the image of a luckless tyrannosaur looking over its shoulder at a colossal fireball sent from the heavens as it streaks across the horizon, the monster's death by vaporisation imminent. The disappearance of most of our beloved dinosaurs, and actually 70 per cent of other species as well, although sad, paved the way for the age of mammals and the eventual appearance of humanoids. This extinction is also popular in the public imagination as it has been linked to a space rock 15km (9 miles) across slamming into the Earth. Sometimes comets and asteroids are forced from their orbits around the Sun and head on a collision path with a planet or moon, even the Earth. When these strike a planet full of life, the dangers can be hard to comprehend and the devastation absolute. Even though there is, compared to the Moon, scant evidence of past strikes on the Earth, this is owing to the Earth's effective cleaning protocols of weathering and erosion erasing the evidence rather than the planet somehow avoiding such catastrophes.

A buried impact crater 180km (110 miles) wide of just the right age has been found in the Yucatan Peninsula of Mexico, dubbed *Chicxulub*. The dinosaurs would not have been killed by the impact itself but rather by the environmental devastation that followed. This event would have triggered tsunamis across the oceans, caused powerful earthquakes and released enough heat to start spontaneous fires around the world. Material thrown into the air would have fallen back to Earth as acid rain thereby acidifying the oceans, and the dust would have blocked out the Sun, plunging the planet into a cold darkness for many years. Around this time, in an unrelated event, huge areas of western India, now called the Deccan Traps, were being smothered in lava, in some places more than 1.6km (1 mile) deep, while huge quantities of greenhouse gases were being pumped into the atmosphere. Asteroid-theory fans have long dismissed this volcanism as an irritating coincidence but many scientists now lean towards the idea of a planet weakened by overzealous volcanoes and then crippled by an asteroid – or vice versa.

There is a number of events we know of that could have dramatically altered the path of human life on Earth. In June 1908, in Tunguska, Siberia, 80 million trees were found burnt or flattened over 2,150km² (830 square miles) with no immediately apparent cause. It is now thought to have been the result of a small comet or meteor that vaporised mid-flight about 5–10km (3–6 miles) from the ground. A short time after the explosion, its noise and resulting air pressure fluctuations were recorded as far away as London, while dust rose into the stratosphere and reduced its transparency for months. Luckily, this impact occurred in a sparsely inhabited location; if it had hit near a city the results would have been ruinous. A bolide – a meteor that explodes in the atmosphere – the size of Tunguska is estimated to strike the Earth on average only once every 300 years, but we are always aware of the looming presence of nearby asteroids and were reminded of our vulnerability most recently in 2013.

On 15th February 2013, a meteor classed as a *superbolide* fell to Earth over Russia, temporarily outshining the Sun. Eyewitnesses felt its intense heat as it burned through the atmosphere at a speed of up to 69,000km/h (42,900mph). Thankfully, owing to its high velocity, shallow angle of entry, and our wonderfully thick protective atmosphere, the object exploded in an airburst over the city of

Chelyabinsk. The explosion released 20–30 times more energy than that from the atomic bomb detonated at Hiroshima, generating a bright flash, a large shock wave and a hot cloud of dust and gas. Many fragments pelted the surface – fortunately, there were no resulting fatalities. The explosion injured around 1,500 people, mainly from broken glass from shattered windows, and damaged some 7,200 buildings in six cities across the region. Completely unrelated, a predicted and even larger asteroid approached close to Earth that same day, the roughly 30m (100ft) 367943 Duende, which passed quietly by some 16 hours later. What is worrying is that the Chelyabinsk meteor arrived undetected before it made contact with our atmosphere. Measuring around 20m (65ft) in diameter, it is the largest known natural object to have entered Earth's atmosphere since the event at Tunguska.

The position of the Sun and its journey through the spiral arms of the Milky Way may also play a part. As the Sun passes through dense regions of stars within the arms, the chances of encounters with supernovae, and the gravitational effects of other stars causing the destabilisation of orbits of asteroids within our Solar System, increase. This takes place roughly every 26 million years. Although more than 100,000 supernovae events have occurred in the Milky Way since its formation, life on Earth has so far been spared. This may not always be the case ...

We have managed to summarise more than 4 billion years of evolution in this chapter, but when we think in terms of astrobiology and the search for life on other worlds we are not expecting to find any life resembling that which has arisen here in the last 400 million years or more. It's the simpler life and the curious forms it took early in its history that can teach us the most. Thanks to our, albeit still limited, understanding of evolution on the Earth we may one day recognise alien creatures as similar to one of the many wondrous forms of terrestrial life that has existed.

Maybe other planetary bodies have life but it has only evolved to the point of the Cambrian, or is only just starting to grow plants, or is in the midst of an age of dinosaurs. Our terrestrial ancestral aliens can teach us so much about the elaborate or painfully simple forms that life could take on another world, and in doing so keep our eyes and our minds open to the unexpected. Now if only we knew where to look for it ...

CHAPTER FIVE

Alien Worlds on Our Doorstep

The search for life in the Universe is not an easy pursuit. There is such a vast repository of information about the many wondrous forms life has taken over the history of the Earth that it is theoretically possible (perhaps almost inevitable) that life on another world could take on any number of guises as it would be affected by and respond to its particular environment. At the very least we have some educated ideas about what to look for and what types of environment on the Earth they like to inhabit. Now we just need to figure out where to look in the cosmos. Planets, moons, asteroids and comets are all options but they are not small targets. The search needs to be narrowed down to particular environments or geological features that hold the greatest chance of supporting any life forms. The Earth, as with life, has an incredible selection of sites from which we can choose and learn from.

A Home Away From Home

Ultimately, the search for life in the Universe begins by looking for localities where all the conditions needed for life to exist can be found together, in the exact same spot. This is called the search for *habitability*. Habitability requires a set of physical and chemical conditions, such as the availability of water, energy and carbon, that if found would first give life the opportunity to become established; and second, sustain it and allow it to flourish over the longer term. Unsurprisingly, any location that displays such *must-have* parameters is termed a *habitable environment* and it is these areas astrobiologists are most interested in finding. One such environment is the Earth itself: a perfect example of a globally habitable world, with billions of smaller niche habitable environments present within it.

The Earth is unique and incredibly special. More than 70 per cent of its surface is covered in liquid water – some might say the most important prerequisite for life. Unlike any other world in the Solar System, it is able to support this liquid water because of its thick insulating atmosphere with a *greenhouse effect* that prevents wild swings of temperature, and keeps the water from globally freezing or boiling away – the greenhouse effect is not always a negative thing. The atmosphere both generates an oxygen-rich ozone layer that absorbs harmful UV radiation from the Sun, and serves as a barrier to protect the fragile life below. The Earth also has a global magnetic field, something that other planets such as Mars have long since lost. The magnetic field protects the planet's atmospheric bodyguard from being blown away by solar winds, and additionally provides another line of defence against cell-damaging cosmic radiation. Finally, the Earth is a rocky or terrestrial planet built mostly of silica-rich rock instead of metal or gas. This allows plate tectonics to be sustained, with this process thought to be crucial for the long-term sustainability of Earth's climate and life. In the search for habitable environments on a global scale, astrobiologists are trying to locate a world similar to the Earth – looking to rocky terrestrial planets and moons with some element of an atmosphere and magnetic field.

The search for life and habitable environments so far has focused on finding a world with water, a source of energy (to power life) and a source of organic carbon. This is, of course, because all terrestrial organisms observed so far are reliant on liquid water for their survival, although fluids other than water have been found on other planets and these may have the potential to support life (see Chapter 8). Life and therefore life-friendly environments also need energy to drive and sustain metabolic processes and encourage growth and reproduction. Ultimately, this energy comes from the Sun, even though it is 149,600,000km (almost 93 million miles) away, and is readily available to any organism or habitat located on or close to the surface of a planet or moon. If conditions do not allow for life on the surface, however, then habitats may be found lurking underground where chemical energy can be used as a replacement for solar. Chemical energy sees microbes break complex compounds into simpler ones to obtain just a small amount of energy from the chemical reaction. Finally, a habitable environment needs organic carbon-based molecules – the building blocks for life. These are not necessarily biological (as they can exist without being part of or created by an organism), but life cannot exist without them. Luckily for life, they are found in every corner of the known Universe, within meteorites that have pelted planets and moons for billions of years, and in comets travelling through our Solar System and throughout the interstellar medium. This is extremely important, as the universal nature of carbon molecules and their delivery across the cosmos greatly increases the habitability potential of millions of worlds across our Galaxy and beyond.

This appears a fairly simple formula – locate carbon, water and energy on a terrestrial world or even within a single palm-sized rock – and you will find a habitable environment flourishing with living organisms. However, nothing is ever that simple. First, think about the relative nature of the term *habitable* and how it changes depending upon the type of life you are looking for. A boiling acidic hot spring in Yellowstone National Park might be the perfect home for a heat-loving bacterium yet it would be fatal for a human. In fact, no world yet discovered in the Universe would be entirely suitable or even remotely habitable for a human being without extensive artificial help. Most have such extreme environmental conditions that it is almost inconceivable that any form of terrestrial-like biology could exist there. Second, environments are not static as they fluctuate and change over time. The conditions present during the origin and first appearance of life are not necessarily those needed to maintain the life forms that are created, or even capable of supporting their long-term survival. Mars is a good example of this. Mars once had a warmer, wetter, life-friendly environment, but today is an inhospitable frozen wasteland. Life that might have arisen early in Mars' history may not have been able to survive as its environment degraded and froze. Third, science is making some mighty assumptions. It assumes that any location that has, or has had in the past, the ability to support life will definitely have contained it. It has to be considered, however, that there are environments where there is no life in spite of there being ideal conditions for it. These are called *uninhabited habitats* and can range in size from a single blade of grass to an entire planet. At present, astrobiologists are searching the Universe for environments that have the potential to support life either now or in the past, but may not prove to be inhabited. We are not just searching for conditions that we as humans would thrive in, of course, since this would be a very short and ultimately futile venture. Rather, we are hunting for environments that push the limits of biological survival to its very extremes, acutely aware that life has the resilience to become established and to survive in some incredibly unusual places.

Alien Environments All Over the Place

When searching for habitable environments, it goes without saying that we have to think about the type of life that might be able to live in them. So in locating potential habitats in the Solar System, it is important to consider the physical limits of life and the constraints this places on a suitable home. The main defining factors affecting cell-based life are temperature, acidity and salinity. Excitingly, certain terrestrial life would be perfectly content in extremes of these conditions and, even more excitingly, such environments are common on extraterrestrial worlds. Wonderfully, these can also be found in hundreds of pockets across the Earth that we can visit.

Alien worlds and even alien life forms can essentially be studied right here on our doorstep. These places are called *analogue environments*, as their biology, geology, chemistry or physical appearance (or a combination of all four) mimic an environment that was once found or currently exists on another planetary body. At present, terrestrial analogue studies are the best way for scientists to examine the habitability potential of alien environments, and they are able to help us design and develop tools and technologies for their exploration. No analogue environment is ever a perfect replica of a location or the conditions present on another world, however. For example, there is nowhere on Earth that naturally mimics the different forces of gravity found on other planets and moons, nor usually their atmospheres. The analogues we have do, however, display a number of extraterrestrial features that can be compared with those on other planetary bodies, to try to understand them better.

Some habitable analogue environments are considered more significant for exploration than others. These are based upon direct observations of their existence on other worlds through space missions, by orbiting satellites and from Earth-based telescopes. For example, we have data and images to certify that Mars has volcanoes, is composed of volcanic rocks similar to those found in Iceland or Hawaii, is covered in impact craters and has ice caps and glaciers, which are all possible sites where life might be hiding, as it is on Earth. This means that volcanoes, basalts, impact craters and ice-covered habitats on Earth are all extremely important analogues, albeit never perfect ones.

Other analogues are based on theories and circumstantial evidence. These are identified by indirect or highly suggestive evidence of their existence, which is still awaiting data to provide confirmation of the theory. Research into the conditions and biota within Lake Vostok in Antarctica is a perfect example, as it is used by scientists to explore the habitability potential of a brine ocean that may lie under the icy crust of the Galilean moon Europa (it was one of three Jupiter satellites discovered by Galileo). There is abundant indirect evidence to support the existence of this ocean and its possible composition, but we have yet to *prove* that it is there. Another example is the lack of flowing rivers of liquid water across the surface of Mars. Evidence of past water action and seasonally stable liquid water is globally present in the form of features that look identical to dried-up river channels, deltas, flood plains, lakes and seas on the Earth. Such indicators would include dark *recurring slope lineae* (*RSLs*) and specific minerals that can only form in the presence of water. While the connection between a river channel and liquid water seems almost undeniable, direct evidence for permanently flowing liquid water is still hard to find.

Finally, we have the analogues that are not backed up by any scientific evidence whatsoever. Unconfirmed UFO sightings aside, there is no physical evidence that life exists anywhere other than on Earth; nonetheless, terrestrial analogues for a mythical alien life form are incredibly important and are integral to the development of scenarios for planetary habitability. The premise that because life is found on Earth in a specific niche environment, and that a similar environment present on another planet could therefore be a habitable environment for life, is perhaps a reasonable one to maintain. The existence on Earth of extremophiles, extreme environment-loving organisms described in the next chapter, is an example of this life. A combination of this analogue research with laboratory experiments and data collected from the Earth itself and other planets and moons is allowing astrobiologists to develop some reasonably educated guesses as to where to look for life.

Extreme Living

The more we explore other worlds, the more we see that their environments are extreme in comparison to those on the Earth. As such, when looking for places on our planet where we can study life forms that might be able to thrive elsewhere, we turn to those localities that depart from our norms, that house conditions where we as humans would struggle to survive without help. These include hot springs and geysers, deep-sea hydrothermal vents, hypersaline environments such as salt flats, deserts both hot and cold, glacial ice, evaporites (sediments precipitated when water evaporates), and even the atmosphere itself. Instead of describing each type of environment, it is more meaningful to show how certain places on the Earth function as analogue sites for some of the most astrobiologically attractive worlds in the Solar System.

A Home Fit For a Martian

In the search for alien life, one instantly thinks about the possibility of *life on Mars*. This single Solar System body is of more public and scientific interest than any other because it is the most Earth-like planet we have seen and have fairly good access to, not that you would think so. I believe we will one day find life there, or at the very least evidence of it having once existed. Owing to their similarities, the Earth boasts hundreds of analogue environments that mimic closely not just the Mars of today but also the various environmental conditions it has experienced over its 4.5-billion-year existence: as it changed from a warm and wet oasis to a cold and arid desert. One of the main steps in assessing the habitability of Mars, therefore, is to study a similar range of Earth-based environments, understand what makes them habitable and what life forms can exist in them, and unearth their level of dependency on water – this is what I do! Needless to say, establishing the presence of life on Mars is a huge challenge, because as the availability of liquid water on the surface of Mars has fallen, so too has the planet's habitability potential and sadly the chances of it hosting life today.

The early years of Mars could be considered an Eden for life, as liquid water was abundantly available on its surface, temperatures would have been higher and its thicker atmosphere would have protected the planet. Rio Tinto, located in southwest Spain, is a fascinating analogue for habitable environments and the life forms that may have existed on Mars during this period of its history. Rio Tinto is a natural acid-rock drainage system, flowing with blood-red, iron-rich waters that teem with life. The pH of the river is an extremely acidic 2.3 (the same acidity as if it were flowing with lemon juice), directly created by its microbial community. Organisms here are *chemoautotrophs* that derive energy from chemical reactions between inorganic compounds such as iron (a process called *chemolithotrophy*), with iron-oxidising, acid-tolerant filamentous bacteria such as *Leptospirillum ferrooxidans* and *Acidithiobacillus ferrooxidans* dominating it. Rusty iron-rich terraces of rock have been forming along the banks of the river for more than 2 million years, and these have trapped bacteria and other microscopic organisms inside them. This site is therefore a wonderful natural laboratory where living organisms can be observed and then matched to their fossil ancestors in the surrounding rocks. This naturally gives rise to the questions 'Might these or similar types of organism once have lived in ancient rivers on Mars?' and 'Could we find evidence of organisms like these preserved in rocks on Mars?'

Time has taken its toll, however, and the Mars of today has lost most of its surface liquid water, has begun to rust and has become a dusty frozen desert. The tendency is to imagine a desert to be a golden, sandy, dry landscape baked by the intense heat of the Sun, but this is not the case on Mars. For starters, it is extremely cold. The most Mars-like environment on the Earth today is actually found at the South Pole, in the vast white Antarctic desert and the spectacular Antarctic Dry Valleys. These are the coldest and driest regions on the Earth, and mimic the harsh arid conditions now prevalent on Mars. Temperatures in the Valleys plummet to −40°C (−40°F), which, combined with the highest UV-B radiation levels on the planet and no source of liquid water, create extreme environmental stresses for life. On first inspection they appear completely barren – what could possibly live in these conditions? Yet within glacial ice and sub-surface rocks, life flourishes. Buried under the surface are warmer wet niches that create microscopic habitats for algae, fungi, nematode worms and tardigrades (the *water bears* whom we will meet in the next chapter). These *endolithic* (within rock) realms give hope that similar habitable environments could persist on Mars today and may have provided a refuge for life when conditions on its surface started to deteriorate.

Observations and investigations on Mars have driven the need for greater analogue research which has in turn allowed for the discovery of more habitable environments, not just on Mars but also throughout the Universe. This has meant the discovery of hundreds of extreme sites on Earth that have drawn attention to new, potentially habitable patches of planets that had been previously overlooked and are even providing an insight into the origins of life itself.

Floating above Venus

On the opposite side of Earth is an unlikely target in the search for habitable environments in the Solar System: its sister planet, Venus. It is common knowledge that Venus is pretty inhospitable for life, now known to resemble our clichéd imaginings of hell rather than a lush tropical paradise. It has the highest surface temperature (an unimaginable 460°C/860°F) of any planet in the Solar System (including that of Mercury, even though this planet is nearer to the Sun), therefore liquid water is an impossibility on its surface. It also has a toxic, unbreathable, carbon-dioxide-rich atmosphere and clouds dripping with sulphuric acid. The Venusian surface is not a habitable environment for life as we know it. High above the sweltering ground, however, is a potential habitable zone where temperatures lie between 0°C (32°F) and 120°C (248°F), and water vapour is available. The lower and middle cloud decks within this high-altitude region may therefore support an *aerial* biosphere. These clouds offer long-lasting droplets of water, although they are highly acidic and rich with dissolved hydrogen sulphide. Energy sources are available through chemical reactions such as sulphate reduction, or indeed photosynthesis, as happens in plants on Earth. Acid-loving organisms found in hot acidic waters on Earth, such as the bacterium *Acidianus infernus*, which grows at 88°C (190°F) and in acidic conditions down to pH0.5, are key analogue organisms for Venus. In addition, there is a precedent set for floating life, from Earth. Evidence shows that bacteria may be actively metabolising, and even reproducing, in clouds way above the Earth. So why not on Venus?

So, although most similar to Earth in composition and distance from the Sun, the terrestrial planets of the Solar System do not present much in the way of enticing habitable environments on their surfaces today. As we've seen, our strongest hopes lie with Mars that it may contain preserved biosignatures of past life forms within surface rocks and minerals, or active communities enduring deep in the sub-surface, while Venus may offer habitable conditions high in its atmosphere, with life floating within the clouds. As such, the traditional formulation of the habitable or Goldilocks zone around a star is perhaps too restrictive as we start to understand just how far life can go to survive. A planet or moon may not need to be around 1 AU (the distance from the Earth to the Sun) from its host star to house environments suitable for life. Suddenly, habitable environments existing throughout the Solar System and in other solar systems across the Universe are becoming a possibility.

The Jovian Moons

Surprisingly, some of the likeliest candidates for life-hosting habitable environments in the Solar System are to be found on moons. These are becoming more important in the search for life than the planets they orbit. The most promising are found among more than 210 frozen natural satellites orbiting the gas giant worlds of Jupiter and Saturn. Recent space missions have revealed many of these moons to be geologically active bodies, with volcanoes spewing ice as well as molten lava, geysers the size of whole countries on Earth, impact craters in their thousands, and vast channels and valley networks. Excitingly, these moons are displaying a wealth of potentially habitable environments. The problem for astrobiologists, however, is that although these geological features could be housing alien life, these moons are so incredibly extreme compared to the Earth that suitable terrestrial analogues of their environments and potential life forms are fewer in number. In addition, our knowledge of the conditions actually present on these icy moons is mainly based on inferences rather than on deductions supported by definitive data. There is a great deal more educated guesswork and imagination needed for detecting life on these worlds than those closer to home ... but that is half the fun.

The Oceans of Europa

One of the most important moons in the search for habitable environments in the Solar System is Europa. This moon is actually built like the Earth and the other terrestrial planets, mainly of silicate rock, but instead of a liquid it is covered in a smooth sheet of water ice that is many kilometres thick. This icy shell is believed to hide a secret ocean of briny water beneath. You might think that this ocean is fairly small, but in fact Europa is only slightly smaller than the Moon, and the volume of its ocean is estimated to be 3×10^{18} cubic metres: this is twice the volume of all Earth's oceans put together. Europa's frozen temperatures ($-220°C/-364°F$ at the poles), resulting from its huge distance from the Sun, provide an extreme environmental challenge for life, although a number of ice-dominated habitats on the Earth could supply analogues for liveable environments here. Most significantly, there is an important analogue site for the ocean itself. Lake Tirez in Spain contains very salty, sulphate-rich waters that may be similar to Europa's salty interior. In addition, salt-loving organisms growing in these Spanish waters provide an insight into how a habitable environment could exist on or beneath Europa's surface.

The Earth also has analogues for the capability of life to survive buried under a shield of ice. Liquid water lakes hidden up to 3.2km (2 miles) beneath the ice sheets of Antarctica, such as Lakes Vostok, Ellsworth, Bonney and

Vida, are thought to be similar to Europa's salty sub-surface ocean. Core samples taken from the ice surrounding Lake Vostok in 2012 revealed DNA from an estimated 3,507 organisms. Similar under-ice realms on Europa are believed to have the best potential to host microbial ecosystems in the entire Solar System, bar the Earth. A habitable sea-floor environment may also occur on Europa. There are extensive communities in the dark, cold, high-pressure environment of the Earth's ocean floor, particularly around deep-sea hydrothermal vent fields such as Lost City on the Mid-Atlantic Ridge and the Mariana Trench in the Pacific Ocean. It is important to investigate these analogues, even if at present any actual search for a deep-ocean biosphere on Europa is impossible. We must instead settle for hunting for indicators of their activity and the presence of this ocean on the surface ice.

The Fountains of Enceladus

One of Saturn's many moons, Enceladus, has attracted great interest thanks to dramatic images of powerful icy jets currently erupting from more than 100 cryovolcanoes near its southern polar region. These geysers explode over 645km (400 miles) into space (about the distance from London to Paris!). Measurements taken of these gigantic plumes by the Cassini Orbiter have found water gas, simple organic carbon-based molecules and volatiles such as nitrogen and methane to be present. These life-essential compounds must have come from source regions far inside the moon, from the area that feeds the jets. The assumption, therefore, is that organic molecules used by and needed for life are present deep within Enceladus. The young volcanic landscapes of Iceland provide a good analogue for these plumes. Iceland is covered in geysers and hot springs, cracks in the Earth's surface where near-boiling water erupts in spectacular fountains, blanketing the ground with mineral- and nutrient-rich waters. Surrounding the hot springs of Iceland are heat- and acid-loving bacteria that form mats of microorganisms, creeping across the surface and thriving in the hot acidic waters. Such terrestrial features are miniscule versions of the gargantuan jets seen erupting from Enceladus but they can inform us about the processes involved in their formation and their ability to create and support a habitable environment.

The Lakes of Titan

One place that greatly resembles the Earth in appearance is another of Saturn's moons, Titan. It is the only moon in the Solar System known to possess a thick atmosphere, and a substantial one at that, and there is evidence that it has Earth-like lakes and seas, rivers with running fluids, sand dunes and weather systems. One lake, Kraken Mare, is three times larger than Lake Michigan-Huron. Titan's lakes are crucial targets in the search for habitable environments and life on this moon. However, surface temperatures of around $-179°C$ ($-290°F$) suggests that the liquid bodies on the surface could not be composed of water, but are more likely to be a mixture of methane and ethane – hydrocarbons. Life might be present here within a range of habitats, from the liquid hydrocarbon lakes on the surface to great depths into the sub-surface, creating a potential biosphere volume double that of the Earth. Owing to the very different chemistries of the liquids on Titan, we can only speculate about what life might be like there, and as such there are very few analogues for this world. The best known one is Pitch Lake, on the island of Trinidad – a natural liquid hydrocarbon or asphalt lake just like those found on Titan, albeit a far smaller version. A unique microbial community is found here, one that includes archaea and bacteria that are actually anaerobic – they are able to live without any oxygen at all. The natural asphalt-soil seeps of the Rancho La Brea Tar Pits in California and the Alaskan Oil Field petroleum reservoirs are also potential habitable analogue sites for Titan.

The Signatures of Life

Once we find these habitable environments on Mars, Europa or Titan, and can send either robotic landers to hunt them down or even, one day, humans to investigate them, what will we look for? It is highly unlikely that organisms will be caught scurrying across the surface of Mars or swimming in the lakes of Titan (although never say never). We will instead be searching for the evidence that life leaves behind. These signs of life or *biosignatures* will be recognisable as they will be composed to a variable extent of carbon.

A biosignature is any substance, be it an element, isotope or molecule, that provides scientific proof of past or present life. The usefulness of a particular biosignature is determined not only by the probability of life creating it, but also by the improbability of non-biological processes producing it. Life processes may produce a range of biosignatures such as nucleic acids (the building blocks of DNA), lipids (fats), proteins and various morphological or visual features that are detectable in rocks and sediments (think dinosaur bones, trilobites, ammonites and any other kind of fossil). In addition, life interacts with its surroundings; for example, it can cause changes through chemical reactions with rocks and fluids, altering their chemistry or creating new materials. These processes will leave features in the geological record that indicate that life was once present.

Biosignatures are commonly used in geochemistry, geobiology and geomicrobiology to determine whether living organisms are or were once present within samples. Now they are applied to astrobiological exploration, founded upon the premise that biosignatures encountered in space will either mimic those found on Earth or be undeniably recognisable as originating from extraterrestrial life. An example of such biosignatures might be complex organic molecules, or structures whose formation is virtually impossible without the help of life. Some categories of *space* biosignatures include: cellular and extracellular morphologies (fossils, in other words); bio-organic molecular structures (e.g. lipids, proteins); chirality (a molecule's left- or right-handedness affected by interactions with living organisms); the presence of biogenic minerals (such as opal, only formed by life processes); atmospheric gases (e.g. methane and ozone that are largely produced via biological processes); and remotely detectable features on planetary surfaces, such as photosynthetic pigments.

Many of these signatures will not be detectable without the help of rocks, minerals or ice to preserve and protect them over millennia. Encasement within these media allows for the preservation of the remains of living organisms to be studied after their death, and their identification after geologically significant periods of time (billions of years). In general, this occurs through the process of *fossilisation*. The most common method is *mineralisation*, whereby hard parts of an organism are replaced by minerals such as calcite, silica, pyrite and phosphate, as well as a number of clays that were dissolved in water present in the sediment in which the organism died, or fell into shortly after death. An environment must satisfy a number of criteria as a suitable site for fossilisation, and some of the most valuable habitable environments we have found on other planets would be excellent sites for this process. As fossilisation and replacement of the original organism progresses, cell contents, cytoplasmic details and wall structures can be destroyed, rendering the identification of the original organisms difficult. In addition, after millions or even billions of years encased inside rocks, these fossils can be broken down, cracked, rearranged, completely destroyed by tectonics, weathering and erosion, or buried so deeply that we might never find them. Ultimately, this makes it incredibly hard to find and recognise a fossil of a once-living organism. Biosignatures therefore can be extremely valuable as they are more easily preserved within rocks, they can survive for much longer periods of time, and they can tough out a number of physical processes that would easily destroy a fossil. They are the key to the search for evidence of past life on Mars, Europa or any solid planetary body, and as such identification of analogue biosignatures in the ancient rock record on Earth is crucial; it provides an opportunity to learn which geochemical signatures are unequivocally produced by life, and how they are preserved over geologic time.

It is important to avoid a false positive result in the search for life. It would be a disaster to cry wolf over such a globally important discovery. Fossil-like objects may resemble once-living life forms, but they must be proven to be biogenic before claims of life are made. To find definitive evidence of living organisms on another world and to prove an object's biogenicity, we therefore need to observe the co-occurrence of biological morphology, *i.e.* fossils and carbon chemistry. Biological information needs to be extracted from any candidate life forms to prove that they were once, or are currently, alive. DNA, the basic building block of all life on Earth, as well as proteins and fatty acids – without which cells could not exist – are key pieces of irrefutable evidence of life. The use of analogue environments on the Earth, such as Rio Tinto, is therefore important in this search. Here, filamentous fossils that *appear* to be bacterial in origin are studied using a range of analytical techniques to identify proteins and fatty acids preserved within them. Bearing such markers, the fossils can be confidently assigned to life and are trustworthy evidence of previous habitable conditions in the area. Studies on fossil localities in Earth's oldest rocks, such as the Greenstone Belts of South Africa and Australia, have shown that some fossils and their associated biosignatures can be preserved and identified as being greater than 2.5 billion years old. Sites such as these provide ideal testing grounds for discovering the best techniques for the identification of markers of life on Earth and on other worlds.

Exploring the Extremes

Finding life anywhere on another world is just one use of analogue sites. Another is to figure out how humanity itself might one day leave the Earth and survive on another planet or moon. As such, a good analogue site is also a location where the exploration conditions of future astronauts can be simulated. Future explorers of the Moon or Mars will need to handle various conditions, such as reduced gravity, radiation, extreme temperatures and working in pressurised spacesuits. Preparing astronauts calls for training on sites that exhibit some or all of these conditions. The operations that can be simulated extend from living in isolation, cooking and gardening, doing fieldwork in a spacesuit and extravehicular activities (EVA) in reduced gravity to the construction of future habitats for humanity.

In order to help develop the key knowledge required to prepare for human exploration of Mars, the Mars Society initiated the *Mars Analog Research Station (MARS)* project. A global programme of Mars exploration operations research, this project includes two Mars base-like habitats located in deserts in the Canadian Arctic (the *Haughton Mars Project, HMP*) and Utah (*The Mars Desert Research Station, MDRS*). In these Mars-like desert environments, extensive long-duration field exploration operations are conducted in a similar style and under many similar constraints as would occur on the Red Planet. MDRS is a laboratory for learning how to live and work on another planet and is a prototype of a habitat that could house humans on Mars and serve as their main base of exploration. The station serves as a home-from-home to teams of six or seven crew members, including geologists, astrobiologists, engineers, mechanics, medics, human-factors researchers, artists and others, who live for weeks to months at a time in relative isolation, as they would on the surface of Mars.

NASA's *Hawai'i Space Exploration Analog and Simulation (Hi-SEAS)* mission is another analogue site used to prepare for human space flight to Mars. Located on the slopes of the Mauna Loa volcano on the island of Hawaii, this isolated dome is surrounded by a Mars-like terrain and houses a crew of *terranauts* who are researching what is required to keep a space-flight team happy and healthy during an extended or even permanent mission to Mars. Research into food preparation and growth, and crew dynamics, behaviour, roles and performance is carried out by the team, who also must live their daily lives, do chores, conduct EVAs in spacesuits and contend with 40-minute delayed communications, as would happen on Mars. A global mission support team of more than 40 volunteers, including myself, provides 24/7 technical assistance and a friendly ear. The first mission in 2013 lasted for 4 months and in 2015 the first year-long mission began.

The *NASA Extreme Environment Mission Operations project* (*NEEMO*) is an analogue mission that sends groups of astronauts, engineers and scientists to live in Aquarius, the world's only undersea research station. Operated by Florida International University, Aquarius is located 5.6km (3.5 miles) off Key Largo in the Florida Keys National Marine Sanctuary. It is deployed next to deep coral reefs 19m (62ft) below the surface. Underwater analogue sites allow for the training of *aquanauts* in neutral buoyancy conditions while operating in a natural but extremely hostile alien terrain. The aquanauts experience some of the same challenges beneath the waves that they would on a distant asteroid, planet or moon. During NEEMO missions, they simulate living on a spacecraft and test spacewalk techniques for future space missions. The underwater condition has the additional benefit of allowing NASA to *weight* the aquanauts to simulate different gravity environments and a technique known as saturation diving allows the aquanauts to live and work underwater for days or weeks at a time. Potential targets for such training are missions to the International Space Station (ISS), the Moon, Mars and asteroids, to test sampling, drilling and field explorations in one-sixth or one-third of Earth's gravity and to test anchoring systems in microgravity. A slightly different type of underwater analogue site is based at the *Pavilion Lake Research Project (PLRP)* in British Columbia, Canada. Since 2004, two-week missions have been conducted every summer to train astronauts how to search for evidence of life in an extreme environment with reduced-gravity conditions – however, astronauts only do EVAs underwater; they do not live there.

There are three permanent, all-year research stations on the Antarctic Plateau: *Concordia Station* (French–Italian), *Vostok Station* (Russian) and the *Amundsen–Scott South Pole Station* (US) at the Geographic South Pole, the southernmost place on the Earth. One of the coldest places on our planet, and the world's largest desert, temperatures here hardly rise above −25°C (−13°F) in the summer and the lowest natural temperature ever measured was recorded at Vostok Station: a frost-shattering −89.2°C (−128.56°F). These stations conduct a great deal of planetary and astronomical research but, perhaps most interestingly, they all allow the study of stressors associated with long-duration space missions, including extreme isolation and confinement. During the winter, crews are without the possibility of evacuation or deliveries for 9 months and live for prolonged periods, up to 6 whole months, in total darkness. Concordia station has been proposed as one of the highest-fidelity, real-life Earth-based analogues for long-duration deep-space missions.

The possibility of finding life somewhere other than the Earth seems to increase the more we understand our own planet, the conditions in which life has been found to survive and thrive, and the more we see data from the orbiters and landers that we are sending to other worlds. Although the planets and moons of our Solar System may prove to be habitable, however, it still does not mean that there is life on them. Earth remains the only example we have of an inhabited planet where life originated and evolved from a single-celled organism to the plethora of species we see today. Through working in areas across the Earth that exhibit similar traits to places on other planets and moons in the Solar System, we know that we need to target habitable environments around the numerous impact craters, ancient volcanoes and sub-surface environments of Mars, within the salty liquid oceans beneath the ice of Europa, in the source regions of the gigantic water jets erupting from Enceladus and within the Earth-like hydrocarbon lakes and seas of Titan. Each of these environments is considered to be *extreme*, and will exert immense stresses and pressure on any organism, including humans, trying to exist within them. Even though the conditions for life are tough ... life is tougher.

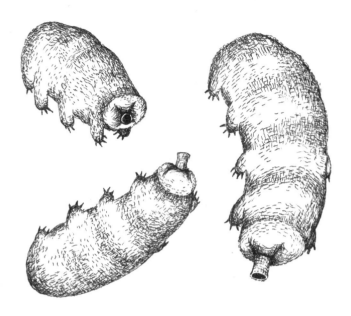

CHAPTER SIX

Everything is Relative!

One of the developments in recent years that really opened up scientists' eyes to the possibility of life on other worlds was the realisation of just how adaptable and versatile life is, and the growing appreciation and understanding of the physical limits of organisms. Since the 1990s, a particular branch of microbiology has been gathering pace – the area of *Extremophiles*. In every corner of our planet in which we look, even in places barely survivable by humans, there is some form of life flourishing. It seems that once life gets going, it will fight to survive and, if needed, will adapt to fill almost any moist niche it comes across. With evidence for liquid water surfacing on many planets and moons in the Solar System, although in conditions beyond any that humanity can survive, organisms that have adapted to life in extreme conditions are taking centre stage. They are providing us with a template for finding life elsewhere and directing us to environments in which we would never have considered searching.

Understanding the range of *current* life on Earth and mapping it to *current* environments in the Solar System is simply the start as it lacks the element of time. Life on Earth was substantially *alien* when it arose around 4 billion years ago because the environments on Earth were so dramatically different. Similarly, the climatic conditions forecast for a billion or so years into the future are depressingly bleak for much of life as we currently know it, including ourselves. The range of what is possible is continually being stretched to incorporate new adaptations displayed by life in its bid for survival. Some organisms have created an *extreme-living* club, and you can only be a member if you can survive somewhere another form of life cannot.

Extreme-lovers

Terrestrial life, as defined in Chapter 2, is made up of carbon compounds and uses water as a solvent and as such has to abide by the limitations imposed by this chemistry. It manages to emerge and survive within boundaries such as the boiling and freezing points of water, the presence or absence of oxygen, extremes of acidity and alkalinity and all pHs in between. The range of tolerances to these are known for the most part for all cells, and the extent to which life can survive any combination of acidity, temperature and salinity determines the *envelope of life*, ranging from cold acidic waters in one corner to hot alkaline brines in the other. The complexity of eukaryotic cells (those with a nucleus, as found within us and all multicellular organisms) means that they are much more sensitive to perturbations of these three conditions. Therefore, the most extreme outer regions of the envelope of life are not dominated by complex eukaryotes but by the simpler prokaryotes. Any organism found thriving in these hostile and extreme environmental conditions on Earth is bestowed with the alias *extremophile*, literally meaning 'extreme love'. When we hear the term extremophile, it immediately conjures up images of tiny microbial prokaryotes, yet the extremophilic taxonomic range spans all three domains, including multicellular sophisticated vertebrates. While adaptation to a single harsh habitat is already impressive, there are species that can survive a variety: the rare *polyextremophiles*. These organisms are exploiting an ecological niche for which they are uniquely adapted, and face little or no competition within it.

The Relativity of Extremity

What is *extreme*? Perhaps extreme is simply an opinion; whether an environment or an organism is extreme is determined by the eye of the beholder. It is clear to us humans that a heat-loving thermophile that dies at temperatures below 21°C (69.8°F), or a pressure-loving piezophile that finds the atmospheric pressure on the Earth's surface too much to bear, is an extreme being in comparison to our own adaptations – but what determines an extremophily? Is it an evolutionary viewpoint? Does the earliest environment to contain life define what is considered *normal*? If life had arisen in a high-temperature, zero-oxygen hydrothermal vent, or around a cooler alkaline spring at the base of the earliest oceans, would that then be considered as normal, and every environment that has arisen since extreme? Or perhaps extremity is a physical state. All physical factors are on a continuum, and any changes in the conditions that make it difficult for organisms to function are therefore considered extreme. Extremophiles are extreme only in relation to the capabilities of other cells. To a bacterium living in the crushing pressures and high temperatures of an ocean-floor black smoker, we humans living at the level of atmospheric pressure present at the Earth's surface – 1 atmosphere (1atm or 0.101 megapascals/MPa) – breathing oxygen and basking in moderate temperatures, are the extreme beings. Obviously, therefore, *normal* is relative to whoever is making the comparison, so from a human perspective a normal condition or environment refers to conditions in which humans could comfortably survive without artificial aid.

Must an extremophile actually *love* an extreme environment as its name suggests or can it merely tolerate it? And must an organism depend on these extreme situations for the entirety of its life cycle? An extreme-loving life form does not need to be completely smitten with the conditions it currently resides in. It may be an *obligate* organism that requires these particular extreme conditions to survive, or *facultative* – meaning it is not only able to tolerate certain extreme environs when necessary, but is also able to thrive in others at particular stages of its life cycle. The bacterium *Deinococcus radiodurans*, the present gold-medallist of radiation resistance, is widely regarded as an extremophile par excellence, yet retains its radiation superpower only as long as other extreme conditions are lacking; it is severely diminished under freezing or desiccating situations. Other examples are spores, seeds and eggs, which are all far more resistant to environmental extremes compared to their vegetative or animal forms. Similarly, trees, frogs, insects and fish shift their physiology as the seasons change, so they can tolerate remarkably low temperatures during the winter months.

The Extremes

Liquid water is the prerequisite of life on Earth and arguably will be the cornerstone of any life in our Solar System and beyond. Life also requires an input of energy but crucially must be able to control this energy as it courses through its system. It does this through *redox chemistry*, whereby the loss or gain of electrons between molecules, atoms or ions occurs through a process of oxidation or reduction. Redox chemistry is universal to life on Earth and as all life is based on carbon organic chemistry, it is assumed that such reactions must be allowed to operate for a life form to exist. In terms of extremophiles, they must either live within environments that adhere to these energy parameters or be able to guard against the hostile outside world in order to maintain these conditions within their cells. Life on Earth has been found enduring *physical extremes* (for example, temperature, radiation or pressure) and *geochemical extremes* (such as desiccation, salinity, pH, raised or absent oxygen levels or redox potential). It could also be argued that there are also *biological extremes* such as nutritional availability, and excesses or lack of population density, parasites and prey.

Temperature

More than 80 per cent of our planet, far from being a balmy paradise, exists at temperatures colder than 5°C (41°F) and, even more incredibly, these frigid places are inhabited. As such, the most well-known extremophiles are those that can work to adjust their thermostats, allowing them to live in the coldest, and hottest, places on the planet.

There are two top prizewinners among temperature-tolerant extremophiles. *Thermophiles* are heat-lovers, commonly found in hot springs and geysers the world over. As microorganisms cannot regulate their own temperature as animals do, they must instead adapt all of their cellular machinery to a particular set of operating conditions. Importantly, they have evolved reinforced proteins to hold themselves together against the violent shaking caused by thermal motion at high temperatures. If a protein shakes to such an extent that it loses its three-dimensional structure and becomes *denatured*, it loses its function and life cannot survive without working proteins. Temperatures approaching 100°C (212°F) normally cause this denaturation to occur in DNA and RNA as well as in proteins, and increase the 'leakiness' of cell membranes to lethal levels. Above 150°C (302°F), many organic molecules decompose entirely and chlorophyll degrades above 75°C (167°F), preventing photosynthesis from continuing within cyanobacteria and all plants, thereby leading to their death from starvation. The most *hyperthermophilic* organisms (extreme heat-lovers with maximum growth at temperatures over 80°C/176°F) are archaea. Among these, *Pyrolobus fumarii* is a *chemolithoautotroph* that obtains energy from the oxidation of inorganic compounds, and carbon from the fixation of carbon dioxide; it is capable of growing at temperatures of up to 113°C (235°F). Another archaean, dubbed *Strain 121*, is found growing quite happily at over 120°C (248°F). At these hotter temperatures, the solubility of gases such as oxygen and carbon dioxide decreases, so many hyperthermophilic organisms are also *anaerobic* (do not require or use oxygen). The more standard thermophiles are mainly found among the phototrophic bacteria, eubacteria and archaea. The eukaryotes, however, such as algae and fungi, are comparative wimps with an upper temperature limit of only around 60°C (140°F), while for vascular plants it is a pitiful 48°C (118°F), and for fish a relatively frigid 40°C (104°F). It is within this thermophilic group that the universal ancestor of life is commonly thought to have resided (see Chapter 4 for more on LUCA), and may be the type of life found on worlds closer to their stars than the Earth, or around the geysers of the gas giant moons.

The cold-lovers on the other hand, the *psychrophiles*, inhabit environs where the temperatures dip below 0°C (32°F). These communities have enzymes and membranes that are loosened so they can remain dynamic and keep the cells active even at temperatures down to −18°C (−0.4°F). Without this adaptation, as the temperature dropped, the cells' contents would become rigid and inflexible, leaving them unable to fulfil their roles. Temperatures below freezing are a challenge for life as a consequence of the properties of its main solvent, water. Below 0°C (32°F), water freezes into ice crystals that can rip cell membranes apart and without liquid water, solution chemistry within cells stops. The freezing of intracellular water is almost always lethal to life. Despite this, many microbes and cells can be successfully preserved at –196°C (–320.8°F), which is the temperature of liquid nitrogen. In fact, human eggs in fertility clinics are preserved using this although they, together with microbes and cells, are not active at this temperature but held in suspended animation. Among animals, the Himalayan midge incredibly is still active at –18°C (–0.4°F), while the poor Antarctic icefish suffers from heat exhaustion above 4°C (39.2°F). Some of the most extreme psychrophiles reside inside solid icebergs within tiny channels of salty water that are kept liquid owing to their saltiness, and are killed at human body temperature. It is these extreme organisms that can survive the commonly lethal effects of the cold, which are of great interest in the search for life on the icy moons of Jupiter and Saturn.

In organisms more complex than microbes, it is perhaps their behaviour more than their biology that enables them to overcome the physical challenges of extreme temperature environments. As a defence mechanism, they can retreat from unfavourable conditions and relocate to a safer home. In the deserts of Earth, some animals have diurnal habits whereby they bury themselves in the more humid and wet layers beneath the surface to avoid the scorching Sun. In particular, the desert ants of the Sahara are among the most heat-tolerant species in the world and can be found sprinting across the scorching sands. They deliberately come out at the hottest point in the day, when surface temperatures are around 60°C (140°F), which, crucially, restricts their predators' activities. The ants scavenge for the corpses of insects that have died of heat exposure and, although they are physically evolved to resist the high temperatures, could still die rapidly from heat shock themselves. They survive because they stay out for short periods and have long legs, enabling them to move quickly with as little contact with the sand as possible to prevent the heat from building up in their bodies. At the other end of the spectrum, some species of nematode worm in Antarctica can withstand the harsh cold temperatures and lack of water by producing antifreeze and drying themselves out, letting the wind blow them around until water is found again, *i.e.* sitting tight and waiting it out. The red flat bark beetle of northern Alaska is an excellent psychrophile; the formation of ice crystals in its internal fluids is the greatest threat to its survival, but the beetle produces antifreeze proteins that stop water molecules from grouping together. Their larvae have been found surviving at temperatures of −150°C (−238°F), for which the antifreeze proteins alone would not be enough. These beetles also deliberately dehydrate their internal tissues; internal water cannot freeze if it is not there any more!

pH

After temperature, the acidity or alkalinity of an environment affects life greatly. Acidity is rated on the pH scale, which measures the concentration of H+ ions (protons) in a solution. Low pH is an acidic environment, while high pH is an alkaline one; pH7 is neutral. Concentrations of protons and their movement from one area to another within a cell are a fundamental mechanism of energy transformation. Biological processes tend to favour the middle range of the pH spectrum, around pH7, and intracellular and environmental pH often falls in this range as well. Proteins commonly denature at exceptionally low pH conditions, yet this is where *acidophiles* are found thriving. Acidophiles are able to survive in highly acidic environments as they can protect the vital molecules inside their cells, such as DNA and proteins, from the high concentration of protons in their environment. These organisms work constantly to pump the excessive levels of protons back across their cell membranes to the outside, like a sailor trying to bail out a leaking ship. Many acidophiles can tolerate pH2 (about the acidity of lemon juice), and some as low as pH0. This is best characterised in the red alga *Cyanidium caldarium*, which has been discovered in nature at pHs as low as 0.5, although it grows most successfully in a laboratory at pH2–3. As well as acidophilic prokaryotes, eukaryotic life forms may also be active in environments lower than pH3, although many of these are acid tolerant rather than truly acidophilic and may grow equally well or even better in more neutral habitats. Most eukaryotic acidophiles are, however, still microbial and many yeasts and fungi can grow in acidic soils and peat bogs of pH3–5. A number of filamentous fungi has been found growing at above pH3, and protozoa within acidic, metal-rich waters of pH2–3. Acidophiles such as these could find quite an acceptable home in the acidic cloud decks of Venus.

Alkaliphiles on the other hand prefer a high pH (commonly 8.5–11) and alkaline environments, although they find it equally challenging. As with low pH, there is often a difference of two or more pH units between the internal and external milieu of the cell and alkaliphiles can struggle to generate energy with too few protons in their environment. If cells are to survive in an alkaline environment they must make their own cytoplasm more acidic to buffer the alkalinity and bring it closer to a comfortable neutral value. Representatives of all domains and kingdoms of life are able to tolerate pH as high as around 11, but perhaps the best understood are the alkaliphilic bacteria and archaea, such as *Natronomonas pharaonis*.

Water Availability and Salinity

Water possesses a number of properties such as a high melting and boiling point, a wide temperature range within which it remains a liquid, and it forms hydrogen bonds, which makes it essential for life. It makes up 95–99 per cent of the total molecules in invertebrates and a typical adult human cannot survive the loss of even 14 per cent of his or her water. As such, a lack of this life-giving fluid constitutes a pretty extreme environment. Organisms that can tolerate extreme water loss or desiccation enter *anhydrobiosis*, a state characterised by little intracellular water and no metabolic activity. A variety of organisms can become anhydrobiotic, including bacteria, yeast, fungi, plants, insects, tardigrades, mycophagous nematodes and the shrimp *Artemia salina*. A further variety of organisms use desiccation-resistant spores to survive dry periods as well as for dispersal, e.g. by the wind. Resurrection plants such as *Craterostigma plantagineum* are unusual in that the plant itself can survive desiccation and can even revive after several months in an air-dried state. Some can even survive a loss of chlorophyll (the pigment required for a plant to be able to photosynthesise). All of these organisms would be very well suited for survival on any planetary body further out from its star than the Earth, where liquid water is scarce.

Organisms can live in a wide range of salty environments, from essentially pure distilled water to completely saturated salt solutions. The latter, however, is much more problematic for life. Salt-loving *halophiles* grow in high-salt solutions including the Dead Sea, which is not actually all that dead! Very salty or briny water outside the semi-permeable membrane surrounding each cell risks drawing water out from the cell, leading to dehydration. Conversely, if the salt concentration of the environment outside is lower than that inside the cell, it could swell to bursting as water rushes in. This process is called *osmosis*. Some halophiles have modified their inner workings to cope with higher salt levels, keeping their insides balanced with the outside, and thus safe from osmosis. Others have taken a different approach and packed their cells with different solutes (chemicals dissolved in the fluid inside the cell) to produce an equally concentrated solution to guard against osmosis, while avoiding the issues of a briny interior. These cells protect their innards from becoming too dry or salty by keeping them agreeably sugary. With these adaptations, organisms are able to thrive in the high salt content of salt evaporation ponds at roughly 10 times the concentration of salt in the ocean. Most halophiles are archaeal and bacterial but humans, along with most plants and other vertebrates, cannot tolerate high-salt environments.

Radiation

Radiation, both ultraviolet (UV) and ionising, is particularly hazardous to life. It can damage every single biopolymer (long chains of molecules strung together, produced by living organisms), causing destruction of nucleic acids, proteins and lipids. Radiation is a huge problem beyond the Earth's atmosphere, both within space itself and on worlds themselves lacking a protective atmosphere to shield life from incoming solar and cosmic radiation. As such, any life form that can survive high levels of radiation, or has the ability to recover from radiation damage, has a distinct advantage for survival. Because of the importance of keeping biopolymers intact and functional, organisms can avoid exposure by living underground or producing UV-attenuating pigments. However, because radiation damage cannot always be avoided, there are multiple mechanisms for DNA repair found in all organisms. Still, a few organisms stand out in their ability to handle radiation damage. The bacterium *Deinococcus radiodurans*, as mentioned earlier, is the reigning champion, having been found living within the cores of decommissioned nuclear power stations. It has the ability to withstand both ionising radiation (doses of up to 20 kilograys of gamma radiation) and UV radiation (doses of up to 1,000 joules per square metre) – levels that are 3,000 times higher than what is fatal for humans – but this extraordinary endurance is in fact thought to be a by-product of resistance to extreme desiccation.

Pressure

Life is sensitive to pressure, be it *atmospheric* (in the air), *hydrostatic* (underwater) or *osmotic* (within cells), since any form of pressure forces changes to the volume within cells. Pilots and divers must remain aware that rapid changes in pressure upon ascent can result in gases – generally nitrogen – coming out of solution in the blood to form gas bubbles and, if not treated, this can result in death. A similar situation occurs in microbes from the ocean floor that have gas-filled vacuoles. If they undergo decompression too rapidly, the vacuole expands and bursts, and they die. However, most microbes found in the deep ocean are able to grow at normal atmospheric pressure if decompression occurs gradually. Organisms that can survive in moderately high hydrostatic pressures, greater than the level of atmospheric pressure (1atm/0.101MPa) present at the Earth's surface, are called *piezophiles* – the pressure-lovers, known until recently as *barophiles* (weight-lovers). The boiling point of water increases with pressure, so water at the bottom of the ocean remains liquid at up to 400°C (752°F). Piezophilic bacteria are found to grow at pressures up to 500atm (50MPa), and the most extreme piezophilic life at even greater pressures. To survive these high-pressure environments, cells have increased binding capacities of enzymes and extra fatty acids within cell membranes to help them retain their flexibility and motion. Piezophiles include microbes, invertebrates and fish. There is life under high hydrostatic pressure even in the deep trenches of the ocean, living at up to 1,091atm (110.6MPa), for example in the Mariana Trench, the world's deepest sea floor at 10,898m (6.8 miles). *Colwellia MT41* is a *psychropiezophilic* bacterium, a polyextremophile (cold- and pressure-loving) microorganism, found growing in the deep sea at 1,016atm

(103MPa,) at only 8°C (46.4°F). Pressure may be a critical factor for higher animals and plants including ourselves, but neither the highest nor the lowest pressures encountered in the habitable parts of the Earth's surface are obstacles to the establishment of microbial life. Low pressures are too rare on Earth for such communities to have evolved here, but that does not mean it would not be possible on other worlds. Earth's pressure-lovers would be excellent organisms to colonise the base of the oceans on Europa or Enceladus, or to live deep underground on Mars.

Oxygen

The Earth has been anaerobic or oxygen-free throughout most of its history, so our reliance on oxygen is only a very recent phenomenon. Living organisms use energy released by respiration for their life processes and there are two types of respiration – *aerobic* (which needs oxygen) and *anaerobic* (which does not). Today, this need for oxygen is limited to only a handful of life forms on the Earth, so even though to us breathing oxygen is normal, we could be considered the odd ones out – the extremophiles. A huge variety of organisms are found to inhabit strictly anaerobic environments, where the mere presence of oxygen would be toxic. Currently, some bacteria and archaea use elements other than oxygen (such as nitrogen or sulphur) as the main source of their energy. However, a metabolism using oxygen is far more efficient, although this efficiency comes at a price. Molecular oxygen is highly reactive. The reduction of oxygen to water occurs during aerobic respiration in animals, and the reverse happens during oxygenic photosynthesis in plants, which creates hazardous chemically reactive molecules containing oxygen, particularly the hydroxyl radical ($\cdot$OH). Without the superior generation of energy from aerobic over anaerobic respiration, it is unlikely that animals would have arisen owing to their high metabolic demands; cellular damage, or more specifically *oxidative damage or stress* caused by an excess of these oxygen-rich radicals, is the price we pay. Current thinking suggests that much, if not all, degenerative human disease involves oxidative damage. The need for oxygen for large and energy-intense organisms such as humans nonetheless outweighs these negative effects.

Nature's Superheroes – the Water Bears

The epitome of a polyextremophile and the kings (or queens) of surviving extreme environments, *tardigrades* are incredibly endearing, eight-legged, all-but-indestructible and mainly microscopic animals. First named *tardigrada* from the Latin meaning 'slow walker', they are also known as *water bears* (a name I love, derived from their resemblance to eight-legged pandas) and even *moss piglets* (drawing comparisons to pygmy rhinoceroses and armadillos). Most tiny invertebrates dart about frantically but the water bears see no need for this; they shuffle along slowly, clambering across bits of debris, ambling around their habitats on pairs of short, stubby legs located under their bodies. The legs are outfitted with a number of hooked claws that resemble the talons of bears. Water bears have five body sections, including one that is obviously a head (with or without a pair of eyes) and are encased in a rugged yet flexible cuticle that must be shed as the organism grows. Animals generally grow by adding more cells or by making each cell larger. The water bears for the most part do the latter, as they must must break out of the cuticle in order to grow. All of this houses a nearly translucent, charismatic miniature creature only half a millimeter in length, about the size of the full stop at the end of this sentence.

These mostly microscopic aquatic animals can be seen with the naked eye in the right light and are found just about everywhere across the Earth, from the Arctic to the Equator, from freshwater droplets within garden moss to the salty deep ocean, and to the tops of forest canopies and the summits of mountains. The vast majority of water bears feed only on plant cells or bacteria, slicing them open with their dagger-like teeth and drinking their fluid contents. Others, however, are vicious predators. Moving incredibly fast on the first six legs, they employ their fourth pair to stand upright and attack prey with the rest of their claws – not unlike an actual bear.

The ubiquity of water bears is linked to their best-known feature, their survivorship – they have survived all five mass extinctions – quite possibly because of their strong determination to overcome a cacophony of spectacularly extreme conditions. This has earned them the title of the *most extreme* survivor of all, beating penguins in Antarctica, camels in the desert and the common cockroach. Only the land-dwelling water bears can boast this title however; marine and aquatic species appear to not have developed these superhero characteristics. All the survival adaptations water bears display were selected in response to their rapidly changing terrestrial-based micro-environments. Terrestrial water bears, for example, technically live on the land but actually reside within thin films of water. Moss and lichens, for example, provide sponge-like homes dissected by a myriad of small pockets of water for water bears to inhabit, but are always at risk of drying out. The water bears have two choices in this situation – die or adapt to new, drier environmental conditions. As such, terrestrial water bears have three basic conditions of life: *active, anoxybiosis* and *cryptobiosis.* When active they eat, grow, fight, reproduce, move and go about their normal daily routines. *Anoxybiosis* commences when a water bear finds itself in a low-oxygen environment. Prolonged asphyxia results in failure of the systems that regulate body water, causing the water bear to puff up like a newly-popped piece of popcorn and float around for a few days until it can resume active life. *Cryptobiosis* effectively resembles death and resurrection. It is a suspension of the water bear's metabolism brought on by the loss of liquid water and extreme desiccation. As its surroundings lose water, the water bear dries up with them, losing up to 97 per cent of its body moisture, shrivelling into a structure about one-third its original size, called a *tun*. In this almost mummified state of *anhydrobiosis* – meaning life without water – this hardy creature can survive just about anything thrown at it. Water bears actually form tuns several times a year in nature simply by retracting their legs and head and curling into a ball, surrendering nearly all of their body's water. The water bear in effect preserves itself by becoming a powder comprising the ingredients of life, held in suspended animation. When finally rehydrated by an adequate source of moisture, it returns to its active life in as little as a few minutes.

Water bears in their hibernating tun state have been experimentally subjected to temperatures far below freezing (down to −272.95°C/−459.31°F) and, once warmed and rehydrated, returned eagerly to active life. They have been boiled alive, exposed to 150°C (302°F), and still been revived. They have also been weighed down by nearly 400atm (40MPa) of pressure (equivalent to that felt at the base of the ocean) and exposed to superfluous concentrations of lethal gases, such as carbon monoxide, carbon dioxide, nitrogen and sulphur dioxide, and still they returned to life. How they can survive all of this remains something of a mystery. It may in part be linked to the fact they make excellent travellers. Water bear tuns are almost indistinguishable from dust grains in both appearance and size, and as such can float on the wind in a similar way to spores, pollen and seeds. Just like the latter, the tuns have a preference for where they land and many micro-environments will be unsuitable habitats for freshly arrived water bears. However, an unfortunately placed tun is able to wait for a change in conditions to something more favourable or to be picked up by the wind again and, with any luck, taken somewhere better. When the right watery conditions are finally found, life can begin again. Contributing to this success is the fact that many water bears are able to produce eggs without mating, and in a few cases are hermaphroditic, so able to self-fertilise. A lone water bear may thus be able to establish an entirely new population once it finds the right landing site. It appears they are creatures with few weaknesses; in fact, their only flaw is a vulnerability to mechanical damage when not in their protective tun phase – in other words, you can squash them!

Their near-indestructability may actually be written right into their DNA. Although still undergoing scrupulous investigation, recent sequencing of the water bear genome has revealed that a certain portion is of foreign origin. Potentially up to 17.5 per cent is made up of a mixture of around 6,000 genes from bacteria, archaea, fungi and even plants, which the water bear has absorbed into itself like a sponge, a process called *horizontal gene transfer*. This is not unusual within bacteria, which trade genes with each other as easily as we might swap emails, but these gene transfers are rarer in animals. A few other examples include ticks that have borrowed antibiotic-making genes from bacteria, aphids that have stolen colour genes from fungi, and wasps that have turned virus genes into biological weapons. One group of genes actually known as the *Space Invaders* has even repeatedly jumped between multiple organisms including lizards, frogs and rodents. Never has this new alien DNA, however, made up more than one per cent of the new, updated genome. The water bears are quite possibly the remarkable exception. How is this possible? It is thought that when they return to life after drying out in times of low water availability, their cells become sieve-like and molecules from the environment, including any nearby DNA, can enter. Since they are so good at repairing DNA damage, this patching-up ability seals in the new DNA and makes it part of the water bear genome. It has been found that the water bears can even switch on several of their borrowed genes, which in other organisms are involved in coping with stressful environments. Perhaps they owe at least part of their legendary durability to these genetic donations.

Most exciting for astrobiology is the water bear's ability to appear ultimately unaffected by the rigours of space travel; they are the first multicellular animals to outlive exposure to the deadly conditions of the cosmic environment. In 2007, researchers in Europe launched an experiment on the European Space Agency's BIOPAN 6/Foton-M3 mission that exposed tun-state water bears to the solar radiation, heat and vacuum of space, while orbiting the Earth at a distance of 260km (160 miles). When they returned to Earth and were given a little water, the animals soon began to move and feed, and over time grew and reproduced. They had survived an environment in which life as we previously knew it could not. Later in the summer of 2011, Project Biokis-Tardikiss, sponsored by the Italian Space Agency, ferried water bears yet again into space, this time on the US Space Shuttle *Endeavor*. Colonies were exposed to variable levels of apparently lethal ionising radiation but upon return to Earth showed a very high post-flight survival rate, apparently unaffected by the cosmic radiation or the microgravity. The water bears are, for sure, creatures that could survive on any number of worlds in the Solar System so long as evolution was able to progress as it did on Earth to allow them to come into being. Could we one day find similar microscopic animals lurking in pockets of liquid water on Mars or Europa?

Extremophiles from Space?

The theory of panspermia mentioned earlier says that reproductive bodies of living organisms can exist throughout the Universe and develop wherever the environment is favourable. This implies that conditions beneficial for the development of life prevailed at different locations in the Universe and at different times, and may be ultimately responsible for the advent of life on Earth. One of the major criticisms levelled at panspermia, however, is that living organisms could not survive their long journey to Earth, owing to exposure to the nutritional wasteland of space with its solar and galactic radiation, frigid temperatures and vacuum, let alone the fiery descent through the Earth's atmosphere. The *Long Duration Exposure Facility* (*LDEF*) and BioPan space experiments sent halophiles into Earth orbit, showing that these salt-loving microbes, as well as water bears, can survive in space. This has led scientists to seriously reconsider the ability of living biological material to travel between celestial bodies, particularly focusing on extremophiles, which are those most likely to survive the trip.

After the water bears, of course, the most probable terrestrial organisms to survive conditions in space are microbes, which might feasibly be stored, protected and transported within comets or meteors. In the vastness of space, microgravity is not lethal to life forms, and the extreme cold and lack of liquid water are survivable by many. Transit times between the expulsion of a rock carrying microbes from its host body to its final destination cannot currently be estimated, however, so we cannot address adequately the nutritional needs of organisms during the journey. We can hypothesise that the exceedingly low metabolic rates resulting from the cosmic extremes of cold and desiccation would render nutritional needs almost non-existent. Thus, we are left with two potential show-stoppers, namely radiation and the space vacuum. Most damage to microbes exposed to space, if they were not protected by a comet or asteroid, would be due to UV radiation, especially in the short term, although heavy ionising radiation has a greater probability of being lethal. Although the data are controversial, *Deinococcus radiodurans*, our extremophilic radiation specialist, did not survive its several-month residency in space and its DNA had extensive unfixable breakages, while *Chroococcidiopsis*, a desiccation-tolerant cyanobacterium that on Earth lives within rocks, survived only 30 minutes when exposed to UV radiation similar to that experienced on Mars. Interestingly, the salt-loving halophiles *Synechococcus* and *Haloarcula-G* were shown to survive for two weeks in space as long as they had some rock or soil shielding them – and could probably last much longer.

The Solar System, and in fact the Universe, is an extremely hostile environment for life as we know it. Even the strongest organisms on the Earth, the extremophiles, would find it a challenge. Yet, knowing these tough organisms exist and have evolved survival strategies to endure within the most extreme environments of the Earth gives astrobiologists renewed hope that something similar, maybe even resembling a water bear itself, may have found a way to thrive in places previously thought inhospitable out in the cosmos. Suddenly the once barren, hostile Solar System has been lit up with biological possibilities, but where could they be hiding?

CHAPTER SEVEN

Searching the Solar System

All members of our inner rocky planetary family –
Mercury, Venus, Earth and Mars – are unique and have
very distinct differences that have ultimately determined
whether or not they might bear witness to life. At the
heart of this lie two key attributes: their distance from the
Sun, or *heliocentric position* (which influences their
temperature), and their mass. Although celebrated in
every mythology throughout history and some even
visible to the naked eye on a clear night, their physical
characteristics only became known in the twentieth
century with the birth of spectroscopy and photography,
and subsequently through space exploration itself in the
1960s.

Beyond the orbits of Mars and the asteroid belt, we find the outer gas giants and icy bodies sitting well beyond the Solar System's traditional Goldilocks zone. However, observing these worlds, and especially their moons, has caused us to re-think what actually constitutes a habitable zone for life, how far this zone reaches across the Solar System and, most importantly, whether there could actually be multiple Goldilocks zones located within different planetary families. The opening of our minds to the many extreme conditions life can endure, and all the extraordinary environments in which life on Earth has been found to be present, has meant that the cold, dark outer reaches of the Solar System have begun to intrigue us from an astrobiology perspective and may actually hold the most promising targets for finding alien life. Wherever there is liquid water on Earth there is life, whether it is in the oceans that envelop the planet, thousands of metres beneath the ground, inside a nuclear reactor, or hidden within glaciers. As long as there is water, there is life. Of course, it is mainly tiny, mostly microbial, life – but it is still life.

Messenger to the Gods

Baked in scorching sunlight by day, and deep-frozen by night, it is far too easy to dismiss Mercury in the search for life in the Solar System. Only slightly larger than Earth's moon, Mercury is already the smallest of the Solar System planetary family and is still shrinking. It was long thought to be something of a relic, a stagnant world that had not changed in eons and eons. Like the Moon, it is covered with craters caused by billions of years of bombardment into its iron-rich basaltic crust. This is because Mercury has very little atmosphere to prevent impacts from meteorites and asteroids damaging the surface. The planet is actually home to one of the largest impact basins in the Solar System: *the Caloris Basin.*

Mercury's day-side is super-heated by the Sun to a sweltering 427°C (800°F), but at night temperatures drop hundreds of degrees below freezing. Its egg-shaped orbit takes it around the Sun every 88 days, although this orbit is quite odd – it takes longer for it to rotate on its axis and complete a day than it takes to orbit the Sun and complete a year. It also has only 38 per cent of the gravity of the Earth (a human would weigh 62 per cent less on Mercury than on the Earth) and coincidentally has almost the same gravity as Mars.

We do not know who first discovered Mercury but it has been known to exist since ancient times. *Mariner 10* was the first spacecraft to visit in 1974 and was also the first spacecraft to slingshot past one planet on its way to visit another, as well as the first probe to visit two planets in one mission. Despite being a spacecraft that seemed to be behaving neurotically, posing problem after problem that confounded its designers and controllers, it still managed to reveal a small, bleak planet with a thin helium atmosphere, a weak magnetic field and a cratered surface reminiscent of that of our Moon. The spacecraft ran out of fuel in 1975 and today *Mariner 10* is presumed to be silently continuing its orbit of the Sun. After the picture painted by this probe, it was another 30 years before humanity returned to Mercury – little did we know that the least explored of the inner planets in the Solar System was hiding a very lively personality ...

When the spacecraft *MESSENGER* arrived at Mercury in 2011, it went down in history as the first spacecraft ever to orbit the closest planet to the Sun. To arrive at this point, *MESSENGER* soared through the inner Solar System, performing one fly-by of Earth, two fly-bys of Venus, and finally three fly-bys of Mercury. Before its self-destruction on 30th April 2015 with a planned impact into the surface, it was tasked to map Mercury's surface geology, study its magnetic field and expose its internal workings. Apart from creating the most detailed and accurate 3D map of the planet to date, *MESSENGER* also revealed Mercury to be a unique, geologically diverse world. It has active geology: hollows formed when volatile materials – probably sulphur-containing compounds buried beneath Mercury's surface – sublimated (turned straight from solids into gas), causing the terrain to sink by several tens of meters, and volcanic vents measuring up to 25km (15.5 miles) across, which may once have been sources for large volumes of very hot lava.

Owing to its small dimensions, many scientists believed that Mercury's once hot liquid core would have long since cooled and in essence the planet had become a dead, roasted chunk of rock. We now know that it has a massive core for its size, and as such is still partially liquid. We know too that its dynamo is still functioning, creating a weak magnetic field. *MESSENGER* also solved another mystery about Mercury. It bounced laser beams off its surface to remotely collect information about the chemical elements that make up the planet's surface. Incredibly, water ice was discovered to be hiding in regions in permanent shadow near the north pole. Even more excitingly, carbon-containing organic compounds were found, forming a thin layer of very dark organic material covering part of the frozen water. This material, which is somewhat like tar, coal and soot, is believed to be similar to what has been observed on icy bodies in the outer Solar System and in the hearts of comets. Scientists suspect that impacts as well as solar and cosmic radiation are triggering chemical reactions in the organic material, turning it about twice as dark as Mercury's surface.

Although not previously the most logical choice for life, Mercury has shown us that it has a few nooks and crannies with the makings of a habitable environment. To be clear, no one in truth thinks that Mercury has microbes. What it does have, however, is evidence of volcanic activity in its past, a hot liquid core, a functioning magnetic field, a thin atmosphere and gloopy tar-like organic materials. Water ice has been found frozen at its poles that, combined with a hot core, may hint at the possibility of liquid water forming at depths below the surface. Mercury is not in the Goldilocks zone of our star but is a key witness to the delivery of ingredients for habitability from the outer Solar System to the inner. Even if Mercury is not itself a good candidate on which to look for ancient or current life, the planet may hold clues as to how life got started on Earth. Finding a place in the inner Solar System, where some of the same ingredients that may have led to life on Earth are preserved, is really very exciting. As a result, humanity is going back. Europe's first mission to Mercury, *BepiColombo*, will launch in 2017, arriving at the smallest terrestrial planet in 2024 to carry out the most extensive exploration of Mercury and its potentially habitable environment to date.

Goddess of Love and Beauty – if You Say So ...

If not Mercury, who is next on the list? With its similar size, mass and composition, Venus's dimensions are very close to those of Earth, hence it is commonly called its twin and is likely to have a still-functioning internal heat source, perhaps from radioactive decay, similar to the Earth's interior. There is, however, one major yet significant difference between these near-identical siblings. Venus's thick atmosphere makes temperatures on the planet hot enough to melt lead, and therefore it is most certainly too hot to sustain life. Blanketed in clouds, the veiled planet once had oceans much like those on Earth, but these evaporated as Venus heated up. Today, Venus is about 100,000 times drier than Earth and is 460°C (860°F) at its surface. Its atmosphere is 96 per cent carbon dioxide with a thick atmospheric pressure of 89atm (9MPa) – a *greenhouse planet* where no life currently found on the Earth could ever hope to survive.

As one of the first planets to be visited by spacecraft, due to its relatively close proximity to the Earth and it being a necessary waypoint for missions to Mercury, Venus has witnessed and probably rolled her eyes at the many failed attempts to try and visit her. Despite these, however, more than 20 unmanned explorations have been successful, with Venus the target of a cornucopia of Soviet, American and European probes. Spacecraft have performed various fly-bys, orbits and landings, and even balloon probes have been sent to float through its atmosphere. The American *Mariner 5* spacecraft can boast the first successful encounter, coming within 35,000km (21,750 miles) of Venus in 1962. As it flew past, it established that Venus has scarcely any magnetic field and with reasonable accuracy measured the planet's temperature as being up to 316°C (600°F). The Soviet *Venera* fleet achieved notoriety in 1966 when the *Venera 3* space probe crash-landed on Venus, becoming the first spacecraft to reach the surface of another planet, despite not being intact. In 1975, the descent vehicle from the *Venera 9* orbiter was the first probe to take photos (and even black and white video) of the Venusian surface from the surface itself, revealing shadows, no apparent dust in the air, and a variety of rocks up to 40cm (16in) in size that did not appear eroded by wind or water, as would be found on Earth. *Venera 9* also detected clouds that were up to 40km (25 miles) thick, with bases from 30km (18 miles) in altitude; acidic chemicals in the atmosphere, including hydrochloric and hydrofluoric acid, bromine and iodine; surface pressures of about 90atm (9MPa); a surface temperature of 485°C (905°F); and light levels bathing the world that were comparable to those at Earth's mid-latitudes on a cloudy summer's day.

Two notable missions for the purpose of understanding the possibilities of life on Venus are those of the USA's *Magellan* and ESA's *Venus Express*. *Magellan* arrived in 1990 and with its radar mapped 98 per cent of the surface with a resolution of approximately 100m (330ft). The resulting maps are comparable to visible-light photographs of other planets, and are still the most detailed in existence. *Magellan* greatly improved scientific understanding of the geology of Venus: a world covered in volcanic rocks and vast lava plains, lava channels more than 6,000km (3,730 miles) long, fields of small lava domes, and large shield volcanoes. The probe found no signs of Earth-like plate tectonics, although the scarcity of impact craters suggested the surface was relatively young (less than 800 million years old).

Venus Express arrived 16 years later in 2006 and took up a polar orbit, focusing on long-term observation of the Venusian atmosphere from the surface right up to the ionosphere. *Venus Express* confirmed that eons ago, Earth's twin must have had substantial oceans. It observed lightning on Venus happening more frequently than on Earth, and witnessed a colossal double vortex swirling over the planet's south pole. The probe photographed a *night glow*, an eerie radiance in the night-time atmosphere of Venus, seen as the Sun's ultraviolet light hit the atmosphere, and infrared light energy was released by high winds from the swirling of oxygen (O_2), hydroxyl (OH) and nitric oxide (NO) molecules. This was also the first detection of hydroxyl in the atmosphere of any planet other than Earth – important because it is created by a reaction between oxygen and water. A major question in Venus science is whether it is still geologically active today. In 2015, nearly 10 years after the arrival of *Venus Express* at our sister world, tantalising evidence was discovered in a rift zone for hot spots that change in temperature from day to day, and are the best evidence yet for active volcanism on present-day Venus. On Earth, rift zones are the result of fracturing and cracking of the crust and are often associated with the upwelling of magma from below the surface. This process allows hot molten rock to be released through fractures as a lava flow. Although the surface of Venus is thus proving to be still geologically alive and so could provide an energy source for biological reactions, the hellish environment means that life would be hard-pressed to survive.

Despite all this, Venus does sit in a very privileged position at the inner edge of the Solar System's Goldilocks zone. Having undergone a runaway greenhouse effect, the surface has become far too hot for liquid water or organic molecules to be stable, and therefore is not a habitable environment for life as we know it, at least not today. High above the surface, however, is a potential habitable zone where temperatures lie in the range between freezing and 120°C (248°F) and clouds offer long-lasting droplets of water, although they are highly acidic. The lower and middle cloud deck of Venus may therefore have the ability to support an aerial biosphere; whether it actually does remains a mystery to be solved.

The God of War

The most Earth-like planet known is our reddish dusty sibling, Mars. Half the size of Earth and lacking a magnetic field or thick protective atmosphere, this world is, believe it or not, currently our best hope of finding life elsewhere in the Solar System due to a number of similarities. Its day is only 29 minutes longer than that of the Earth and it takes 1.88 Earth years to orbit the Sun. It has seasons just like on Earth, 38 per cent of our gravity, and has more than five million cubic kilometres (almost 1.2 million cubic miles) of water ice, mostly hidden just below the surface. A toxic atmosphere of 95 per cent carbon dioxide, minimal oxygen and an average temperature of −63°C (−81.4°F), however, makes the surface of Mars appear rather inhospitable to life, especially human life. Astrobiologists are most interested, however, not in the possibility of life existing on Mars today, but in the past. Could life once have existed here and if so, where did it go? Where might it be hiding if it were still present? Mars is a planet that we are becoming as familiar with as our own, and so no astrobiological discussion can be started without first acknowledging the many missions that have provided us with this window into such a familiar yet alien world.

Mars Mission History

As we saw in Chapter 1, popular culture had it since the nineteenth century that Mars is or was an inhabited planet, crisscrossed with canals of liquid water built by some advanced civilisation that might or might not be on the verge of colonising the Earth. Once technology caught up with the desire for exploration, however, satellites were tasked to orbit the planet and take the first ever close-ups of the Martian surface. After several catastrophic failures, many of which occurred even before the spacecraft left Earth's atmosphere, in 1965 NASA's *Mariner 4* finally flew by Mars after a 7.5-month journey through 54.6 million km (33,926,870 miles) of open space, snapping the first pictures of the Red Planet. This eagerly anticipated arrival shattered any imaginings of a lush, Earth-like world with flowing rivers and cities full of humanoid Martians. Instead, it was clear that Mars is a rocky, barren world, scarred with impact craters and cavernous valleys – a world that in many ways is more reminiscent of the airless, lifeless Moon than the Earth. It also discovered that Mars has no global magnetic field, which would be necessary to protect any life forms on its surface against dangerous solar winds of charged particles. We now know that Mars's magnetic field disappeared around 4 billion years ago, but we do not know why. With the loss of its magnetic field, the planet's atmosphere was no longer protected and was stripped away, exposing the surface to solar and cosmic radiation, gradually making it even more inhospitable.

Viking

Undeterred by the disappointment of Mariner 4, humanity returned to Mars. In 1976, NASA's *Viking Project* became the first US mission not only to land a spacecraft on the surface of Mars in one piece, but also to return images of the surface. Twin spacecraft, both consisting of a paired lander and orbiter, entered Mars's orbit before detaching the landers to begin their fiery descent to the planet's surface. The *Viking 1* lander touched down on the western slope of Chryse Planitia (the Plains of Gold) just north of the equator, while the *Viking 2* lander settled down at Utopia Planitia, the largest recognised impact basin on Mars, and indeed the Solar System. Besides taking photographs of a vast number of rocky vistas, the probes became renowned for finding evidence of water action on Mars, including sweeping valleys and deep fluvial erosion patterns. Most famously, however, the landers conducted three biology experiments designed to look for possible signs of life. These discovered unexpected and mysterious chemical activity in the Martian soil, but were unable to provide clear, undeniable evidence for the presence of living microorganisms near the landing sites. The conclusion made was that Mars is self-sterilising: that the solar ultraviolet radiation saturating the surface, the extreme dryness of the soil and the oxidising nature of the soil chemistry combine to prevent the formation of living organisms in the Martian dust. As depressing a result as this seemed to be, scientists now claim that the method by which the samples were collected could actually have destroyed the evidence of life they were looking for ... bad news for *Viking*, good news for astrobiology.

The lack of life found on Mars by *Viking* was an enormous blow to the global community, and it took another 20 years before we successfully went back to Mars. From 1996, *Mars Global Surveyor (MGS)*, accompanied by *Mars Pathfinder* and its little rover *Sojourner*, orbited and mapped the entire planet. *MGS* achieved so much in its seven-year life, including the characterisation of surface features and geological processes; the determination of the composition, distribution and physical properties of surface minerals, rocks and ice; and the mapping of the global topography, planet shape, and gravitational field. The mission also monitored global weather and, importantly, imaged possible landing sites for the 2007 *Phoenix Lander* and 2011

Curiosity rovers. Since then, the space around Mars has become rather full, as NASA's *Mars Odyssey* (2001), ESA's *Mars Express* (2003), NASA's *Mars Reconnaissance Orbiter* (*MRO*, 2005), ISRO's *Mars Orbiter Mission* (*MOM*, 2013) and NASA's *Mars Atmosphere and Volatile Evolution Mission* (*MAVEN*, 2013) have now joined *MGS*, with ESA's *ExoMars Trace Gas Orbiter* (*TGO*), scheduled to arrive at the party in 2016. A total of 13 orbiters to date has been sent to circle the planet and map and explore the surface, while several rovers have scoured its landscape searching for clues that might indicate life is, or once was, possible.

MAVEN

The *Mars Atmosphere and Volatile Evolution* mission, or *MAVEN* mission, launched in 2013, is currently orbiting Mars to explore how the Sun may have stripped the planet of most of its atmosphere, turning a world once wet and habitable for microbial life into a cold and barren desert. Scientists want to know what happened to the water that once flowed across the surface and also where the planet's thick atmosphere disappeared to. Each time *MAVEN* orbits Mars, it plunges temporarily into the ionosphere – the ion- and electron-laden atmospheric layer lying uppermost, at 120–480km (75–300 miles) above the planet's surface. This layer serves as a form of shield around the planet, deflecting the intensely hot, high-energy particles of the solar wind. Today, *MAVEN* has shown a plume of atmospheric particles breaking free of the planet's gravity, escaping from the polar region, extending behind Mars like a tail. *MAVEN* has also detected a long-lived layer in the electrically charged ionosphere of Mars, made up of metal ions (iron and magnesium) that are the remains of incoming comet dust and meteorites. The spacecraft has also seen the Red Planet glow under the impact of violent *Coronal Mass Ejections* (*CME*) sent from the Sun. These blast billions of tons of solar material into space at millions of kilometres per hour but because Mars is not protected by a global magnetic field as is the Earth, CME particles directly impact the Martian upper atmosphere, driving the escape of atmospheric gas into space. This generates some stunning displays of aurora.

Roving on Mars – *Sojourner*

The great-grandfather of Mars' rovers, *Sojourner* (meaning *'traveller'*) was the first moving robot on Mars, and indeed the first wheeled vehicle driven on any other planet in the Solar System. It travelled just over 100m (330ft) within the ancient floodplain of Ares Vallis, snapping over 550 photographs of the rocks it encountered. The first one it chemically analysed was dubbed *Barnacle Bill* and this changed our view of Mars forever. The rock was found to have more silica in it than the surrounding environment, a clear sign of past thermal activity. Suddenly Mars's geological history became a great deal more interesting. Further rocks, nicknamed *Yogi* and *Scooby Doo*, were recognised as being not just volcanic rock (basalt), but also sedimentary. On Earth, sedimentary rocks are made by deposition of material on the surface and, importantly for Mars, within bodies of water. Images beamed back supported this, exposing rounded pebbles and *conglomerates* that told a story of rock movement by water in the past. A more water-rich planet was starting to reveal itself, and where once there was water there may have been life.

Spirit and *Opportunity*

In 2004, siblings *Spirit* and *Opportunity* bounced on to the surface and finally delivered conclusive proof that liquid water had once been present on Mars. *Spirit* landed in a possible former lake within a giant impact crater given the name of Gusev, while *Opportunity* (fondly known as *Oppy*) headed to the flat plain of Meridiani Planum, where satellite data had found a high level of the mineral haematite, an ore that requires liquid water to form. Their goal was to search for signs of past water activity on the Red Planet and this did not take long at all. As soon as *Oppy* opened its panoramic camera eyes, scientists knew they had struck gold – actually, haematite. Landing in a shallow impact crater, *Oppy* was facing a layered sedimentary rock wall, surrounded by marble-sized iron-rich mineral balls dubbed *blueberries*. This amazing rover, on its first day of operation, had found an area that had formed in an ancient acidic and oxidising shallow lake. Its mission was already a complete success. The rover had discovered the evidence needed to prove that ancient Mars may have been habitable for life for potentially millions of years. *Spirit* was not letting *Oppy* take all the glory, however, as it also completed its initial mission in record time. At a location in Gusev Crater dubbed *Home Plate*, *Spirit* discovered opaline silica, which would have formed in volcanic fumaroles or hydrothermal vents, showing that water had interacted with magma in the past at that site. It also finally discovered the elusive carbonate rocks, which, given its atmosphere of carbon dioxide and evidence of water, scientists had been expecting to come across far sooner. Equally interesting, *Spirit* also observed complex coatings on olivine basalts, created by modern-day water on Mars, or possibly frost.

Phoenix

Although not a trundling rover, a hugely important astrobiological mission to Mars came in 2008 with the arrival of the *Phoenix* lander. *Phoenix* was designed to study the history of water on Mars and the habitability potential of the Martian Arctic's ice-rich soils. It landed in a flat landscape shaped into 2–3m- (6.5–10ft-) wide *polygons*, and had been sent there because such geometric features are created on Earth by ice expanding and contracting inside soils when the temperature changes. *Phoenix* found water ice on Mars just a few centimetres below the surface in the middle of the polygons, and amazingly the ice was photographed slowly sublimating (turning straight from solid ice into gas) when exposed to the Martian atmosphere. *Phoenix* also observed snowfall on Mars, and found calcium carbonate in the soil, indicating a wetter past environment at the landing site. It also located something pretty dangerous for life – *perchlorate salts*. The big question regarding the presence of organic compounds in the soils surrounding *Phoenix* was left open, since heating of samples containing perchlorate would have caused any organic materials present to break down and be destroyed. Under certain conditions perchlorate can inhibit life, but all is not lost since microorganisms do exist on Earth that can obtain energy from it by anaerobic reduction. Also, the chemical, when mixed with water, can greatly lower the liquid's freezing point, just as salt can when it is applied to roads to melt ice. Thus, although a potential problem for life itself, perchlorate may allow small quantities of liquid water to form on or beneath the surface of Mars today and therefore, ironically, provide microhabitats for life.

Curiosity

Finally, we come to the best-known, and it must be said, most Twitter-savvy rover to date: *Curiosity*. The centrepiece of NASA's Mars Science Laboratory (MSL), this BMW Mini-Cooper-sized robot was detailed with finding out for certain whether Mars is, or was, suitable for life. Its immense size has allowed it to carry a suite of instruments designed to crush, bake and photograph any rock within 2m (6ft) of its robotic arm. Weighing in at 900kg (1,984lb), it can rove up to 200m (650ft) per day, faster than any rover before it (although still literally at a snail's pace), and is powered by a radioisotope thermoelectric generator (or nuclear-powered generator, using plutonium-238). The $2.5-billion MSL spacecraft launched from Cape Canaveral, Florida, on 26th November 2011, and arrived on Mars on 6th August

2012, after a daring landing sequence that NASA dubbed the *seven minutes of terror*. This intricate sequence used a supersonic parachute, rocket thrusters and the now famous *skycrane*, which allowed the landing assembly to dangle the rover beneath the rockets on a 6m (19.5ft) tether, gently positioning *Curiosity* on to the ground while simultaneously severing the link to crash-land elsewhere on the surface. Fun fact: as *Curiosity* trundles across Mars, it leaves in its tracks a message from home in Morse code. The wheels contain embedded cut-outs of dots and dashes that the rover can use as reference points to estimate how far it has travelled. In dot-dash notation, however, each wheel carries three characters (• − − − / • − − • / • − • •), which just so happens to spell out *JPL*, the acronym of the Jet Propulsion Laboratory in Pasadena, California, which manages the rover mission for NASA.

Curiosity is tasked with searching for habitable environments at the landing site of Gale Crater, a 154km- (95.5-mile-) wide impact crater and central 5.5km (3.5 miles) geologically layered mountain called Mount Sharp, formed by a meteor strike some 3.5–3.8 billion years ago. Scientists chose Gale as the landing site for *Curiosity* because it displays many signs that water was present over its history, and as we are all aware by now, water is a key ingredient for life as we know it. Some of these indicators are minerals manifested as clays and sulphates, formed only in the presence of water. They are also exciting to study, as on Earth many preserve signs or biosignatures, of past life.

To achieve its goal, *Curiosity* has many instruments and experiments set up on board, including one that bombards the surface with neutrons whose speed would slow if they encountered hydrogen atoms: one of the elements of water. It has a robotic arm that can collect samples from the surface, an oven to bake them inside its main body and the ability to test the gases that are given off, analysing them for clues about how the rocks and soil formed. It has high-resolution cameras surrounding the rover that, besides taking great selfies, can take pictures as it moves, providing visual information about the landscape that can be compared to analogue environments on Earth. Panoramic images especially are taken to help scientists select promising future geological targets and to help the rover drivers steer *Curiosity* to those locations to perform on-site scientific investigations.

Within six months of arriving at Mars, *Curiosity* had its answers and the mission was deemed a complete success. Gale Crater had the right ingredients and environments to support ancient microbial life, should it ever have arisen. The landing site itself contains at least one lake that would have provided a deliciously habitable environment. Surprisingly, the clays drilled out from inside some rather informative mudstones at a site known as *Yellowknife Bay* were found to be much younger than expected. This discovery does not just prove that Mars was habitable but also extends the window of time when it may have been suitable for life. If that were not exciting enough, powder from the very first drill samples *Curiosity* obtained from the surface of Mars included the elements sulphur, nitrogen, hydrogen, oxygen, phosphorus and – you guessed it – carbon! Finally, we have unequivocal evidence that Mars has the chemistry for a habitable environment and the basic elemental building blocks for life.

In December 2014, *Curiosity* went one step further and made the first definitive identification of organics on Mars. It found chlorinated hydrocarbons such as chlorobenzene, dichloroalkane and chloromethane. Also in December 2014 came the news that *Curiosity* had detected wafts of methane in the Martian air. From time to time, Mars belches out a gas that on Earth comes largely from life forms (from one end or the other). This may well hint at communities of microbes living under the Martian surface and churning out the gas. Nonetheless, any number of other non-biological, probably more likely, processes can and do make methane. Rocks on Mars contain the mineral olivine, which can react with water to release methane. Also, clathrates or molecular cages harbouring methane in the icy sub-surface could be a source, releasing the gas in bursts over time. Unfortunately, detecting methane alone is not enough to claim life.

In addition to its main mission, *Curiosity* has been carrying out radiation observations to determine how suitable an area like Gale Crater would be for an eventual human mission. *Curiosity* operates its Radiation Assessment Detector for 15 minutes every hour to measure radiation on the ground and in the atmosphere. In December 2013, NASA decreed that the radiation levels were viable for future human crews heading to Mars. A mission comprising a 180-day journey each way to and from Mars and 500 days on the planet would administer a dose of 1.01 sieverts. This is only a touch over the total lifetime limit of 1 sievert currently set for ESA astronauts, and is associated with *only* a 5 per cent increase in fatal cancer risk over a lifetime, so is tolerable ...

Despite the fact that organics have finally been found on Mars, the question of whether it has or had life still remains. That revelation, and I believe it will come, still lies ahead of us, and will hopefully be provided by the next rover to head to Mars in 2018 – *ExoMars*.

ExoMars

The *Exobiology on Mars* mission (*ExoMars*), set to launch in 2016 and again in 2018, is the first space operation designed chiefly to search for biosignatures of past and present life on Mars. This hotly anticipated astrobiology-led mission is currently under development by the European Space Agency (ESA) in collaboration with the Russian Federal Space Agency (Roscosmos). Due, at time of writing, to launch in early 2016, the *ExoMars Trace Gas Orbiter* (*TGO*) and an Entry, Descent and Landing Demonstrator Module

(EDM) stationary lander called *Schiaparelli* will head to Mars first. After delivering the lander to the surface, the TGO will stay in orbit to map the sources of methane and other gases on Mars, and will confirm the ultimate landing site for the *ExoMars* rover, scheduled to head to Mars in 2018. It will also act as a crucial communications relay between the *ExoMars* rover and Earth. The unique selling point of the *ExoMars* rover is its drill. This little rover will be able to drill 2m (6ft) into the Martian sub-surface, cutting through and exposing millions of years of Martian history, and possibly buried life forms.

Where would you send *ExoMars* if you had to pick just one spot to visit on Mars? At the time of writing, this is the decision being made – where could *ExoMars* land that would offer the best chances of finding life? As with every space mission, it comes down to a delicate yet familiar balance between engineering constraints and scientific goals. Unfortunately, owing to the way we have to land the rover on Mars the engineers win, and so most of the planet is already ruled out as being too dangerous. The landers need to touch down at as low an elevation as possible to give them more time to come through the atmosphere and therefore more time to slow down (so as not to crash into the surface). To help narrow this already small list of landing choices, a further engineering requirement is for the rover to access as much sunlight as possible since it runs on solar power. *ExoMars* therefore needs to land in a latitude band straddling the equator of Mars that is a meagre 30 degrees wide from top to bottom. Finally, landing on another planet is never possible with pinpoint accuracy; it is much more likely that *ExoMars* will touch down somewhere near its intended target rather than directly on it. This area is called the *landing ellipse*, and for *ExoMars* is the equivalent of landing anywhere within a 104km by 19km (65 mile by 12 mile) area of where you aimed.

With all these requirements met, the scientific goals start to come into play. Four possible sites were identified for *ExoMars* to make its stand and hopefully achieve its mission to find signs of past or present life – *Mawrth Vallis, Oxia Planum, Hypanis Vallis* and *Aram Dorsum*. Over the coming years, one of these will become the most studied and talked about spot on Mars. Found clustered within the same equatorial region of Mars, but covering an area the size of Western Europe, these sites feature ancient rocks containing a record of the environment on Mars over 3.5 billion years and, of course, display evidence that liquid water once flowed there.

Mawrth Vallis is a veteran landing site, having also made it to the final four for the *Curiosity* rover. Named after the Welsh name for Mars and the Latin for valley, it is an ancient channel carved by catastrophic floods. It has layered cliffs resembling Neapolitan ice cream that are rich in clay minerals. Such minerals, called *phyllosilicates*, form in the presence of neutral pH water and tell us that habitable conditions for life once existed and, as said before, are also good at preserving signatures of long-dead life. Oxia Planum, 400km (250 miles) away from Mawrth, is also made up of layers of clays and has an ancient channel emptying into a now dry shallow lake. Hypanis Vallis is thought to represent ancient river delta deposits. Here, sediments were built up slowly and may have concentrated the evidence for life, making it easier to find. Finally, Aram Dorsum is an inverted river system, with a hill-like relief instead of a stereotypical depressed river channel. This is quite common on Mars. It happens when water carves a channel and deposits sediments that, once cemented and hardened, survive intact while everything outside is worn away by billions of years of erosion, leaving evidence of an ancient river system, now rising above the landscape instead of below it. Water was flowing throughout this region about 3.8 to 4 billion years ago, a period when life was probably just getting started on Earth, and possibly also on Mars. It may be that evidence of past life on Mars is hiding just beneath the surface at one or all of these sites.

At least for now, it looks as though *ExoMars* will be heading to Oxia Planum, Mawrth Vallis lost out again, so let us all hope we have made the right decision.

Mars 2020

NASA's *Mars 2020* rover is a mission under development and forms part of a long-term campaign to bring Martian rocks home to Earth. Based on the successful design and operation of *Curiosity*, *Mars 2020* will be sent to investigate an as yet undecided, astrobiologically relevant ancient environment on Mars to uncover its surface geological processes and history, including the assessment of its past habitability and potential for preservation of biosignatures. It has been proposed that the rover collect and package as many as 31 samples of rock cores and soil for a later mission to bring back to Earth. The *Mars 2020* rover will also help pave the way for future human explorers by investigating the ability to use natural resources available on the surface of the Red Planet. Designers of future human expeditions can use this mission to understand the hazards posed by Martian dust and demonstrate technologies to process carbon dioxide from the atmosphere to produce oxygen for human respiration, and potentially as an oxidiser for rocket fuel (see Chapter 10 for more information on humans travelling to Mars).

When on Mars ...

Although scientists have not (yet) found life populating the Martian surface, we have not lost hope and are looking harder than ever. This is because in so many respects Mars is the most Earth-like planet in the Solar System, and with its much warmer and wetter habitable environment in the past, the conditions for the emergence and persistence of life may have been present on Mars just as they were on the Earth. Mars has famously undergone global climate change over its 4.5-billion-year life, so we are not just looking to environments on Mars today that might support life, but also at different points in its history. Mars has transitioned through three climatic stages: from relatively wet to semi-arid to hyper-arid conditions, and consequently the surface habitability has deteriorated greatly over its planetary lifetime. The history of Mars can thus be divided into Early, Middle and Present Mars phases. *Early Mars* covers roughly the first billion years of its lifespan, when liquid water was still presumed to be present on the surface. This was an environment similar to the Earth, supporting the hypothesis that life may have had the chance to flourish on Mars as it did on Earth during this time. However, after the first few hundred million years the environmental histories of these two planets diverged drastically. Mars underwent a global climate shift that resulted in a drop in surface temperatures and loss of liquid water. This is the onset of *Middle Mars*, defined as the second billion years when a global *cryosphere* (global 'ice age' during which the entire surface froze) took hold of the planet and paved the way for the Mars we know today. *Present Mars* started some 2.5 billion years ago and is characterised by a hyper-arid climate. The existence of life on the Martian surface today seems unlikely, given the extremely cold and desiccating conditions, high UV radiation levels received on the surface or *flux*, and the lack of magnetospheric shielding against ionising radiation. Beneath the surface, however, partially protected from radiation by rocks and dust, and where it is slightly warmer so that isolated pockets of liquid water may remain, who knows what (or who) might be hiding ...

King of the Planets

The terrestrial planets do not present many especially habitable conditions on their surfaces today. Mars may contain preserved biosignatures within surface materials, or active communities deep in the sub-surface, and Venus may offer habitable conditions high in its atmosphere. That said, they are a much better bet than the planets beyond the asteroid belt. Once we cross this rotating barrier of rock, we enter the realm of the gas and ice giants, such as Jupiter. While there have been no samples taken that could test for microscopic life on Jupiter, there is considerable and compelling evidence against life as we know it existing or ever having existed there. Composed mainly of hydrogen and helium, there is virtually no water present that could support a life form. The planet does not have a solid surface anywhere for life to develop and the only real (tiny) possibility of finding it would be in floating microscopic form high up in the atmosphere. However, this too has its problems. The atmosphere of Jupiter is in constant chaos, so even if life somehow held on near the lower pressure regions in the upper reaches, and could resist the harsh solar radiation found there, it would eventually be sucked down into realms where there is 1,000 times Earth's atmospheric pressure and temperatures are over 10,000°C (18,000°F); it would be almost instantaneously destroyed. No life on Earth could survive in anything close to these environments.

Known, therefore, as completely inhospitable, the gas giants are not truly included in the search for life, although it is fascinating to think about ways in which it might work. The most intriguing astrobiological targets in the Solar System are actually found on the moons orbiting these gaseous behemoths. The first is Europa, which on the face of it does not look or sound particularly appealing to life as it is constantly bombarded with ionising radiation owing to its location within Jupiter's magnetosphere. Temperatures at its surface range from −187°C to −141°C (−304.6°F to −221.8°F), far below the lowest limits for microbial growth − not surprising since it is an average 805 million km (500 million miles) from the Sun. In 1979, the *Voyager 2* probe whizzed past and spotted a network of cracks on Europa's surface, confirming earlier theories that the moon was coated in a thick shell of ice. When the Galileo probe showed up in the

1990s, it became clear that the cracks were occurring because the ice was moving, floating on top of a hidden layer of liquid encircling the moon. Beneath Europa's estimated 100km- (62-mile-) thick icy crust we believe there resides a liquid ocean with more water than covers the surface of the Earth. Within the cracks and fractures of the ice is a salty dark material, quite possibly the same as regular table salt, sodium chloride, which has risen up from the ocean beneath. Suddenly, Europa is a tantalising world for astrobiologists – if there is liquid water, where might life, if it exists, be hiding?

The surface ice itself is not an environment that any currently known terrestrial life could withstand, so we will not be seeing microbial igloos popping up there any time soon. However, the ice could provide just enough protection from the intense bombardment of radiation and encourage more favourable temperatures beneath it, to allow for the preservation of organics and even life forms. Just as a layer of ice over a pond allows the water beneath it to stay liquid and aquatic life to go on living through a freezing winter, Europa's rind of ice shields its enormous ocean and helps to keep it warm enough to remain fluid in spite of the moon's great distance from the Sun. Yet as Europa orbits Jupiter, the moon is contorted by the giant planet's gravitational field, generating an interior heat, by far the dominant heat source, which also keeps its water from freezing altogether. Potentially, active volcanoes and vents may exist at the base of the ocean, further heating the water, and providing sites where bacterial life may congregate, as it does on Earth. Plumes have also been observed erupting from the southern hemisphere but interestingly, and perhaps worryingly, these now seem to have vanished – are they simply sporadic events or were they ever really there at all? Europa has many elements thought to be key for the development and even persistence of life, such as water and heat energy; astrobiologists are now keen to detect the presence of organic chemicals.

The much-awaited *Jupiter Icy Moon Explorer* (*JUICE*) mission is an ESA spacecraft planned as part of the Cosmic

Vision science programme, scheduled to pay a visit to the Jovian system in 2030, to study Ganymede, Callisto and Europa (Io will be left out this time). Hopefully launching in 2022 and taking eight years to reach the system, its aim will be to analyse the character of these three worlds and evaluate their potential to support life, as all are thought to have significant bodies of liquid water beneath their surfaces. In particular, the focus on Europa will be on the chemistry essential for life, including organic molecules, and on the non-ice material criss-crossing its surface.

Lord of the Rings

If life is near impossible on Jupiter, you can guarantee the same can be said for Saturn. Comprised almost entirely of hydrogen and helium, with only trace amounts of water ice in its lower cloud deck, it has no surface upon which life could live. At the top of the clouds, the temperatures are around −150°C (−238°F), and although it gets warmer as you descend through the atmosphere, the pressures increase too. Sadly, once temperatures are warm enough to have liquid water, the pressures are simply too high for life. It is also extremely windy up there, with speeds of up to 500m/s (1,640ft/s). As with the Jovian system, the quest to find life near Saturn is turning its focus away from the planet and towards the moons.

Titan, Saturn's largest, haziest moon, is getting scientists really rather excited. Deceptively Earth-like, Titan has a dense nitrogen-rich atmosphere (the only moon known to do so), complete with clouds and seasonal rainstorms that soak the surface. Sunlight and electrons stream across Titan from Saturn's magnetosphere and break apart the nitrogen and methane in its atmosphere, setting off a cascade of reactions that produce organic compounds, and creates a solid organic haze that fills the atmosphere and shrouds the surface from view. It has a very familiar land-scape beneath this seemingly impenetrable veil, with mountains, dunes, riverbeds, shorelines and seas. Indeed, Titan is the only place in the Solar System, besides the Earth, that has liquids pooling and flowing across its surface. It is likely that Titan would be a promising place to look for extraterrestrial life in the Solar System, if not for its coldness; Titan is far too chilly for life as we know it. All water on Titan is found as rock-hard ice. In fact, the many rocks that litter the moon's surface are not made of rock at all but actually water. At Titanian surface temperatures (−179°C/−290°F), phospholipids − the chemical compounds that provide structure to cell membranes − cellular water bodies would be frozen solid. Any life that evolved on Titan's surface would need to be made of a very different set of chemicals and not be reliant on water, as it is locked in a state inaccessible to it. But potentially lucky for life, Titan's puddles are not filled with water; the surface is instead soaked with hydrocarbons. Methane and ethane, which on Earth are gasses, are able to flow as liquids across the surface owing to Titan's frigid environment. The volume of liquid hydrocarbons resting in Titan's second largest sea, Ligeia Mare, is actually 100 times greater than all the oil and gas reserves on Earth combined. Could a bizarre non-Earth-like life form exist on Titan that uses these slick, liquid hydrocarbons in a similar way to how life on Earth uses water?

During the 1990s, the Hubble Space Telescope (HST) offered hints that Titan was a wet world, but this was not confirmed until the NASA-managed *Cassini* mission allowed scientists to get a good look at the moon. This was a collaborative mission that included 16 European countries together with the US. On 14th January 2005, after a seven-year voyage, the *Cassini* spacecraft sent the Huygens probe parachuting through the haze to a spot on Titan's equator, to become the first terrestrial robot ever to land in the outer Solar System. It then sent transmissions from the surface for another 70 minutes before *Cassini* moved out of range. *Cassini* is the fourth space probe to visit Saturn but the first to enter orbit and is still sending data at the time of writing. It has revealed a world on Titan that looks very much like ours – but with a completely different chemistry. As well as a hydrocarbon-drenched realm, Titan also may have a deep sub-surface ocean similar to that within Europa and another of Saturn's moons, Enceladus. It may prove to be a water-ammonia mixture, which could be an environment habitable for organisms with biochemistry similar to that of terrestrial life – although requiring them to power a metabolism at the temperatures present on Titan would be a real challenge, even if the chemistry were usable. At this point, we do not really know what kind of life might be able to survive on Titan, as we have no examples of similar life on Earth. But this does not mean it isn't possible.

Saturn's sixth-largest moon, Enceladus, discovered by William Hershel in 1789, is a tenth the size of Titan, and is covered by fresh, clean ice with a surface temperature at noon of −198°C (−324.4°F). When Cassini flew by in 2005, it drew renewed interest from astrobiologists with the sighting of present-day geological activity occurring at its surface. Jets of fine icy particles and water vapour were observed erupting from cryovolcanoes at the south pole. Over 100 of these jets have been seen so far, feeding into a large plume that soars several thousand kilometres into space and containing not only water vapour but also simple organic compounds and volatiles – such as nitrogen (N_2), carbon dioxide (CO_2) and methane (CH_4) – similar to the chemical make-up of comets. Some of the water vapour actually falls back on to Enceladus as snow, while the rest escapes and supplies most of the material making up Saturn's E-ring. The southern polar terrain surrounding the source regions of the plume is surprisingly warm considering it is made of ice, and analysis of icy particles within Enceladus' plume strongly suggests the presence of a salty sub-surface alkaline ocean. Most models regarding the origin of this plume include a sub-surface liquid water aquifer, and it is this aquifer with its potential to support the origin and evolution of life that is of particular interest for habitability. A plausible sub-surface ecosystem on Enceladus would be unlike many terrestrial biomes, as life forms would have to be independent of oxygen and not rely on organic materials produced by photosynthesis.

Gods of the Sky and Sea

To sustain life on Uranus or Neptune, these distant planets would need a source of energy that even the simplest life could exploit, as well as some type of standing liquid water. A sister ice giant to Uranus, the surface of Neptune dips to a glacial –218°C (–360°F), while the cloud tops are –224°C (–371°F) in temperature. They are both far too cold to host bodies of liquid water and have no solid surface on which they could form in any case. Uranus is composed mostly of methane, water and ammonia ices enshrouded by an atmosphere of hydrogen and helium; it is methane that gives it its blue-green colour. Tremendous pressures inside Uranus created by the overbearing atmosphere raise the planet's temperature to more than 4,700°C (8,492°F), and would instantly crush and burn life. Add to this the lack of sunlight and internal heat and there is an absence of essential energy for life. Even though it seems impossible, technically there remains a chance some bizarre incarnation of life might be able to survive on Uranus but we are unlikely ever to be able to send a spacecraft down into the planet to check. *Voyager 2* is the only spacecraft to have flown by Uranus, back in 1986. The planet revealed few secrets but there were hints that there exists an ocean of boiling water some 800km (500 miles) below the cloud tops. The five *natural satellites* in orbit close to Uranus, such as Titania, would be more likely to support life, but currently are not deemed to do so and humanity is in no desperate hurry to explore further in the Uranus Planetary System.

Neptune similarly offers little hope of life. It is a cold and dark world, whipped into a frenzy by supersonic winds.

About 4.5 billion km (2.8 billion miles) from the Sun, it is mostly composed of a very dense atmosphere of hydrogen and helium, with ices of water, ammonia (NH_3) and methane (CH_4) over a possibly heavier, approximately Earth-sized, solid core. As is the case for the appearance of Uranus, Neptune's blue colour is also the result of methane in the atmosphere. There is very little water in the cloud tops, but the percentage increases as you descend towards the core. Perhaps there is a band on Neptune where there is enough pressure and temperature for liquid water to form into an ocean layer. The only spacecraft ever to have visited Neptune is the same one that flew by Uranus – *Voyager 2* – passing by Neptune three years later in 1989.

A slight glimmer of hope may exist within Triton, Neptune's largest and backward-orbiting moon. It is tremendously cold with temperatures on its surface of water ice of about -235°C (-391°F). Its unusual orbit, essentially heading the wrong way round, implies that it did not form around Neptune but was captured after being ejected from the Kuiper Belt. Triton is quite dense, suggesting that, unlike its parent planet, it may have a solid core of silicate rock. In spite of its frigid state, *Voyager 2* found geysers belching icy matter into space for over 8km (5 miles). This, as with other moons in this distant neighbourhood of the Solar System, could imply that a liquid ocean is hiding beneath an icy crust, kept fluid by tidal friction and the decay of radioactive isotopes, as happens on the Earth. Similarly recorded by *Voyager 2*, Triton's sparse atmosphere has also now been detected from Earth and is growing warmer – we do not yet understand why.

The increasing number of sub-surface oceans on icy Solar System bodies could provide potential habitats for primitive extraterrestrial life forms, yet astrobiologists do not expect to find these inhabiting either Neptune or Triton, as neither fit the standard definition of a habitable world. If the ammonia that may well be present in Triton's subsurface ocean were able to lower the freezing point of water, however, it might be a more suitable host for life. There is nothing to say that life (but not as we know it, Jim) could not be thriving on either body, just waiting to be discovered.

The Underdog

Now that the *New Horizons* spacecraft has completed the first Pluto fly-by (in 2015) after a nine-year journey, we have finally visited every member of the Solar System and the secrets of this dwarf planet too are starting to be revealed. But could this once-upon-a-time planet have the theoretical potential to support life when it is more than 4.8 billion km (3 billion miles) away from the warming embrace of the Sun?

It is amazing what, until 2015, we didn't know about Pluto. For starters it is larger than we first thought. About two-thirds the size of the Moon, it is 2,370km (1,470 miles) across and could comfortably fit inside the area of Russia. The fact that we were wrong about something as simple as its dimensions demonstrates the importance of visiting a world to get accurate information, but is also significant in showing that Pluto is less dense than we thought – it turns out to be made of more ice than rock. Ancient surfaces, like those on the Moon, record the history of impacts – and therefore the history of the Solar System – in the form of craters. Pluto, it was assumed, would also be covered in a very old cratered crust but, amazingly, it has areas that are smooth and unscarred by impact craters and composed of much newer icy deposits as seen in the heart-shaped region of Tombaugh Regio. This tells scientists that the surface can only be about 100 million years old – fairly young in geological terms. How is this possible? To smooth away the craters created during Pluto's history, as they were on most of the planets and moons in the Solar System, Pluto would need to have some kind of internal heat to soften or melt the icy surface. We have no idea what this source of warmth might be. It is probably too small to generate much radioactive heat inside its body, and there is no larger parent world to squeeze it and generate tidal energy; yet it is obviously geologically active. Figuring out this conundrum will be a huge revelation for planetary science and astrobiology alike.

Pluto is also losing its atmosphere (yes, surprisingly it has one) and as such has merely 1/100,000th of the atmospheric pressure at sea level on Earth. It has 3.5km- (2-mile-) high mountains made of rock-solid water ice, a frozen copy of the Earth's Rocky Mountains, and a surface that in appearance resembles boiling milk. The smooth plains of Tombaugh Regio have officially been titled *Sputnik Planum* after the first Russian satellite, launched in 1957. An ice sheet within these plains appears to have flowed in a similar way to glaciers on Earth and may actually still be flowing. There are surface patterns resembling the convection cells seen in steadily boiling milk (yes, another milk analogy). One interesting feature is that Pluto has a tail rather like that of a comet, as it is losing an estimated 500 tonnes (550 US tons) of nitrogen into space every hour. *New Horizons* flew through this nitrogen tail, which extends for 109,000km (67,730 miles) away from Pluto, and is sculpted by electrically charged particles that have travelled all the way from the Sun and are continuing past.

Unsurprisingly, there are no signs of life on Pluto, yet it is showing hints of the ingredients we normally use to describe a habitable environment. There is an as yet unknown heat source, there is water – albeit frozen as ice – and the most exciting find, organic carbon-based molecules. Pluto's tenuous atmosphere has haze layers where methane molecules (CH_4) are broken apart by the Sun's UV radiation. These recombine in various ways to form larger, more impressive molecules, but eventually group into solid specks called *tholins*. These have at best been described by Sarah Hörst, an Assistant Professor in the Department of Earth and Planetary Sciences at Johns Hopkins University, as 'abiotic complex brown organic gunk'. These fall as tar-like rain on to the surface, giving Pluto its surprisingly Mars-like reddish-brown colour. With flowing ice, exotic organic surface chemistry, mountain ranges and a vast carbon-rich haze, Pluto is showing a diversity of planetary geology and even astrobiology that is truly thrilling and highly unexpected this far out in the Solar System – Pluto's payback for being demoted to dwarf status!

Comets

In the quest to find evidence of life elsewhere in the Solar System, comets have been implicated in a number of stories, from the extreme notion of transporting living cells or even fully formed microbes from planet to planet, seeding each new world with life, to the more plausible idea of icy rocks carrying the basic organic building blocks to Earth, which led to the origination of life. It is theorised that 4 billion years ago the Earth was bombarded with rocks and balls of ice carrying organic molecules which, through their violent impacts with the newly formed Earth, were split up into the elements needed to form sugars, and ultimately DNA and life.

It is widely known that there are organic carbon-based molecules in interstellar space, with large quantities trapped in interstellar clouds and comets. When a European spacecraft analysed dust particles from Halley's Comet in 1986, it turned out to be some of the most organic-rich material ever measured in the Solar System, even though meteorites that have hit Earth already contain a whole suite of molecules, including amino acids. We now know for sure that comets could have provided the raw ingredients that the Earth would have needed for life. A regular visitor to the inner Solar System, 67P/Churyumov-Gerasimenko was the chosen target for the ESA catch-a-comet *Rosetta* mission. It has a short orbital period of 6.45 years, controlled by Jupiter's gravity, and is believed to have originated from the Kuiper Belt. When these Jupiter-family comets cross the orbit of Jupiter, they gravitationally interact with the massive planet. Their orbits gradually change as a result of these interactions until they are eventually thrown out of the Solar System or collide with a planet or the Sun.

In November 2014, everyone's favourite comet lander, *Philae*, hopped, skipped and jumped its way into history. Instead of the planned single landing, *Philae* had an initial bouncing touchdown followed by a collision with a crater rim and two further touchdowns. Important for astrobiologists, analysis of data from the UK-led instrument *Ptolemy* discovered molecules that can form sugars and amino acids. Ptolemy sampled ambient gas and detected the main components of the coma gases (those in the halo around the nucleus of the comet), including water vapour, carbon monoxide and carbon dioxide. Smaller quantities of carbon-bearing organic compounds were also identified, such as formaldehyde and acetone. Formaldehyde is implicated in the formation of ribose, which ultimately features in molecules such as DNA, and acetone is best known as the chief ingredient in nail polish remover (both equally important creations). While this is a long, long way from finding life itself, Philae has shown that the organic compounds that eventually translated into organisms here on Earth were present in the early Solar System and within moving bodies that could have transported them to the newly formed planets. So far there are no signs in 67P of amino acids, the building blocks of proteins. However, they are probably there somewhere, since they appeared in samples from NASA's *Stardust* mission, which returned material to Earth from the tail of comet Wild 2 (81P/Wild) in 2004, and have also been traced in meteorites that crash-landed on Earth.

There are no life forms as yet identified within comets but there are the ingredients for life. Comets therefore act as messengers, delivering water and organic-rich dust throughout the Solar System – sowing the ingredients for life far and wide. The challenge now is to discover where else they may have ended up.

Every day, our understanding of the envelope of life expands and with it the possible places in which life might exist in the Solar System. Not just that, but after a century of certainty the Solar System itself can still surprise us. At the time of writing, two astronomers from the California Institute of Technology have found evidence of a possible ninth planet lurking in the farthest reaches of our planetary neighbourhood. *Planet Nine*, as it has been dubbed, has not actually been seen yet but its existence has been inferred. Should this mysterious world existing as far away as 1200 AU be proven to be in fact real, who knows what it might be like or if it might have habitable environments. One day we could find the envelope of life stretched to even greater extremes. Nearly every planet and moon observed so far has the potential to support a habitable environment (not that this proves they ever have had or currently host life), so future studies of these worlds will be extremely exciting. But why stop at the edges of the Solar System when there is an entire galaxy of potentially habitable worlds beyond ...

CHAPTER EIGHT

Extraterrestrial Worlds: Life Not As We Know It

The Milky Way contains over 100 billion stars, and the whole Universe is made up of more than 100 billion galaxies. Surely there is at least one planet out there, just teeming with life, orbiting around one of those stars? We know that other planets exist in other solar systems. On 6th January 2015, NASA announced the Kepler Space Telescope had discovered its 1,000th *exoplanet* – a planet orbiting another star in place of our Sun. In fact, as of November 2015, 1,977 planets in 1,257 planetary systems have been found. Nonetheless, of all the worlds discovered to date, only a handful closely resembles the Earth. Instead, they exhibit a truly spectacular diversity, varying immensely in their orbits, sizes and compositions, and have been seen circling a wide variety of stars, including ones significantly smaller and fainter than our Sun. We are starting to see that any kind of world imaginable (within the realms of physics, of course) might be possible somewhere out there, and if that were true then theoretically a huge variety of alien life is possible too. The search for ET often focuses on planets that resemble Earth, the only world known by humans to host life – but does this always need to be the case?

Alien Worlds

Only in the past two decades have astronomers been able to confirm the existence of thousands of worlds orbiting distant stars, and could finally then legitimately question the possibility that some of these exoplanets might be home to extraterrestrial life. However, the conviction and belief that planets outside our Solar System exist goes back long before this. The Catholic monk *Giordano Bruno* proposed in 1584 the notion of 'countless suns and countless earths all rotating around their suns' – he was accused of heresy and burned at the stake. And yet, even in Bruno's time, the concept of a plurality of worlds was not entirely novel. The scientists and philosophers of ancient Greece also pondered whether other solar systems might exist and whether some would harbour other forms of life. The astronomer *Edwin Hubble* (1889–1953) used the world's most powerful telescopes of the day at the observatory on Mount Wilson in California and by 1923 had established that tiny nebulae visible in the heavens were in fact fields of hundreds of billions of stars, located way beyond the Milky Way. Hubble's observations proved the existence of countless potential worlds out in the darkness of space, and any number of these could be a habitable planet bustling with life.

Too far off from our own planet for direct observation, exoplanets can only be detected through their effects on their host star. Since our Solar System provides an excellent example of a planetary system with life, not surprisingly astronomers began the search for new worlds by examining stars similar to our Sun. Ironically, however, the first genuine discovery of a planet beyond our system came in 1994, when two or three planet-sized objects were found orbiting a pulsar – a dense, rapidly spinning corpse of a supernova explosion – rather than the expected Sun-like star. Although the existence of this small group of planets remains controversial, there is a consensus that these worlds could not support life as we know it, being permanently doused in high-energy radiation. The first discovery of a planet orbiting a star similar to our Sun came in 1995. A Swiss team proclaimed their finding of a new planet at least half the mass of Jupiter, set in a speedy orbit near the star 51 Pegasi. Thus began a surge of exoplanetary discoveries and by the arrival of the twenty-first century, several dozen more worlds had been detected.

Planet Hunters

In the beginning, there was *Hubble*. This first-generation space telescope, launched in 1990, has provided some of the most breathtaking images ever taken of our cosmos, and has been celebrated as the first to take an image of an exoplanet, *Fomalhaut b*. Launched in 2003, the *Spitzer Space Telescope* observes objects in the infrared spectrum and was the first instrument directly to detect light coming from an exoplanet. The data it has collected has revealed the composition, temperature and possible wind patterns on many distant extrasolar worlds. From its launch in 2006, the French *CoRoT* (*Convection, Rotation and planetary Transits*) mission, was the first exoplanet-hunting space operation, looking specifically for signs of planets transiting in front of their local star. It was a major contributor to the list of confirmed exoplanets, including some of the best-studied planets beyond our Solar System. CoRoT ceased to function in 2012, and was retired in 2013.

The $600m Kepler mission was launched in March 2009 and its primary mission came to a premature demise in May 2013. Its mission objective to establish how frequently Earth-like planets, in or near the habitable zone of their host star, occur across the Milky Way galaxy was a hunt for Goldilocks planets. It used a specially designed telescope called a *photometer* (light meter), that continuously records the brightness of stars. To make its discoveries, Kepler targeted a dense field of stars, allowing it to monitor simultaneously and unceasingly 150,000 balls of burning light. As a planet drifts across the face of its star in *transit*, it blocks a percentage of the light as viewed by the observer, and it is these dips in brightness that enable the planet to be detected. The drops can be miniscule, often around 0.01 per cent for an Earth-sized world, and last between 1–16 hours. The change must occur in a regular sequence to be attributed to a planet orbiting the star. Errors are quite possible at this subtle level, so once a candidate has been identified, Earth-based observatories take over, searching for telltale fingerprints of the host star's wobble as it responds to the pull of the orbiting planet's gravity. This is an invaluable double-check and shows that some one in ten of Kepler's candidates are false alarms. Even though its original mission has ended, it continues to observe the heavens, and scientists and the public alike will be combing through the massive treasure trove of publicly available data for years to come. This is how new exoplanets continue to tumble out of the sky and the number of potentially habitable exoplanets found is still climbing, long after the mission to detect them has ended. Kepler has discovered more than half of all known exoplanets to date, with over 2,000 confirmed and at least another 3,000 unconfirmed candidates.

Owing to its resounding success, new space telescopes capable of finding Earth-sized worlds around nearby stars are being designed to succeed Kepler. At the time of writing, the European Space Agency is scheduled to launch *CHEOPS* (CHaracterising ExOPlanet Satellite) in 2017, followed by

NASA's launch of *TESS* (Transiting Exoplanet Survey Satellite) in 2018. By 2024, ESA hopes to have followed CHEOPS with a larger planet-finder dubbed *PLATO* (PLAnetary Transits and Oscillations of stars). This mission's objective is to identify and study a large number of extrasolar planetary systems, with the emphasis placed on finding Earth's twins. If all goes to plan, the *European Extremely Large Telescope* (E-ELT), currently being built in Chile, will then be able to analyse the atmospheric composition of these newly found planets. By analysing the mix of gases in an atmosphere, E-ELT will be able to determine whether the planet in question is potentially habitable – or even inhabited. In addition to all these missions, the shiny new *James Webb Space Telescope* (JWST) is a sophisticated new observatory currently under design that is tasked with unlocking some of the greatest mysteries of the Universe, and which could also play a key role in the hunt for alien planets. Sold to the public as a replacement for the Hubble Space Telescope, this $8.8-billion infrared telescope is planned for launch in 2018 and will orbit 1,496,690km (930,000 miles) from Earth, in a region called the *Lagrange Point 2*. Here, the gravitational forces from the Earth and the Sun essentially cancel one another out, so JWST will be able to maintain a stable orbit while using minimum energy. From this orbital perch, it will be able to stare uninterrupted at stars through its sensitive infrared eyes and allow astronomers to *sniff* the atmospheres of alien planets to break down their molecular composition.

Habitable Worlds

Everyone wants to find a planet that might have life on it, either now or in the past, whether this is a second Earth or a world with sufficiently similar features and conditions that could make it habitable for life as we know it. An Earth-twin would have an *Earth Similarity Index* (*ESI*) of 1.0, and all exoplanets get assigned their own ESI. Astronomers remain committed to the idea that planets and moons with liquid surface water are the best bet for finding life, so the goal is to find a Goldilocks planet or moon. With this in mind, they are searching for one that is neither too hot nor too cold nor too large nor too small, but *just right* for liquid water. As with the Goldilocks zone of the Solar System, an exoplanet too close to its star would be superheated and any liquid oceans would boil away, while one that is further from its star would be too cold and any oceans would freeze over. But there is also a Goldilocks size to the perfect exoworld. Too small a planet or moon would not be able to hold on to a protective atmosphere, while if it were too huge, it would have an immense atmosphere of hydrogen and helium, making the surface too hot to support life. This holy grail of a perfect world does not need to be a complete replica of the Earth, but should simply enjoy some of its finest features. In fact, the more exoplanetary worlds we see, the more we are starting to consider that the Earth may not even be the gold standard for life. There may conceivably be *superhabitable worlds* out there that are even better suited than the Earth to support life.

A *Periodic Table of Exoplanets* divides most of the known candidates into groupings based on mass or dimensions and temperature. Exoplanets in the *Hot Zone* are too close to their parent star to have liquid water, whereas those in the *Warm Habitable Zone* are at the right distance for liquid water to be stable, given that they are the right size (from half that of the Earth up to 10 Earth masses). Water will only be in existence as ice for those in the *Cold Zone*. The *Mercurians* are low-mass bodies, most likely spherical and lacking an atmosphere, like Mercury and the Moon. The *Subterrans* are comparable to Mars, *Terrans* to Earth and Venus, while *Superterrans*, or *Super-Earths*, are up to 10 times as massive as Earth, a category with no comparable examples in the Solar System. *Neptunians* are similar in mass to Neptune and Uranus (are you starting to see a naming pattern yet?), and *Jovians* are compared to Jupiter and

Saturn-sized worlds, or greater. The two largest types of exoplanet are, unsurprisingly, the most commonly detected as they are the easiest to spot. These *Hot Jupiters* have similar characteristics to Jupiter itself but generally orbit closer to their parent star and so have far hotter temperatures. *Giant Neptunes* are large gaseous planets, considerably more massive than the Earth but smaller than Jupiter. Both of these types of world are believed to be inhospitable to life.

Searching for Super-Earths

Instead of hunting solely for Earth's twin (in terms of both the planet and its star), we are fascinated by planets similar to, yet larger than Earth – the so-called *Super-Earths*. This name denotes the size of the worlds, not their capabilities. These are worlds that feel both familiar and yet completely alien. They may be made of rock and metal, or ice and gas. These planets may have oceans and atmospheres, or contain nothing but hydrogen and helium. The goal, of course, in studying these is to find a rocky Super-Earth located in the Goldilocks zone of its parent star. More than 30 Super-Earths had been discovered up to 2016, with the first found around a pulsar in 1992. The first one discovered around a main-sequence star, the red dwarf *Gliese 876*, was not observed until 2005. The first discovery of a potentially habitable super-Earth was in 2007, this time around *Gliese 581* and on the edge of that star's Goldilocks zone. In fact, not one but two worlds were discovered, with *Gliese 581c* getting the most attention. This planet has a mass of at least five Earths and sits on the overly warm side of the Goldilocks zone (conversely, *Gliese 581d* sits on the cold side). Scientists believe that 581c suffered a runaway greenhouse effect, as is thought to have occurred on Venus.

At the time of writing, the most Earth-like planet yet has been discovered and named the ever-imaginative *Kepler-452b*. It is the first almost Earth-sized planet to be found in the Goldilocks zone of a star very similar to our Sun. It orbits a star known as *Kepler-452*, located in the Milky Way and some 1,400 light years away in the direction of the Cygnus constellation. Its size – 1.6 times that of Earth – hints at it being a rocky world that is likely to have an atmosphere, good cloud cover and possibly active volcanoes. This is our best candidate yet for *Earth 2.0* and could also be the ideal place to look for evidence of extraterrestrial life. What is most fascinating about it, however, is its age: it is a staggering 1.5 billion years older than our own Earth. This world may give us a glimpse of what awaits our planet in the future. We have also found *Kepler-438b* orbiting not a red but an orange dwarf star in the constellation of Lyra, which is 470 light years away. It is slightly larger than the Earth and is bathed in 40 per cent more heat from its star than the Earth is from the Sun. Its small dimensions imply that it is a rocky world, and it sits within the Goldilocks zone. Despite being exciting candidates, these worlds will surely not hold the podium finishes for long.

Gliese 832c is not one of the top three potentially habitable exoplanets but this super–Earth is located only 16 light years from the Earth. It is a rocky planet orbiting in the interior of a planetary system thought of as being similar to a miniature Solar System, with a gas giant in the outer reaches. Gliese 832c has a mass 5.4 times that of the Earth and takes 35.68 days to orbit its sun. Given its large mass, it seems likely it would possess a massive atmosphere similar to that of Venus, making it inhospitable for life, although this is not known for sure. Its Goldilocks orbit should allow for liquid water to persist on its surface; the planet's atmosphere, however, would determine whether any such water were usable by life. The number one question is, 'Could a super-Earth such as this support life?' So far, all super–Earths have been found orbiting smaller dwarf stars (yes, this may have something to do with the fact that they are easier to detect), yet to be capable of supporting life, these worlds will need to orbit dangerously closely to their star to maintain the best temperature for liquid water to be stable on their surface. Super-Earths will also have a larger gravity than the Earth. Life inhabiting any oceans would have no problem with this, as the buoyancy of water would balance out the greater gravity of a super-Earth. On land and in the air, however, it would be a different story. We will describe later what kind of life might evolve, should it live on a world with higher gravity and a thicker atmosphere, but the key message is that it *is* possible!

Revealing Red Dwarfs

The vast majority of exoplanets detected so far lie within planetary systems orbiting red dwarf stars, which are smaller, colder and dimmer balls of light than the Sun. For a world to be habitable in this type of star system, it must hug a tight orbit around its sun to keep it warm enough for liquid water to be stable. Such a close orbit means there is a high probability that the planet would become *tidally locked*. This means that one face of the planet would always be looking towards the star, bathed in eternal sunshine, and one would always be turned away, in perpetual darkness, similar to the Moon's experience as it orbits the Earth. This creates a huge temperature dichotomy between the two sides and could produce global gale-force winds. Neither face of these worlds is attractive for life, although there is a sliver of hope. A thin zone could exist, encircling the planet on the boundary between day and night, sitting in the aura of a never-ending twilight that could potentially have a temperature range suitable for life. Sadly, however, intense heating caused by the proximity of planets to their host red dwarfs would nonetheless be a major impediment to life developing in these systems. There would be a very small circumstellar Goldilocks zone owing to low light output from the star, and this light would be shifted into the infrared spectrum, unlike light from our Sun. Finally, if that were not tough enough for life, many red dwarfs earlier in their life are also far more violent and unpredictable than their more stable, larger cousins such as the Sun, in a matter of minutes erupting with flares that double their brightness and send torrents of atmosphere-stripping charged particles towards any unsuspecting nearby planets. You may therefore wonder why we are bothering to look here? First, red dwarf stars are the most common type of star, making up 73 per cent of all those in the Milky Way. Second, they are very long-lived. Red dwarfs could live for trillions of years (in fact, it is thought that no red dwarf has actually died yet) since their nuclear reactions are far slower than those of larger stars, meaning that life would have both longer in which to evolve and to survive.

Exploring Exomoons

As the name implies, an *exomoon* is a satellite in orbit around an exoplanet or extrasolar body. The number of natural satellites found in our Solar System orbiting terrestrial worlds and gas giants alike suggests that exomoons should be equally common in other planetary systems. Sizeable moons in a stellar Goldilocks zone could quite possibly outnumber planets. When we focus on moons in our Solar System, there are quite a few with many potentially habitable environments through the presence of liquids, heat and nutrients on and within them, such as Europa, Enceladus and Titan – so why could the same not be true in other solar systems? Furthermore, only four worlds in the Solar System other than the Earth show evidence of current tectonic or volcanic activity, and these objects are not planets but moons. Exomoons are, however, extremely difficult to detect and confirm, owing to their size. Observations from missions such as Kepler have hinted at a number of candidates, including some that may one day turn out to be habitats for extraterrestrial life. As yet, no exomoons have been confirmed, but they are sure to lurk within the vast Kepler data sets, awaiting discovery.

Exomoons may prove to be better candidates for life than exoplanets, as moons can have multiple energy sources. While the habitability of terrestrial planets is generally influenced by the levels of sunlight reaching their surfaces, moons also receive reflected starlight from their parent planet as well as thermal emissions from the planet itself. If a moon were to orbit a planet similar to Jupiter, which is quite possible given how many exoplanets have been classified as hot Jupiters and since Jupiter itself has 67 moons, even more energy sources would be available. A planet such as this would still be shrinking and thereby converting gravitational energy into heat, so it would actually emit more heat than it received from the Sun, providing yet more illumination on to its nearby moons. Besides this, moons orbiting close to a gas giant are *flexed* (affected) by the planet's gravity, providing potential tidal heating as an internal, geological heat source. The distance of the moon to the planet would also play a role in determining habitability, because the closer they lie together the stronger this tidal heating would be. Too close and it is likely that the moon would suffer from a catastrophic runaway greenhouse effect, boiling away surface water and leaving it uninhabitable. These complex interactions between a planet and its satellite could affect the latter's climate enough to make it suitable for life, even if the host planet were completely inhospitable. It seems there is even a Goldilocks zone for exomoons around their exoplanets, as well as exoplanets around their star.

A Pale Blue Dot

If there were an alien civilisation on a planet currently orbiting one of the 100 or so nearest Sun-like stars, what would they see, were they to look towards the Earth? Could they tell it is teeming with carbon-based life forms ready to shake their hand/tentacle? And how is the Earth helping us to identify signs of life in nearby planetary systems? If we look at the Earth from over 4 billion kilometres away, it fits within a single pixel as a tiny pale blue dot, but intelligent alien life could learn a great deal from this infinitesimal speck of light. The Earth varies in brightness over time as clouds and continents move across its surface, so extraterrestrials could infer that this little planetary object has weather, water and even rocky continental bodies. This blue spot on the horizon could also reveal to our inquisitive neighbours what kinds of gases are in its atmosphere. Each gas present will either remove or absorb a separate wavelength of starlight, leaving gaps in the complete rainbow spectrum of light. By looking at the different missing pieces from Earth's spectrum, the aliens could make an educated guess about what comprises Earth's atmosphere. There is plenty of water vapour in our atmosphere, which would suggest liquid oceans are lapping across the planet and therefore that a key ingredient for life, as hopefully they know it, is present. The atmosphere would also be found to contain an unusually high amount of oxygen. Since oxygen is a highly reactive gas it normally combines with other substances and does not exist on its own for very long – it should not really be in Earth's atmosphere at all. But plants and photosynthetic bacteria continually produce oxygen so on Earth, at least, there is always a large amount in the atmosphere. We say that oxygen is a *biosignature gas*: a gas produced by life itself. This would tell the aliens that there is oxygen-producing life, as well as oxygen-consuming life, on the planet.

ET would also be able to see carbon dioxide, methane and other important trace gases in Earth's air. Methane is composed of one carbon and four hydrogen atoms stuck together, and can be a tiny, but powerful, biosignature gas as the product of life as well as one of life's most basic energy sources. Most of our methane comes from countless tiny microbes feasting in the depths of Earth's oceans and swampland as a by-product of their metabolism. It can also, however, be created without any input from life whatsoever. *Abiogenic methane* arises when volcanically heated water reacts with rocks containing high levels of iron and magnesium. Because of the heating, hydrogen in the water is liberated. This free hydrogen then meets with carbon that has come from carbon dioxide dissolved in the water. The result is methane that has nothing to do with life forms. And yet while not every process that produces methane is generated by life, the overwhelming majority of known sources are alive. Knowing that methane exists in the atmosphere of a planet serves another life-related function as well: it can inform one about the surface temperature of an exoplanet. Methane is one of the most notable greenhouse gases. Like carbon dioxide, atmospheric methane acts as a sort of planetary thermal blanket; it wraps around the Earth and absorbs surface radiation that would otherwise make its way into space. In fact, of the two, methane is a far more efficient warming agent and has at least 20–25 times the global warming potential of carbon dioxide. Fortunately for us, however, methane only persists for a few years after it is produced; otherwise things on Earth would be pretty toasty.

Interestingly, and sadly, alien astronomers would also be able to see evidence of humanity itself and the negative effect it has had on the world. The Earth is surrounded by at least 500,000 pieces of greater-than-marble-sized debris or 'space junk' – natural fragments of meteoroids and leftover remnants of now-defunct spacecraft, satellites and launch vehicle stages. Who is to say whether distant observers could spot this orbiting belt of debris or perhaps even glimpse sunlight reflecting off from it? In the atmosphere, they would see evidence of an industrialised civilisation and its pollution. Chlorofluorocarbons (CFCs), in particular tetrafluoromethane (CF_4) and trichloro-fluoromethane (CCl_3F), are the key ingredients in many mass-produced products on Earth, for everything from holding hair in place to eating holes in our ozone layer. These are compounds that can only be produced by advanced industry. Alien searchers might be tempted to shake whatever passes for their heads in sadness, and move on to contemplate other options.

Designer Life

What might life look like on some of these exoplanets, assuming they had sufficient conditions and the time available for complex multicellular plants and animals to arise? If life developed on a world with a lower or higher gravity than that of the Earth, or with no landmass, or it orbited a red dwarf star instead of a Sun such as ours, what adaptations would have developed to enable it to survive? What common traits might we expect to evolve on any planet regardless of the starting conditions? Would we even recognise this life as *'living'*?

The Degrees of 'Alienness' ...

There may be a number of ways to arrange and assemble organic molecules to create a living being, but it is incredibly hard for us to imagine one better suited to run and support the functions of life than the system of DNA/RNA storage, the operating manual of a cell and proteins. If any life form arising in the Universe were to be built with a similar sugar-phosphate backbone, then these alien beings would essentially be terrestrial and biochemically similar to us. Many scientists also believe the symbiotic evolution of the eukaryotic cell and the building of multicellular organisms to be all but inevitable.

Owing to the distribution of organic material in the Universe and carbon being the third most abundant element in the cosmos, the first degree of *alienness* is a population based on the same organic building blocks as Earth-based life, such as amino acids and sugars, but assembled in different ways or using different sets. To recap from Chapter 2, all proteins within life on Earth are built from a combination of just 20 amino acids, yet a catalogue of more than 70 different types of amino acid has been found within rocks from space. Most are alien to terrestrial life. Also, most molecules within a cell have a particular *chirality*, described earlier. As such there are two possible mirror-image versions of a molecule, which are called *enantiomers*. All terrestrial life uses one enantiomer – biologically-produced amino acids are left-handed and sugars are right-handed. Perhaps on another world life will use amino acids, but right-handed forms instead of left. And as mentioned in detail back in Chapter 2, life on Earth depends on water and carbon. The most alien life we could imagine would not be based on water and maybe not even on carbon.

We are looking for life in the middle range of alienness, put together using the same building blocks as Earth life but arranged slightly differently. Furthermore, its organic chemistry would have been designed (evolved) to help the organism survive the environment within which it existed. We are not looking nor do we expect to find life identical to that on Earth. For a start, it is a very narrow-minded point of view, but also, if it were found, there would be no way of proving it were alien and not simply terrestrial contamination. Even focusing on the possible variants of life as we know it, there turn out to be a number of familiar features we might not be too surprised to see staring back at us ...

The Predictability of Evolution

The most difficult question about evolution is 'Why?', since this is not posed by evolution itself – it is not working to a game plan or plotted timeline. Instead, the current prevailing conditions represent the only place where evolution occurs, and organisms change in response to fluctuating opportunities or crises imposed by their environment. Evolution is driven by random mutations and natural selection. If an adaptation (or mutation) is useful to a lineage, chances are that it will be preserved and passed on to future generations. Individuals best suited to their particular environment will prevail while those that are not will perish. It is rational to assume, therefore, that an alien organism developing on another world in the distant reaches of our or another galaxy would be subject to the same evolutionary demands as terrestrial biology.

Useful adaptations for life seem to emerge throughout evolution again and again. Evolution is not particularly original but it is innovative, upcycling existing proteins to play new roles and turning previously negative traits into a positive adaptation for survival. This has its limits, however – everything does – and Mother Nature seems to hit upon the same designs over and over again. If it worked well the first time, then why not a second time – Earth's own 'If it ain't broke, why fix it?' philosophy. We call this *convergent evolution* – a process whereby species not closely related live in similar ways and/or in similar environments, and by having to face the same environmental challenges are likely to evolve similar traits. An example of convergent evolution is the similar nature of the wings of insects, birds, pterosaurs and bats. All four designs of the wing serve the same function, to enable the organisms to fly, and are similar in structure, yet each evolved completely independently of the other. Convergent evolution is extremely common on Earth. In their own exploration of what life might lie waiting in the Universe, popular British science writers Jack Cohen and Ian Stewart, a reproductive biologist and mathematician respectively, listed the *four F's* of universal evolution in terrestrial biology: fur, flight, photosynthesis and ... sexual reproduction.

The late evolutionary biologist Stephen Jay Gould, in his 1989 book *Wonderful Life: The Burgess Shale and the Nature of History*, discussed the Burgess Shale fossils described back in Chapter 4. You may recall that they are a collection of strange alien-style life forms that inhabited the Earth's oceans about 520 million years ago. Many species from this time in the Cambrian have since died out because they were not fit enough to compete for survival or were in the wrong place at the wrong time during volcanic eruptions, asteroid impacts or other extinction events. Gould theorised that life today would have been very different had history unfurled in another way, that life is a result of the outcomes of past accidents – *historical contingencies*. Random mutations and chance extinctions would build on each other, driving the evolution of life down one path or another. In Gould's view, the existence of every animal, including humans, was a rare event that would have been unlikely to recur if the tape of life were rewound to the Cambrian Period and replayed. For example, it is widely believed that the chance asteroid impact 65 million years ago that killed off the dinosaurs allowed mammals to arise and humans to become the dominant species on the Earth. Without this impact, would we even be here?

Life is a lottery of convergence and contingency, a potluck of inevitable adaptations and some lucky chances. The same interactions between convergence and contingency may play out on other planets, with many features of an alien being partially predictable, while others can only be based upon quirks in their evolutionary and environmental history. If extraterrestrial life has faced similar evolutionary pressures as life on Earth, future humans may discover aliens that have convergently evolved to resemble us, and have intelligence similar to ours. On the other hand, if contingent events build on one another and are responsible for driving the development of life down unique paths, as Stephen Jay Gould suggested, then extraterrestrial life may be remarkably strange. This means, however, that in order for us to speculate on what alien life might look like we should pay attention to the convergent adaptations life has created, as the number of lucky breaks is probably infinite. Furthermore, if an alien were evolving in an environment very different to the Earth, then it might have developed a number of unique design solutions to allow for its survival. One of the most important questions in evolutionary biology is what features of organisms are universal and might be expected to re-appear every time life arises or is restarted, regardless of the planet or moon it finds itself on.

A Body and Brain

In popular culture, we predominantly portray ET as humanoid with four limbs, standing upright and with a forward-facing head. Although this probably is not alien enough, we know it is as a result of the budgets placed upon costume departments and that it is more engaging and believable to witness Captain Kirk talking to a human-like alien than a gelatinous blob of goo. However, there is some truth behind the idea. On Earth, birds, reptiles, fish and insects are all constructed with bilateral symmetry. This means the left and right halves of their bodies are reflections of each other. Alien life may quite possibly have chosen the same layout. Yet it could also have a different fundamental plan, such as the radial symmetry of jellyfish, whereby it has no left or right side, only a top and a bottom. Most vertebrates have an entrance and an exit – mostly separate, sometimes shared – and some form of *skin* to contain all their organs. There is also a common need for lungs or gills in creatures, once they reach a certain size, in order to be able to access oxygen. And before you ask, there is good reason to suppose that alien life would enjoy a deep breath of oxygen as much as we do. Burning organic carbon-based fuels, such as glucose in oxygen, provides greater levels of energy – enough to satisfy the enormous power demands of animal life.

Larger animals colonising the land would also require some kind of support or scaffolding to hold their body together against the force of gravity, as well as a frame against which muscles can push. They will therefore most likely have a skeleton that can either be an 'innie' like ours or an 'outtie' like that of crustaceans. But what about limbs? These are obviously needed in some form for grasping objects and in most animals for movement, but how many would an alien have? Humans and all land vertebrates have a four-limbed body plan (two arms and two legs), as a result of contingent evolution – our fishy ancestors by chance had two pairs of lobed fins, and so we have four limbs. An alien ancestor could just as easily have had three pairs of limbs, creating hexapod descendants along the lines of terrestrial insects, and maybe even have adapted these limbs so that the front pair are no longer used as legs but as arms or claws similar to those of crabs on Earth. Six legs would be a very fortunate adaptation for life on a world with stronger gravity, supporting the movement of much heavier, although not necessarily larger, life forms. At the end of our limbs, humans have 10 fingers and 10 toes, but we could balance or grasp objects just as well with four or six digits, just as long as we kept our opposable thumbs. Who knows how many fingers an alien might have – the point is that the chances are they will have them.

The Face of Life

The development of the eye is seen as a universal evolutionary feature. It makes good design sense to have a way of *seeing* where you are going and, to that end, placing the eyes at the front of a head. It is clever to put the best surveying organ available close to the brain and for it to be protected by a hard shell (the head). The human eye is an exquisitely complicated organ that acts in a similar way to a camera, collecting and focusing light and converting it into an electrical signal that the brain translates into images. Instead of photographic film, it has a highly specialised retina that detects light and processes the signals using dozens of different types of neuron. Humans and most other vertebrates, and cephalopods (which includes octopuses, cuttlefish and squid) have *camera-type* eyes, which took shape in fewer than 100 million years. Eyes first evolved during the Cambrian Explosion from light-sensitive proteins based in a single illuminated spot, and were used to monitor circadian (daily) and seasonal rhythms. They then evolved into light-sensitive pits, into compound insect eyes and finally our optically and neurologically sophisticated eyeballs by 500 million years ago.

Complex, image-forming eyes have evolved independently some 50 to 100 times, which is not particularly surprising, given that any model or method allowing organisms to see and rapidly focus on an image would confer an enormous evolutionary advantage for survival, regardless of whether they are based on land, air or sea. Many genes are responsible for making the eye. One holds instructions for making light-sensitive pigments, another provides information for making the lens, and other genes orchestrate it all, directing various parts when and to where they need to be assembled. These are called *master control genes*, and for eyes the most important one is *Pax-6*. The ancestral Pax-6 gene controlled the formation of the first very simple eye and still controls today's most complex incarnations. Given that a variety of eye-type structures has arisen independently numerous times, it seems highly likely that an alien life form will have eyes. To be at the pinnacle of evolutionary adaptation, it would quite possibly have an eye similar to that of an octopus – one step better than the eye of a human as it lacks the *blind spot* created where the optic nerve leaves the eyeball.

Sensory organs give animals an acute awareness of changes in the environment around them and throughout their bodies, so that they can physically respond. A very satisfactory evolutionary adaptation, these touchy-feely organs enable animals to avoid hostile environments, sense the presence of predators and hunt down sources of food. Animals can perceive a wide range of stimuli that includes touch, pressure, pain, temperature, chemicals, light, sound, movement and position of the body. Some animals can also sense electric and magnetic fields. The *special* senses of smell, taste, sight, hearing and balance are particularly useful, and the organs used for these relatively complex. Life forms need to process this sensory information as fast as possible so most have a centralised nervous system, and to reduce data transfer times nature houses this near to the organs. It seems, therefore, that the development of a head at the front of the body may prove to be universally essential among higher animals, although the positioning not so much.

Skin and Bones

Human skin colour ranges from the darkest brown to the lightest pinkish-white, even yellowish, hues. Human skin pigmentation is the result of natural selection; it evolved primarily to regulate the amount of ultraviolet radiation penetrating the skin, controlling its biochemical effects. There is a direct correlation between the geographic distribution of UV radiation (UVR) and the distribution of indigenous melanin skin pigmentation around the world. Areas that receive higher amounts of UVR, generally located closer to the Equator, tend to have darker-skinned populations. Areas far from the Tropics and closer to the poles have a lower intensity of UVR, which is reflected in lighter-skinned populations.

Alien life would not, however, necessarily follow the same human melanin spectrum. It might more closely resemble that of terrestrial plants than Earth's vertebrates. Might aliens live up to their fictional reputation and be a greyish green? This colouration of particular life forms on Earth is a consequence of two things: in plants it comes from the photosynthetic pigment *chlorophyll*; and in animals from the need to be camouflaged and remain hidden within our planet's vast vegetation. Some biologists believe that chlorophyll may be a universal molecule, used by any number of organisms to soak up the light of their parent star. However, the wavelength of light emitted by a star varies, depending upon its temperature. A star cooler than the Sun, such as a red dwarf, will shine more in the infrared than in the visible portion of the electromagnetic spectrum, so any photosynthetic pigment would need to be tuned to absorb this differing wavelength of light. It might well be perfectly camouflaged to its own vegetation but to our eyes would not look green. If an alien did appear green to us, then it is a pretty fair bet that its sun would be very similar to ours. An alien might also appear green if it used chlorophyll to provide the organism with a source of nutrients. Unfortunately, although perfectly adequate for the energy budgets of plants, photosynthesis cannot provide nearly enough energy to meet an animal's high demands, especially powering muscles and a brain. Complex life must be carnivorous, devouring the nutrients contained within plants and other animals (which themselves may feed on photosynthetic plants) to draw the energy it urgently needs. There is nothing to say, however, that a carnivorous life form could not have a chlorophyll-rich skin for times of famine or for use as a top-up source of energy and nutrients for survival in harsh or seasonally challenging environments.

An internal circulatory system is needed in any life form to move nutrients effectively to where they are needed, as well as to remove waste products. For terrestrial life, rich red blood is the main mechanism, although in actual fact blood can be a number of colours, including colourless, as a result of the specific chemicals it carries. Humans and most other vertebrates use the iron-containing protein *haemoglobin*, and so have red blood. Haemoglobin is a *respiratory pigment* and plays a vital role in the body, ferrying oxygen to cells and helping waste carbon dioxide return to the lungs where it can be exhaled. When it is *oxygenated*, i.e. full of freshly breathed-in oxygen, it is bright red in contrast to when it is deoxygenated, when it is a deep, dark red. It is a commonly held myth that deoxygenated blood is blue – after all, if you look through your skin at any of your veins carrying deoxygenated blood away from your body's cells, they have a definite blue-grey hue. However, this appearance is in fact caused by the interaction of light with both the blood and the skin and tissue covering the veins. There are some creatures, however, for whom blue blood is the norm. Unlike haemoglobin, which is bound to red blood cells, *haemocyanin* can float freely in blood and contains copper instead of iron. When deoxygenated it is colourless, but blue when carrying oxygen. This is the shade of blood found in spiders, crustaceans and some molluscs, octopuses and squid. Green blood also exists in some segmented worms, leeches and sea cucumbers, which contain *chlorocruorin* or a mixture of haemoglobin and chlorocruorin. Finally, violet blood has been found within marine worms and brachiopods as it contains *haemerythrin* as the oxygen transporter. What is perhaps most interesting about the varying colours of blood is that it showcases evolution coming up with different solutions to the same problem – in this case, how to transport oxygen.

One adaptation I consider particularly useful, and could easily imagine any alien life form adopting, is being streamlined. It turns out that there are not many ways of remaining streamlined while pushing yourself through the water. On Earth, salmon, whales, penguins and water boatmen all come from very different lineages and yet have independently converged on the same body plan of a sleek bullet-like shape helped by fins and flippers. There is no reason why this may not have occurred elsewhere as well. Perhaps on another world, jet propulsion would be a more dominant mode of movement. Terrestrial squid contract an outer cavity to move backwards in pulses and it has been speculated that animals larger than sharks on another world could also propel themselves this way by contracting water or air through a hollow tube running the inside length of their bodies. The need for an aerodynamic body is not just good for swimming, but for the one thing we all wish we could do – fly.

A Flight of Fancy

The evolution of flight might be expected or even inevitable on any terrestrial planet. But before there was to be flight, life needed wings. The way in which these evolved on the Earth is not precisely known although some theories perceive an evolutionary step from arms used by bipedal animals to leap into the air to capture small prey, which evolved into large wings to assist in said leaping. Perhaps wings arose from gliding ancestors who began to flap their gliding structures in order to produce thrust so as to move faster and further. We know that flight evolved millions of years ago in all of the groups that are capable of flight today and the reasons differ depending on the species in question. These range from helping them to escape from predators or catch flying or speedy prey, aiding movement from place to place (leaping or gliding), freeing the hind legs for use as weapons, or gaining access to new food sources or an unoccupied niche.

Gliding – a controlled descent using gravity as the driving force – has evolved many times and in many different groups including frogs, lizards, snakes and several different mammals, and even the seeds of some plants. Gliding is also known among some fossil reptiles. On the other hand, active flight, during which flapping powers an organism through the air, has only evolved four times in nature: once in arthropods and three times in vertebrates. It has only become *extinct* once … in the *pterosaurs*. The first animals to evolve flight were insects some 410 million years ago, and the pterosaurs were the first vertebrates to evolve active flapping flight, although the origin of this adaptation is something of a mystery. The transformation from non-flying, perhaps gliding, animal to fully-flying pterosaur probably occurred in the forests of the Middle Triassic. Unfortunately, this environment rarely yields fossils, so the search for the oldest or even original pterosaur may be in vain. Shortly after the Cretaceous, bats appeared – the first active flying mammals – and about 50 million years after that another group of vertebrates achieved the ability to fly. Instead of evolving wings directly, this group used its ingenious brain to skip that step and build machines to fly for them: this was our species.

On Earth, the energetics of staying airborne impose stringent limits on the size of flying animals, but this may not be the case on planets and moons with different gravities and thicknesses of atmosphere. Planets smaller than the Earth have a lower gravity and so tend only to hold on to a thin atmosphere. This would mean that flapping wings would generate less lift and flight would be rather difficult, even though the physical pull of gravity holding the organism to the ground would be reduced. Wings with very large surface areas and spans of up to 75cm (2.5ft), similar to those of prehistoric dragonflies, might help. Flight would actually be easier on a larger world with a stronger gravity, as its pull on the atmosphere would be stronger, and the air would be denser, maintaining a thicker, more flight-friendly environment. Animals as massive as elephants would be able to glide through the air and *sky-whales* could dominate the clouds, carried on thermals and slowly flapping their immense wingspans.

If I had to design a flying alien species, I would give them wings modelled on those of a bat. Bat-style wings have evolved several times in mammals. They use up less energy during flight as a result of flexible skin membranes and are held together by more than 24 joints. As a matter of fact, bats are operating with the same skeletal structure as humans. Every joint in the human hand is found in a bat's wing, and indeed a couple more. The wings provide more lift and less drag, thereby increasing manoeuvrability.

Lighting up Life

Bioluminescence is the production and emission of light by a living organism. It is a form of *chemiluminescence,* whereby light energy (luminescence) is released as the result of a chemical reaction. Bioluminescence occurs widely among animals, particularly in the open sea, including jellyfish, comb jellies, crustaceans and cephalopod molluscs. This characteristic is also present in microorganisms including some bacteria and fungi, and terrestrial invertebrates such as insects. The most famous, perhaps, are the dinoflagellates frosting breaking waves in a blanket of phosphorescence and weaving light ribbons across the sea, while on land fireflies are amazing to watch as they dance around on a warm summer's evening. Fireflies actually provide so much light that they were once carried underground in jars to provide light for miners working deep in the bowels of the Earth.

Bioluminescence can serve several functions depending upon the needs of the organism using it, which can range from *counter-illumination camouflage,* in which the animal matches the overhead environmental light as seen from below (such as in the oceans), to attraction of a mate or, conversely, attraction of prey, snaring food in glowing threads and webs. Furthermore, it can be used in defence and in warnings, for communication, mimicry and, of course, simple illumination.

In some animals, the light is not their own, coming instead from symbiotic organisms such as *Vibrio* bacteria. Other organisms on Earth contain a light-emitting pigment called *luciferin* and the enzyme *luciferase,* which reacts with oxygen to create light both within and outside cells. In evolution, luciferins generally vary very little, with one in particular, *coelenterazine,* present in the light-emitting pigment of nine ancient groups of organisms. Not all manufacture coelenterazine themselves – some obtain it through their diet. Overall, bioluminescence has arisen over 40 times in evolutionary history and is found within at least 70 genera of squid. Most marine light emission is in the blue and green light spectrum. However, some loose-jawed fish emit red and infrared light and the genus *Tomopteris* emits yellow light.

An Alien Greenhouse

Unsurprisingly, convergent evolution is also common in the plant world and can give a number of clues as to what vegetation might arise on an exoplanet or moon. Plants, especially those on land, need to satisfy four fundamental constraints to survive. They must be able to catch as much light as possible from their Sun to allow for photosynthesis to work and they must be able to disperse pollen or seeds as far as possible to ensure the survival of their species. They also need to ensure mechanical stability so as not to topple over and must have ways of retaining, or not losing too much, water. Depending upon the demands of the local alien environment, plants might meet these requirements in a number of ways. Slow-growing vegetation arising on a world with a low availability of light would be likely to develop wide, flat canopies to maximise the amount of light intercepted (although this could cause a stability problem, increasing the risk of being uprooted in strong winds); while those on water-poor worlds might evolve in a similar way to squat cacti with highly modified leaves, such as spines. As well as defending against hungry herbivores, spines help prevent water loss by reducing airflow close to the cactus and providing some shade. As such, the shapes of trees and plants in an alien forest are likely to resemble those found in similar environments on the Earth and might be recognisable to us. On a planet with high wind speeds, mechanical stability would be of paramount importance and trees may resemble terrestrial firs, or seaweed with its submissively flexible stem. Worlds with a higher gravity might have low-lying trees with stout trunks and fewer branches. Potentially on these worlds, plants might evolve novel ways to reach the sunlight, reproduce and access water. Perhaps instead of desperately trying to grow towards the sky, alien plants would simply float upwards. Photosynthetic plants on Earth use the hydrogen produced by the splitting of water molecules to generate food, and release oxygen as a waste product. If an alien plant released this hydrogen inside an inflatable sac, it might float into the sky like an airship to find what it needed, anchoring itself to the ground with a vine. Going one step further, this vine might have the ability to detach during reproduction to allow the plant to be carried in the wind and disperse its seeds across vast distances. This adaptation is found in the seas on Earth when kelp forests release seeds contained in small flotation bladders, pumped full of oxygen or carbon dioxide.

We would hope to recognise the shapes and even life strategies of a plant or tree on another world, but would we recognise its colour? Would an alien biosphere be as green as the vast majority of healthy vegetated areas on Earth? If alien plants were found on a world orbiting a Sun-like star and use chlorophyll as a pigment, then quite possibly yes. However, even the Earth hosts a variety of organisms other than green plants that photosynthesise other than green plants. On land, plants may also display foliage that is red, yellow, orange, cream, purple or demonstrate a variety of other effects, while underwater algae and photosynthetic bacteria are also found in a wide palette of shades. The dominant colouration of extraterrestrial foliage will depend on how alien photosynthesis evolves in response to the spectrum of light received from its parent star, combined with the filtering effects of the planet's or moon's atmosphere (which may be very different to our own) and, for aquatic creatures, of liquid water (or the liquid they are residing in). In general, plants on Earth use the broad spectrum of visible light (red–orange–yellow–green–blue–indigo–violet) from the Sun, profiting most from the blue-green range. The Sun transmits predominantly red *photons* (particles of energy from light or other electromagnetic radiation), useful for their quantity, though lower in quality than blue photons, which supply more energy. Green photons in between are lacking both in such energy and numbers, so vegetation on Earth has evolved to screen much of these and thus reflect green.

As always, the answer to the puzzle of what vegetation may be found on other worlds lies once more in the stars. Astronomers grade stars according to their colour, which is related to their temperature, size and longevity. It is clear that only certain types of star are long-lived enough to allow the evolution of complex life to occur. From hottest to coldest these are the F-, G-, K- and M-class stars (our sun falls into the G category). F stars are larger, burn more brightly and bluer, and exhaust their fuel over a couple of billion years. K and M stars are smaller, dimmer, more red in colour and survive longer. We know that light of any colour from deep violet through to near-infrared could power photosynthesis. For another Earth-type planet orbiting around a G-class star, we can comfortably predict green, yellow or orange plants. Around stars that are hotter and bluer than our Sun, the abundance of blue photons would be so overwhelming that plants might need to shield themselves against it, using a pigment similar to anthocyanin, so that they would reflect blue. Since, however, they would still try to absorb a percentage of the energetic blue light, they would actually appear green to yellow to red. The span of M-star temperatures would make possible a wide spectrum of colours in alien plant life. A planet around a cooler M star, such as a red dwarf, would receive about half of the energy that Earth gets from the Sun, with less visible light and a spectrum closer to the near-infrared range. With less energy available, plants might try to absorb as much as possible, and with little light left over to reflect, appear black.

Once we have observed and hopefully recognised life on another world, be it animal, plant, microbe or maybe even mineral, what do we do next? Why ... we try and say hello, of course.

CHAPTER NINE

Is the Truth Really Out There?

At a 2015 press conference, NASA's Ellen Stofan and John Grunsfeld predicted that astrobiologists would finally detect alien life within the next 20 years. Once, this would have been viewed as a rash statement, but today, weighty evidence suggests that warm, wet environments habitable by forms of life we would recognise exist throughout the Universe. Our understanding of life's fingerprint and evolutionary manoeuvres grows by the day. The potential existence of sentient aliens and extraterrestrial cultures, on the other hand, remains controversial. It is the loneliest question in the cosmos – are we the only life forms in the Universe? The enormous size of our Galaxy, containing potentially 400 billion stars, makes it difficult to imagine that our planet is isolated in its status as the host of intelligent life. Somewhere out there, surely, are other life forms with whom we might be able to communicate – at least at some level. If they are out there, why have they not contacted us and are we even capable of detecting their presence? One assumption is clear – that any civilisation, by the mere fact that it has become a developed society, is intelligent. So what exactly is the fingerprint of intelligence? Who decides what intellect actually is? And do we as a species have enough of it to be able to find and recognise it elsewhere?

The Search for Answers

Our interest in whether or not life is out there stems from our ability to see the stars, and recognise that we are but one lowly planet orbiting just one of them. The notion that vast galactic empires may be conducting their own business in outer space remains conjecture that is based on apparently logical conclusions drawn from our own origins. We know that microbial life evolved on the Earth at least, and that life then took many twists and turns via natural selection and some chance events to develop complex multicellular bodies and brains, societies and finally technologies that could provide a means of transport to other planets – maybe one day to other stars. Who is to say this might not equally occur on any of the billions of other habitable planets we believe twirl out in the cosmos? The search for sentient life is not just scientific but also spiritual, based on a belief it is out there somewhere.

We want to answer one of the world's oldest questions: 'Are we alone in the Universe?' There was intensive debate about this issue even in antiquity. The atomists, who, as their name suggests, perceived correctly that atoms were the basic material of which everything is made up, believed in a plurality or a number of worlds. Yet, the Aristotelians held the opinion that we live in a closed cosmos with Earth at its centre. In the medieval age, philosophy and theology were dominated by the Aristotelian world view, until finally the Copernican revolution paved the way for the belief, and later proof, that there are many solar systems similar to ours in the vastness of space. Two widely assumed principles supported the idea that life is abundant in the Universe: the principles of *plenitude* and *mediocrity*. The former holds that a Universe made by a perfect Creator should be as rich as possible – and what universe could be richer than one that gives birth to and provides a home for a plenitude of life? The latter suggests that every place in the Universe that has similar molecules and shares similar laws of physics to Earth, would be likely to develop along a more or less similar route as our planet. The resulting multiplicity of Earth-like planets is a principle held by many in modern science. Nevertheless, whether or not that principle also applies to the existence of life remains an open question.

The Oddity of ET

In an attempt to quantify the possible number of cultures present in our Galaxy, the astronomer Frank Drake formulated a completely unsolvable equation in 1961 that, despite its unknowable and currently improvable answer, has gone down in history and is taught on all planetary science courses. The equation below is not some mind-boggling mathematical calculation – just a useful, relatively simple tool to help us contemplate the variables we must incorporate when considering the question of life elsewhere, and it is actually quite intriguing. Here it is:

$$N = R^\star \times f_p \times n_e \times f_l \times f_i \times f_c \times L$$

We are trying to figure out the value of **N**, which represents the number of civilisations in our Galaxy with whom radio communication might be possible. To arrive at this number, a variety of factors must be taken into account. Starting at the beginning, $\mathbf{R^{\star}}$ is the average rate of star formation in our Galaxy. Estimates for the number of stars in the Milky Way vary from a low of 100 billion to a high of 400 billion. Estimates for the age of the Milky Way also vary from an infant of 800 million years to a grandfather of 13 billion years. If we go with the lowest star count and the oldest age for the Galaxy, the average rate of star formation works out at 7.7 new stars per year. If we go with the highest star count and the youngest age for the Galaxy, the average rate of star formation becomes 500 new stars per year. The rate of star formation in the galaxy is not constant over time, however; stars were formed at a much faster rate in the Galaxy's earliest moments, and not all stars are created equal or deemed useful for hosting life. Today, estimates for the overall rate of star formation range from 5 to 20 new stars per year and the rate of formation of Sun-sized stars, around which intelligent life may arise, is in the order of one per year.

The next term, $\mathbf{f_p}$, is the fraction of those stars that have planets. At the time Drake wrote his equation, this was a complete unknown. Since then, nearly 2,000 exoplanets have been found orbiting a variety of stars. Estimating the total number of planets in the Universe is difficult, but it is possible that, in the Milky Way, each star has an average of 1.6 planets – yielding 160 billion alien planets in our home Galaxy alone. This number is making the chances for finding communicable life look a little better. The third term, $\mathbf{n_e}$, is the average number of planets that can potentially support life per star that has planets. In his original equation, Drake optimistically assigned a value of 2 to this parameter, meaning that he proposed on average two Earth-like planets per star for those stars with planets. The answer to this remains unknown, but out of the thousands of exoplanets discovered, small, rocky worlds similar to our own are popping up everywhere, and some of them may be capable of hosting life as we know it. The last four parameters, f_l, f_i, f_c and L, are, as you may have guessed, also not known – perhaps forever unknowable – and are very hard to estimate. They are in order: the fraction of planets that actually go on to develop life at some point, the fraction of those that actually go on to develop intelligent life, and the fraction of those intelligent civilisations that develop technology that releases detectable signs of their existence into space; finally, L is the length of time for which civilisations exist.

The most contentious is f_i, unsurprisingly. We have only one example, Earth, where life is abundant and humanity has reached a level of technology that allows it to scour the Universe for other life, and can broadcast its own existence into space. Is human-like, technological intelligence likely to be common across the Universe? Are we merely an evolutionary blip? Or is intelligence something that the entropy-driven, complexity-producing Universe will inevitably converge on? It may even be that Earth (and all intelligent life on it) is an early bloomer and that we are not hearing from advanced alien civilisations because the Universe has not had the time to spawn other habitable worlds on which they could flourish.

In case you are wondering, the estimated solutions to the Drake Equation range from 0 intelligent, communicating civilisations in the Galaxy, to 10,000 – not especially illuminating. We may be one of a myriad of intelligent species or we may be alone. Even if one day we were to receive signals from another intelligent species, the problem would remain of how to reply and stay in contact over such measureless distances, even ignoring the obvious barriers of communication media and language. It could well be that extraterrestrial life exists in parts of the vastness of the Universe that are beyond the possibility of contact or even of mere observation. Yet finding life outside the Earth – even non-intelligent microbial life – would be an important step towards a better understanding of the Drake Equation, and take us further along the yellow brick road to communication.

Conversations with my Cat

As far as we know, no cat can compose an email, no whale can sing to us in our own language and no bird can solve mathematical equations. Only humans can perform such intellectual feats, presumably, some may say, because we are smarter than all other animal species – at least by our own definition of intelligence. Just as with life itself, there is no globally accepted definition of intelligence. It has been described in many ways, from a capacity for logic, to abstract thought, understanding, self-awareness, communication, learning, emotional knowledge, memory, planning, creativity and problem-solving. At its most simple, however, intelligence is the ability to identify and receive information and retain it as knowledge for later use: now the scope for recognising other intelligent species on Earth widens.

Life based on one basic blueprint has existed on Earth for 3.7 billion years – more than a quarter of the age of the Universe – and it took 1.8 billion of those years for the first multicellular versions to appear. Life on Earth is divided into bacteria and fungi, plants, and animals, but nervous systems and brains only developed in animals. Of these animals, some 60–80 lines developed, but only in the chordate vertebrates did intelligence appear. Within the vertebrates, such as fish, amphibians, reptiles, birds and mammals, higher intelligence only developed in mammals. The hominids first appeared some 3–6 million years ago, but *Homo sapiens* evolved only in the last 200,000 years, producing a number of different civilisations, with only the most recent developing technology capable of seeking out other intelligent life. This last development of space-voyaging folk took place only in the last 100 years of the immense 4.55-billion-year lifespan of the Earth. The evolution of hominid intelligence is attributed to specific environmental challenges and it is a misinterpretation of evolutionary theory to see this rise of intelligence in us as a *necessary* process. Should we accept that it was pure chance and a lucky mutation or two? It could have appeared in fish or dinosaurs, or may not have arisen at all, but intelligence is the only adaptation to have allowed a single species to establish complete domination over the rest of the natural world. Will humanity with all its knowledge survive 100,000 years from now? We as a species are good at reproducing to ensure the longevity of our race, but are yet to prove we can use our gift of intelligence to survive across the ages.

Cosmic Conundrums and Fermi's Paradox

This hope of the existence of long-lived alien civilisations capable of first contact is what drove the Italian physicist Enrico Fermi to utter his famous phrase, 'Where is everybody?' In 1950, amid a spate of rumours of flying saucers crashing into New Mexico, Fermi reasoned that if only one in a million stars in the Milky Way had planets with intelligent beings and they began space travel, then within a few tens of million years they should have spread throughout all regions of our Galaxy, including our Solar System. So why, he wondered aloud, have we not seen them? Why have they not made their presence known? This became known as the *Fermi Paradox*. If Earth is not unique in having intelligent life, then civilisations should already have evolved many times over in the Galaxy, since there are billions of stars older than the Sun. If any of these civilisations wished to colonise the Galaxy, they could have done so by now. There are two answers to his question: (1) we are alone, or (2) we are not alone, and the first solves the paradox. Fermi was obviously posing the question because of his belief that we are not the only intelligent life forms floating in the sea of space. A number of solutions has been proposed, none of them provable yet, of course, but an answer I particularly like is that we are akin to animals in a zoo. Humans are bound by our current level of technological intelligence to travel only within our own Solar System. Any civilisation able to overcome these limitations would need to be vastly more advanced – so advanced, in fact, that they may see striking up a conversation with us with our current science, technology and social abilities, as futile, as we would view trying to chat to an ant colony scurrying around an anthill. Hence, we have heard no news. Perhaps more advanced civilisations are waiting until we are worthy. Or, if they don't exterminate us for being so inferior, they may assign us (or already have assigned us) to conservation and study in a galactic zoo with the aliens as our keepers. Perhaps they are reading this and laughing at us for not already realising.

Barriers to Life

The Great Filter is a probability barrier, a concept that some mechanism we cannot yet understand may have prevented life, or will prevent life in the future, from expanding into the Universe. We think there may be one or more highly unlikely evolutionary stages whose occurrence is paramount for an Earth-like planet to form and to produce an intelligent civilisation of a type that would be visible to us with our current observation technology. If you begin with trillions of potential germination points for life, and end with a total of zero extraterrestrial civilisations that are observable – *something* is happening *somewhere* along the line to affect (arrest or slow down) evolutionary development. The critical evolutionary step(s) towards intelligent life must be essential enough, yet unlikely enough, that even with many billion rolls of the dice one ends up with nothing: no aliens, no spacecraft, no signals. This very powerful Great Filter can change the course of history. So what could this Great Filter be? And importantly when did it happen? There are three possibilities: it already transpired in the distant geological past; it has not yet taken place; or ... it is happening right now.

If the filter were in the past, this would explain why we have not yet come across aliens, because if the rise of intelligent life on any one planet is sufficiently improbable, then it follows that we are most likely to be the only such civilisation in our Galaxy or even in the entire known Universe. A potentially unique and extremely improbable step occurred at some point in our history that allowed for intelligent technological life to arise on the Earth. If the Earth movie were stopped and played again from the start, the rise of sophisticated intelligence might not happen in its re-run. Evolutionary biology, at least for the moment, does not enable us to calculate the probability of the evolution of intelligent life on Earth, but we know that some events were critical to its success and may therefore be good candidates for a Great Filter that led down the path to intelligence. One criterion is that the Great Filter must only have happened once (as there is only one example of intelligent life), since features that have evolved multiple times on Earth are demonstrably likely to occur on other worlds. The evolution of flight, sight and limbs, which have all occurred on Earth several times, are ruled out as possible candidate events. Another possible Great Filter is that an event took a very long time to come to pass even after the perfect conditions for it to occur were present. The emergence of life in the first place is an example. As far as we know, the transformation from building blocks into a reproducing, metabolising organism may have occurred only once and have taken hundreds of millions of years to get going, even after the planet had cooled sufficiently to enable a wide range of organic molecules to be stable. It actually took 1.8 billion years for prokaryotes to evolve into eukaryotes, which is quite a long time. This transition is a good candidate for being the Great Filter.

A worrying possibility is that the Great Filter lies in our future. This would mean that some cataclysmic unknown event prevents almost all technological civilisations at our current stage of development from progressing to the point at which they engage in colonisation of space and make their presence known to other technological civilisations. For example, it could be that any sufficiently technologically advanced culture always discovers or creates very powerful weapons and causes its own annihilation. We will never know whether this is the case or not until it happens to us, or until we chance upon another civilisation at this point in its own evolution. A final thought to ponder is whether the Great Filter is happening right now! The greatest obstacle to exploration of the cosmos is the distances involved and the ability of humans to undertake and survive the journey. Could distance and physical frailty in fact prove a Great Filter, and indeed prevent other species from contacting us?

The Search Begins ...

The vast immeasurable expanse of the Universe and the enormous impact that first contact would have on our world has led a few brave souls to take on the scientific challenge of searching the cosmos for intelligent beings. What drives them is the belief that humanity is a normal outcome of physics, chemistry and biology. Since the 1950s, a small number of astronomers across the world have risked ridicule by joining in a search for other sentient beings. In 1984, they founded the *SETI Institute* (the *Search for ExtraTerrestrial Intelligence*), based in California. Utilising massive arrays on Earth, as well as space telescopes, SETI scans the heavens for any indication of radio or other communications beamed in our direction. At the time of writing, no verifiable signal has yet been received. The Universe may be teeming with life, but it is currently preserving its secrets.

Project Ozma

Between April and July 1960, Frank Drake, who wrote the quirky unsolvable equation presented earlier, undertook humanity's first effort to identify radio transmissions from alien sources. Based at the *National Radio Astronomy Observatory (NRAO)* in Green Bank, West Virginia, *Project Ozma* was born, named after the queen of L. Frank Baum's fictional land of Oz, described as 'very far away, difficult to reach, and populated by strange and exotic beings'. Drake initially directed his search towards two stars, similar in age to our Sun, known as Tau Ceti and Epsilon Eridani, located some 11 light years (66 trillion miles) away. For six hours every day, Project Ozma's radio telescope scanned frequencies emanating from regions of cold hydrogen gas, looking for repeat sequences of pulses or series of prime numbers such as 1, 2, 3, 5 or 7, that might indicate some form of artificial intelligent message. A thrilling red herring early in the programme proved to come from a now not-so-secret military experiment; besides that, there came only static. Nonetheless, the pioneering Project Ozma generated enormous public interest, and made the search for the technological fingerprints of civilisations on other worlds scientifically feasible.

Prime Numbers and Laser Pulses

In the story *Contact*, published in 1985 by Carl Sagan, a young SETI researcher finds strong evidence of ET life within a radio transmission and is chosen to represent humanity to make first contact. The signal is a repeating sequence of prime numbers apparently sent from the star Vega, and contains 60,000 pages of data outlining plans to build a machine to allow one human occupant to communicate with the alien life forms. This story, written by an astrobiologist and SETI researcher himself, was based on real techniques, real theories and even real scientists.

Jill Tarter (who gave a fantastic TED talk on this topic) acted as Sagan's muse for the novel and was portrayed in the film adaptation by Jodie Foster. The book draws on the idea that alien signals could take many forms – from radio and light signals to laser pulses and even genetic manipulation. We can still only guess at the means by which a more advanced civilisation might choose to make contact.

So far the hunt for alien signals has mostly used radio waves, based on the theory that radio is a relatively easy and cheap way to send signals long distances through space. The SETI Institute uses powerful radio telescopes on Earth to search for signals focused at a single spot on the radio dial, called *narrow-band signals*, and those that repeat in a mathematical pattern. Huge numbers of natural bodies make radio noise, such as small pulsars (pulsar actually being short for 'pulsating radio star'), although not in regular arrangements; yet the only thing that makes a narrow-band signal, as far as scientists know, is an artificial transmitter.

The SETI Institute's *Allen Telescope Array (ATA)* is solely dedicated to the search for signals broadcast by intelligent alien life. Located at the Hat Creek Observatory in the Cascade Mountains of California, the ATA is an ambitious array of multiple small dishes whose power can be combined to form the equivalent of a single large-dish antenna, but positioned in several different directions to make a more powerful radio ear than ever before. Because of its ability to study many areas of the sky at once, every day of the week, it has the ability to listen to a truly significant sample of the cosmos.

Exquisitely sensitive, the ATA could detect emissions from powerful radars equivalent to those we have on Earth at a distance of dozens of light years. Any society even slightly more advanced than our own could manage a deliberate radio transmission that the Array could tune into. For SETI researchers, it is only a matter of aiming the antennae in the right direction and establishing the correct frequency. Among its targets are the exoplanet candidates discovered by NASA's Kepler space telescope. For the first time in the history of the search for sentient life, telescopes can be pointed at stars known to host planetary systems, including those that may feature planets similar to Earth – just the type of worlds that might be home to a civilisation capable of building radio transmitters and receivers.

We assume that other intelligent civilisations would broadcast radio signals just as we do, but although radio-loud ourselves over such a short phase, we are already reducing our interference through switching to fibre-optic cables and telecommunication satellites. Furthermore, we are assuming that other intelligent civilisations would even want to talk to us, or know to look in our direction. What if other planets were host to hyper-intelligent space dolphins, who never rise above the sheltering waters of their world, in an attempt to evade dangerous stellar radiation? They would not even know there were other stars, let alone other intelligent beings wanting to communicate with them, nor would they probably care.

If listening for the one unexplainable radio message is a bit of a long shot, how else could we go about it? *Laser pulses* are a favourite choice. Russian and American scientists have scanned the skies periodically over the last couple of decades hunting for laser light, which is not only distinguishable from other natural types of light such as starlight, but as far as we know can only be produced by an intelligent source. Ghostly subatomic particles called *neutrinos* are perhaps better suited for transporting a message over long stellar distances than radio or optical signals, so it may be wise to look out for neutrino-based alien Morse code as well. We could also look for evidence of asteroid mining – humans are already seeing the potential benefits to our own civilisation of obtaining mineral resources from our local rocky belt, so why would an alien civilisation not do the same? Perhaps evidence could be found through unusual changes in the chemical composition of the asteroid belt, irregular-shaped chunks missing from images, an increase in the size and amount of debris surrounding a celestial body, or other changes detectable from Earth. An unfortunate side effect of our own culture is pollution, but this means we could search for similar dirty signatures in alien atmospheres. If there are non-natural chemicals, such as chlorofluorocarbons, in a planet's atmosphere, this would also be a sign that there might be someone with technology on the ground.

Taking this a step further, we could actually look for evidence that may have been sitting right here on earth for billions of years – who is to say that aliens have not been here at some point already and left behind some artefact or message for us to find? Our DNA encodes information – could it have an alien message written into it? It is of course highly unlikely, but still in the outer realms of possibility. We could even take a cue from science fiction and look for the signature from an alien spacecraft zooming by. We may just get lucky one day and receive an email. A group of scientists have set up a website inviting ET to get in touch, and although 99.9 per cent are hoaxes, only one needs to be real.

The Power of Civilisation

Believe it or not, should we ever make contact with ET there actually exists a ruler by which alien civilisations can be measured. It is called *The Kardashev Scale*. Currently classed on this scale by Carl Sagan as a Type 0.7 civilisation, the question being put is whether humanity will ever advance past the Moon and finally make our way into the ranks of the Type Is? As a civilisation grows and advances, its energy demands will increase rapidly as a result of population growth and the power requirements for the technology this greater number of people will supposedly build and operate. The Kardashev Scale was created to measure a theoretical civilisation's mechanical progression against how much energy it has available. The scale was originally designed in 1963 by the Russian astrophysicist

Nikolai Kardashev, who created three base classes, each with an energy disposal level: Type I (10^{16}W) Type II (10^{26}W), and Type III (10^{36}W). Recent astronomers have extended the scale to Type IV (10^{46}W) and Type V (all the energy available in all universes and in all realities). The human race still has a long way to go before being awarded Type I status as we continue to sustain our energy needs from fossilised plants and animals, and is therefore at the bottom of the civilisational heap.

A *Type I* designation is bestowed upon populations who have been able to harness all the energy available from their host planet and the energy that reaches it from their own star. The population will then have the knowledge and know-how to collect and stockpile this energy to match the demands of its growing numbers. However, humans being able to harness all Earth's energy is hard to fathom – it would mean we could control all the natural forces on the Earth, such as volcanoes, the weather and even earthquakes.

A *Type II* civilisation can harness the power of its local star directly, controlling the star itself. One hypothetical method of doing this is called a *Dyson Sphere*, named after the physicist Freeman Dyson, who had the idea that a growing technological culture would ultimately be limited by access to energy, and that advanced power-hungry civilisations would be driven to harvest all available light from stars. Such a device would consist of vast clusters of machines that would encircle a star, harvesting most or all of its energy output and transferring it to the civilisation's own planet for later use. Another idea for capturing stellar power involves the control of nuclear fusion, the mechanism that runs stars, and the harnessing of this power in an incredibly large reactor. Perhaps nearby gas giants could also be utilised for their hydrogen, slowly drained of their chemical life source by an orbiting nuclear reactor. What is attractive about this level of advancement is that should a moon-sized object enter the Solar System on a collision course with our little planet we would have the ability to vaporise it. Perhaps we could even play a planetary game of chess – moving our planet out of the way or sacrificing another planet of our choice to block the invader's path – cosmic checkmate.

Searching for evidence of this theory, at the end of 2015, scientists monitoring NASA's Kepler space telescope observed a bizarre star snappily entitled KIC 8462852 that was shown to be emitting a strange light pattern. As detailed in Chapter 8, Kepler searches for dips in starlight created when a planet transits in front of its host star. KIC 8462852 stood out as being strange because the star was witnessed dimming by 20 per cent, unlike the normal one per cent created by the passing of a planet. It was also seen to be surrounded by a mass of matter consistent with debris found around a young star soon after its formation; this star, however, is not young and the debris appeared to be recent. Could this debris in fact be a megastructure similar to a Dyson Sphere? SETI astronomers have so far found no evidence of radio signals coming from this potentially alien astro-engineering project, but KIC 8462852 will now undoubtedly be the subject of SETI observations for years to come.

Once a civilisation has graduated from gaining control over a planet and then a star, making its own extinction almost impossible, what could possibly be next? Well, a *Type III* civilisation, of course: a galactic space-roving population with total control of energy, resulting in a master race with dominion over the Universe. These beings may even have evolved into self-replicating cyborgs or cybernetic organisms, both biological and robotic. In this scenario, the descendants of regular humans would be seen as a weak, inferior and primitive clan. The dominant humanoid species would have a population boom as they colonised the Galaxy, building numerous Dyson Spheres to leach the energy from each new star they came across, creating a huge network of stellar energy funnelling power back to the home planet.

Not alone in his beliefs, Kardashev considered a *Type IV* civilisation too advanced to contemplate. Could anything be more theoretically advanced and fictional than Dr Who-esque cyborgs harnessing the power of hundreds of stars? Nonetheless, some believe that even greater advancement is possible for a society. Step forward the *Type IV* civilisations that would be capable of harnessing the energy content of almost the entire Universe and travelling across the accelerating expansion of space. A Type IV civilisation would need to tap into energy sources unknown to us using bizarre, or currently unknown, physics. There is a further level – a *Type V* civilisation, where beings would essentially be gods, with the knowledge and power to manipulate the Universe and beyond at their will.

Cosmic Sightseeing

The human brain is the most powerful entity in existence as we know it – a biological supercomputer. As such, it gives humans a massive advantage over automated machines such as telescopes, rovers and space probes. It has superior pattern-recognition capabilities and allows for ingenious problem-solving strategies. In space, the unexpected is the norm and no being is better than a human at responding quickly to the unanticipated. Despite the fact that we would be the best entities to send in search of other life forms, long-distance space exploration is highly problematic for the human body. If we ignore the obvious issue of a lack of advanced-enough technology and propulsion systems even to blast humans off to far-flung star systems, our weak little bodies would not survive the trip. A short lifespan of up to 120 years is not compatible with the up to 80,000 years it would require with current technology to reach even the closest star, not to mention what spending that length of time in microgravity and exposed to the radiation of space would wreak physically on the human body and mind. It represents a perfect storm of immeasurable distance, slow travel speed, human frailty, short lifespans, and extreme cost, which in combination necessitate our reliance on technology to reach out to the stars and make the introductions for us.

This is not a bad second choice. Automated robotic probes have been sent to planets, moons, comets and asteroids, and to the very edges of our Solar System, and for the most part have been successful beyond our wildest imaginations. However, what about going beyond the Solar System to search for other life forms? That is a goal far beyond our current capabilities. In 1978, the probes *Pioneer 10* and *11*, were launched and after successfully completing their missions around Jupiter and Saturn, continued along paths that would eventually take them out of the Solar System. Today, they are heading towards the star Aldebaran, 68 light years from the Sun (which will take in the region of 2 million years). After 30 years of flight, they are still somewhere well within the Solar System and sadly all radio communications have been lost. Even though we will never know what, or even who, these probes meet on their journey, *Pioneer 10* does bear a plaque inscribed with information about Earth and humanity – just in case it bumps into some beings from the Aldebaran civilisation. But if they reply to our message, will there still be anyone left on Earth to receive it?

Since voyaging into the cosmos looking for friends is challenging, and two-way communication is not possible with our current technology and short lives, we are focusing instead on sending *messages in bottles*, as well as listening out for them calling to us. Alien civilisations may even be able to eavesdrop on humanity by tapping into our TV and radio broadcasts. Considering that one of the first TV transmissions was of Hitler opening the 1936 Olympic Games – and we all know what happened soon afterwards – a worry is that this will not exactly inspire them to get in contact. In 1951, the first episode of *I Love Lucy* was broadcast and some 0.0002 seconds later, the signal headed into space. Maybe this, or re-runs of *Friends* or David Attenborough documentaries could make humanity and the Earth seem more appealing.

Given that stars in our galactic neighbourhood are separated by about 4 light years, in the past 50 years roughly 10,000 star systems may have been exposed to our TV shows. They must be rather confused about what on <insert alien planet name here> is going on over on that little pale blue dot – or perhaps they are as hooked on *Game of Thrones* as we are.

Hello?

We are not only broadcasting BBC Radio 2 and reality TV shows, but have actually sent complete messages into space. SETI most famously transmitted a communication to the stars in 1974 using radio waves from the *Arecibo* telescope in Puerto Rico, aimed at a globular cluster, M13, more than 25,000 light years away. Frank Drake and Carl Sagan composed the message, which included the numbers 1 to 10, atomic numbers of the elements of life such as hydrogen, carbon and oxygen, information on our DNA, a figure of a human (non-gender specific) and a graphic of our Solar System highlighting the Earth as the origin of the message. Sadly, the stars this message was aimed at will no longer be in the same spot by the time it arrives, but who knows who might pick it up along the way.

Three years later in 1977, the *Golden Records* were launched on both *Voyagers 1* and *2*, intended to communicate a story of our world to extraterrestrials, interestingly only portraying the positive sides of Earth – no warfare, hunger or disease – which makes sense. Who wants to make first contact with an alien civilisation only to highlight the less attractive aspects of life *back home*? In August 2012, *Voyager 1* took its first steps towards becoming that beacon as it entered interstellar space, leaving our Solar System behind. The spacecraft is trekking towards a star called Gliese 445, and has a date with it in 40,000 years' time. Of course, by this date it won't be able to transmit home any data – in fact, by 2025 all of its scientific equipment will have stopped working (the equipment on board is already more than

40 years old, created before the CD and colour television).
The *Voyager* message, however, is embedded in a 12-inch
gold-plated copper disk containing sounds and images
selected to portray the diversity of life and culture on Earth.
Again, Carl Sagan led the charge and with his associates
assembled 115 images and a variety of natural sounds such
as surf, wind and thunder, birds, whales and other animals.
To this they added musical selections from different cultures
and eras, and spoken greetings from Earthlings in 55
languages, together with printed messages from the then
President Jimmy Carter and UN Secretary General Kurt
Waldheim. The launching of this record says a great deal
about the hope and positivity of humanity. Since then, all
missions to other planets and those designed to orbit and
explore the Solar System have contained messages including
information about the Earth and humanity, just in case any
being comes across them.

After *New Horizons* flew by Pluto in 2015, it began a new
journey towards the Kuiper Belt, following which it may
one day become the fifth spacecraft to leave the Solar
System and may even be the first to be discovered by an
alien species some millions of years from now. Unlike
Pioneers 10 and *11* and *Voyagers 1* and *2*, *New Horizons* was
launched in 2006 without a welcome message, but following
completion of its active mission there will be some space
available on its computer for a message to be uploaded
digitally. Unlike previous messages, however, this one,
fondly known as the *One Earth Message*, will be a unique
crowd-sourced message in a bottle, sent by people from all
over the world. Who speaks for Earth? The answer is
everyone. This literal selfie of our planet will aim to
communicate to ET the real essence of the Earth, humanity
and the other life forms that share our planet. If we did not
believe there was even the slightest chance of intelligent life
out there, why would we bother?

Much of today's scientific exploration and data analysis
looks to the public for help and support, such as the

Zooniverse, which calls upon citizen scientists to help comb through mountains of data to aid scientists with classifying distant galaxies, spotting black holes, characterising surface features on Mars and even hunting for exoplanets. The quest for ET is no different. The SETI@home project has involved the worldwide public in a search for radio-wave evidence of life outside Earth for 16 years. Based at the Space Science Laboratory at the University of California (Berkeley), this project records and analyses data from the Arecibo Observatory by searching for narrow-band signals of possible extraterrestrial origin. As yet, no such signals have been found. Today, SETI@home continues its search for evidence of extraterrestrial life with hundreds of thousands of volunteers each hoping to be the one to find it.

What Happens if We Find it? What Happens if We Don't?

As Carl Sagan wrote in *Contact*, 'The universe is a pretty big place. It's bigger than anything anyone has ever dreamed of before. So if it's just us ... seems like an awful waste of space.'

NASA's Kepler space telescope has helped scientists discover thousands of exoplanets, and has a very large field of view of 105 square degrees – comparable to the area of your hand stretched at arm's length. Most astronomical telescopes have fields of view of less than 1 square degree so, although Kepler can monitor more than 100,000 stars, it is still a miniscule area of the Galaxy, let alone the Universe. Set to launch in 2018, NASA's next-generation James Webb Space Telescope, together with its larger successors, will give scientists the opportunity to look for signatures of life in the atmospheres of exoplanets – although they will not be capable of distinguishing whether life forms are brainy beings or single-celled microbes. Astronomers now know that every star in the Milky Way galaxy has at least one planet orbiting it, so humanity's first contact with alien life may one day be possible. It is also not just a case of where to look, but also when. The Arizona State University astronomer and author Paul Davies points out that even if a fairly close civilisation, say one 1,000 light years away, were to look through a telescope and find Earth, it would see the planet 1,000 years in our past. Why would they bother to send a message to a planet that had not yet discovered electricity, let alone built a receiver to intercept their message?

Even the discovery of some simple sort of ET life would be extraordinary. Finding non-sentient extraterrestrial life would help piece together our own origins and the history of life on Earth, and would be a momentous watershed event for the entire globe. If the discovery were of life that could say *hello* back to us – life as we know it would change forever.

UFO-spotters, Raëlian cultists and self-certified alien abductees notwithstanding, humans have to date seen no sign of any extraterrestrial intelligent civilisation. We have not received any visitors from space, nor have our radio telescopes detected any unusual transmissions from other worlds. But although no one has yet found life elsewhere, there's no reason necessarily to despair. Mass extinctions have wiped out vast majorities of species in our planet's nearly 5-billion-year history, and yet here we are. We can only assume and hope that any life existing elsewhere would be just as resilient.

But what if this really is all there is – and our isolation extends far into the Universe, or, and perhaps more likely, we do not recognise different life forms because some of our presumptions concerning how an alien civilisation might look and behave, based on our own experience, are incorrect? In 2015, the close examination of 100,000 galaxies near to our own concluded that none presented any irrefutable evidence of civilisations with highly advanced technology. Instead of listening for voices from the skies, scientists looked instead for heat signatures that would be produced by advanced civilisations, just as Freeman Dyson and later the Kardashev Scale predicted might exist. The idea is that, once a star is encased in a Dyson Sphere, its glow would be suppressed, but the engineered construction itself could be detected by the wasted heat oozing out from it. The same process is happening when your iPhone warms up during prolonged 'Googling'. In some sense it doesn't matter by what means a galactic civilisation generates or uses its power, because the second law of thermodynamics makes energy use hard to hide. They could construct Dyson spheres, draw power from rotating black holes or build giant computer networks in the cold outskirts of galaxies. Any of these would produce waste heat, but the search for objects emitting more heat than light in over 100,000 nearby galaxies has yielded, perhaps unsurprisingly, no positive results. No Type III civilisations have been found – yet.

Over the years, to explain away the endless silence of deep space, researchers have created a vast assemblage of possible explanations for the disappointing lack of any intelligent alien life. Perhaps we are indeed alone. Perhaps the laws of astrophysics and biology make intelligent life vanishingly rare, and the rise of humans was serendipitous. Perhaps technological civilisations always destroy themselves once they reach a certain point. Perhaps interstellar travel is simply too hard, too slow or too boring for any advanced civilisation to bother undertaking. It could be that galaxy-sterilising explosions such as gamma-ray bursts in the cosmic past suppressed the rise of advanced civilisations and now that these have quietened down, we humans had the chance to arise and are the foundations for civilisations yet to come. Perhaps, and I like this idea best, any advanced civilisation will have become in tune with its natural environment, value nature's role in its survival and will be working in harmony with it. In this scenario, our supremely intelligent and compassionate aliens would not produce waste heat, light, nor electromagnetic signals from a repository of profligate technologies – so it will be less easy to find them until we use our intelligence to do the same.

CHAPTER TEN

The Next Generation

Imagine the Earth in the future. Are there flying cars, floating cities, outposts scattered across the ocean floors, and artificially intelligent cyborgs? This is the magical, technologically advanced world that science fiction paints. But is it realistic? By 2050, the UN predicts that Earth's human population will have grown from 7.1 billion to between 8.3 and 10.9 billion and may only continue to grow. In this version of the future, many questions will surround the sustainability of world populations, the growing pressures on the environment, global food supplies and energy resources. Will the Earth be able to sustain us? With the answer to this question unknown but worrying nonetheless, humanity needs to start planning for the future and to contemplate leaving the safety net of the Earth and looking towards the stars. Stephen Hawking has stated that the colonisation of space would be the best way to ensure the survival of humanity. Although I believe there are other ways to ensure our species lives on, space settlement is the next logical step after space exploration – it implies the permanent or long-term presence of humans in an environment outside Earth. But if we leave our home, suddenly we will be living outside of what we consider to be 'normal' and will be attempting to inhabit environments in which we are not originally biologically designed to survive. We will have to become the extremophiles, a generation of aliens and Life 2.0.

Why and Where Should We Go?

When in 1961 Russian cosmonaut Yuri Gagarin was blasted into orbit and safely returned, he became the first man in space and people were finally given substantial evidence to support the idea that humans could travel off-world. Subsequently, and since the year 2000, humanity has been continuously living in space. Although a colony of fewer than 10 people, the International Space Station is our first extraterrestrial outpost, an inhabited satellite orbiting the Earth. No *terrestrial* or land-based space colonies have been built thus far, yet this is the dream as investigating the habitability of other worlds not only benefits our understanding of the versatility of life, it also takes us closer to answering one of humanity's oldest questions – are we alone? Our permanent residence in space is helping us prepare for a future when humans may need to be able to live and work on other planets and moons.

In the long term, *i.e.* another 3 billion years, our Sun will start to expand and enter its red-giant phase as it draws closer to its death. It will engulf Venus, and even if it doesn't swell enough to reach the Earth, it will still boil off the oceans and heat the surface to temperatures that even the hardiest extremophile could not survive. This, however, is a rather long way off and not really a good enough reason to start the process of moving right now. So why would we want an off-world colony today? Or more importantly, why *should* we want one. There is no denying that it would be magnificent to have people living on multiple worlds, nor that sadly the Earth is beginning to sag under the pressure of humanity. We are on the verge of self-inflicted destruction, whereby the damage we are doing to our planet is progressing faster than our capabilities to fix it. Off-world colonies could, and I strongly emphasise *could*, improve the chances of human civilisation surviving in the event that the Earth becomes uninhabitable. Life is fragile and any number of natural or man-made catastrophes could occur, such as another Snowball Earth, asteroid impact, nuclear war or complete depletion of our natural resources. This paints a very bleak and somewhat depressing picture of our future. Hopefully long before any of these scenarios come to pass, I believe we will choose to leave Earth for the purpose of exploration and scientific enlightenment, because it is built into us to want to travel and unravel the mysteries beyond our physical and intellectual borders. If we happen to set up humanity's lifeboat in the process, then even better.

As such we need to explore how humans might be able to live and work on other planets, moons and in space itself, as one day that need may become an imperative and that imperative a reality. What might it be like to live on other worlds in our Solar System? A great thought experiment with a similar theme and plot-line to the film *Interstellar*, assumes that we have developed the capability to skip across the Solar System to its farthest reaches and have the knowledge and technology needed to build a human outpost on any world of our choosing in the Solar System. Where would it be?

Mercury

Starting from the inside out, humanity could move to Mercury – and it goes without saying, its surface would be an extremely inhospitable place in which to land unprotected. It would not be our first choice, that's for sure! Like the Moon, it lacks a protective atmosphere, so colonists and their equipment would need thermal protection from the intense heat of the Sun, and require shielding from the powerful solar radiation that reaches the surface and infrared radiation of any very hot region of Mercury's crust. Because of its rocky, barren and airless similarities with the Moon, any settlement of Mercury might be performed using the same general technology, approach and equipment as a colonisation attempt on the Moon. Unlike the Moon, however, Mercury has the advantage of a magnetic field that protects it from cosmic rays and solar flares, and a larger surface gravity of about 0.37g, almost exactly equal to that of Mars – just over one-third of the gravity on Earth. This means that heavy equipment and building materials would be easier to lift and move around and, as an amusing bonus, a human could jump three times as high. Due to its proximity to the Sun, the surface of Mercury can reach 427°C (800°F) near the equator during the day (hot enough to melt lead) and fall to –180°C (–292°F) at night, with temperatures at the poles being even colder – that's a lot for the human body to deal with. For a planet located so close to the Sun, it is perhaps surprising that significant deposits of ice lie hidden in the shadows of polar impact craters. Could this ice be mined to access water on Mercury? These polar regions could actually be a good spot for settlements, providing a source of water and a break from the intense heat of the Sun. Weirdly, a colony would not really have to worry about any natural disasters wiping them out as, without an atmosphere, Mercury has no weather and with no bodies of liquid water or active volcanoes, there is very little risk of devastating tsunamis or volcanic eruptions. Interestingly, this lack of atmosphere would mean that during the day, the sky would appear black, not blue – that would just be odd! Sadly, like all planetary bodies in the Solar System, however, there is always the threat of asteroid impacts and, potentially, earthquakes (Merquakes?!), owing to compressive forces that shrink and squash the planet. Happily, it only takes around five minutes for signals to bounce between Mercury and Earth, so there could be a stunted but very achievable conversation with home. Who would have thought that Mercury would actually be quite an attractive option?

Venus

Next for consideration is Venus, our Solar System's equivalent to the mythical realm of Hell. Already it sounds appealing, doesn't it? Without technological help (which is far beyond our capabilities at the present time), our fragile human bodies would die in less than 10 seconds on the surface, instantly crushed while being simultaneously cremated. The last, very quick, breath taken would be of toxic gas. Life on Venus would be nauseating, brutal and very short. If we could somehow surmount these issues, then the best place to set up camp would be somewhere on the flat, smooth plains that can be found on more than two-thirds of the planet. Walking around would not be a pleasant experience with surface temperatures of 465°C (869°F), and air so thick that every step would be like trying to run in water. The planet's gravity would not be a problem, however, as it is almost 91 per cent of that of Earth so would probably not feel much different, but the atmospheric pressure is 92 bars – tantamount to living more than 900m (3,000ft) beneath the ocean on Earth.

High in the atmosphere on Venus, winds travel up to 400kph (249mph) – faster than any tornado or hurricane witnessed on Earth – interspersed with fierce bursts of lightning that, as a small mercy, never reach the already challenging surface. The roasting heat prevents any rain from touching ground so water is never able to collect or even wet the surface. The active volcanoes on Venus may add yet another danger to colonists as the eruptions are thought to be so large that they could re-surface the whole planet. It would take only a few minutes to get a distress call home when the planets are closest, but when Venus disappears to the other side of the Sun it would take up to 15 minutes. Not that any help would be close at hand should it be needed, nor could anyone really offer assistance against such an inhospitable surface environment.

The type of habitat that could use the strengths of Venus' extreme conditions is one filled with gases of the same composition as Earth's atmosphere at sea level (so colonists could breathe) but floating high in the dense Venusian atmosphere. The atmospheric pressure at 50km (31 miles) above the surface of Venus is similar to that on Earth at sea level (1 bar), and temperatures are just over 0°C (32°F) at that altitude. Just like a weather balloon, a floating habitat with internal pressure like that on Earth would rise to an altitude on Venus where the external pressure was the same. If this were actually possible, a human could walk outside on to a ramp using just an oxygen tank and look out over the Venusian clouds below. The habitats would produce their own oxygen through photosynthesising vegetation, which would not be difficult to grow in Venus's carbon dioxide-rich atmosphere, and water could be extracted from the sulphuric acid in the clouds. Theoretically, anything is possible.

The Asteroid Belt

Although perhaps a surprising choice, there is a real option of moving to a dwarf planet such as *Ceres*, the largest object in the Asteroid Belt. The objects of this orbiting rock garden have been suggested as potential sites for future space-mining operations hoping to reap water for its hydrogen to make rocket fuel; oxygen to provide breathable air to make long-distance space missions possible; and ore minerals. They are also seen as potential staging posts and transport hubs for deeper space exploration due to their lower escape velocity. The main fear any colonists would have living on these objects would be of one asteroid bumping into another, and the resulting threat of knocking objects out of the belt and on to a collision course with Earth.

Comprising one-third of the mass of the entire asteroid belt, Ceres could quite possibly become the main asteroid base for future trips to Mars, as it is not a dead lump of pockmarked rock, as commonly comes to mind when we think of an asteroid. Ceres may actually contain more water ice buried beneath its surface than all the fresh water flowing across the Earth, and although its gravity is less than 3 per cent that of the Earth, it is one of the most suitable locations for a permanent human base. Ceres is currently not believed to have a magnetic field so its surface is not shielded from cosmic rays or other forms of radiation, and it does not have a significant atmosphere, so there is no weather (adverse or otherwise) and it always remains well below freezing. NASA's *Dawn* spacecraft was the first to visit Ceres, having arrived in orbit in March 2015, and was greeted by a complex and beautiful landscape full of weird-shaped craters, a 6.5km- (4-mile-) high mountain, mysterious bright spots that might be huge deposits of salt, and an entirely dry surface. Excitingly for life, however, there may be liquid water inside the dwarf world as water vapour has been seen erupting from it into space, possibly from volcano-like icy geysers. Thankfully, these vapour jets would be far too weak to pose any danger to humans but they hint at the world's potential to support life. The relatively small size of Ceres is a selling point as well. Hiking across its surface to find a suitable site to live would not take very long (relative to travelling around a planet or moon that is) – Ceres has a diameter of 950km (590 miles), just short of the distance from the south coast of England to the north of Scotland.

Europa

Despite depictions within some entertaining science-fiction films, humanity could not even contemplate living on

Jupiter. A purely gaseous world, there is probably no solid surface on which a crew might touch down, which makes colonisation impossible – unless you fancy setting foot directly on to its core and can tackle the crushing weight of liquid hydrogen bearing down on you. We might be able to live in orbit around Jupiter, however, and harvest its energy to provide the resources for colonisation of any number of its 60 nearby moons. If you ask an astrobiologist they will instantly suggest setting up a base on Europa due to the tantalising idea that life may already live beneath its icy shell. In reality, Callisto with its own large amounts of water ice, low radiation levels and relative geological stability would be ideal. However, where is the adventure in that? For human explorers setting up a research base on Europa, the cold, icy surface would actually be quite suitable. It is relatively flat and, although crisscrossed with small ridges, these are little more than a few metres high so should not prevent construction nor journeys across the landscape. A serious threat to life, however, is Jupiter's magnetosphere, which bombards Europa with deadly radiation. The best location for a base would therefore be either protected below Europa's icy crust or on the hemisphere of the moon that faces away from Jupiter, as this receives the least amount of radiation. Like our Moon, gravity is low (about 13 per cent that of the Earth), so going for a walk on either moon would be a similar experience, and also means that both have an almost imaginary weatherless atmosphere. Colonists, if daring to live on Europa's surface in inflatable igloos, would need them heated to help deal with the blistering cold outside (down to −220°C/−364°F at the poles), reinforced to withstand icequakes, and located away from possible powerful plumes of water shooting out through the icy surface from layers far beneath. If you wanted to email research findings home, a message would take at least 30 minutes to arrive, and only when the gargantuan bulk of Jupiter wasn't blocking the way. Oh, and don't even think about making a voice call.

Enceladus and Titan

For the same reasons as Jupiter, Saturn is not a place where you want to end up. However, if you had to make an emergency landing somewhere in this system and could make it to Titan, then you might have a chance of survival as you could jump out of your ship without the need for a pressurised spacesuit – you'd simply need a tank of oxygen and some insulating clothing. With its thick atmosphere, standing on the surface of Titan would feel rather like being submerged in a swimming pool on Earth. The landscape also resembles that of the Earth and there is a number of flat areas of land for a colony to build upon. If this weren't enough good news, Titan is primarily composed of water ice and rocky material and NASA's *Cassini* mission showed exciting hints of an ocean inside it, which might be as salty as the Earth's Dead Sea. Colonists would just need to melt this surface ice, and/or access the ocean and filter out the salt. One downside is that although the surface is covered in aqueous bodies, humans could not drink the hydrocarbon-rich liquid – it would be like trying to drink tar. Excitingly, Titan offers a lot to work with, as it already possesses an abundance of all the elements necessary to support life. Water can easily be used to generate oxygen and nitrogen to add to breathable air. Nitrogen, methane and ammonia can all be used to produce fertiliser for growing food. The best thing about Titan concerns transportation, which takes on a whole new dimension because of the moon's low gravity (more or less 14 per cent that of Earth) and dense atmosphere – colonists could strap on wings and fly! It has weather in the form of methane rain and thunderstorms but no cyclones or tornadoes, and its atmosphere would protect colonists from cosmic rays and many incoming projectiles. In addition, there are no moonquakes as far as is known and the existence of cryovolcanoes is still debated – it is a pretty comfortable, safe and quite possibly enjoyable place in which to live. It gets my vote!

If a spacecraft carrying colonists ended up on Enceladus, one of Saturn's other moons, then life would be a lot harder. The main dangers here are the freezing cold temperatures, minimal air pressure and explosive geysers. Due to the moon's icy surface, most of the sunlight it receives is reflected back into space, lowering the temperature to an average −201°C (−330°F) throughout the day. As a result of its sparse atmosphere, it has no extreme weather for colonists to worry about, but is left exposed to incoming space debris and radiation. The best locations for a human base would be near to the *tiger stripes* in the southern polar region as these would provide a source of heat and power. These giant fissures spew plumes of frozen ice particles and cold vapour into space, thereby producing nearly 16 gigawatts of power – a reasonable trade-off for the danger of living close by. The source of this power is believed to be the ocean lurking beneath the ice, which may also harbour indigenous life forms. The moon's tiny gravity, just 1 per cent that of the Earth, would hamper travelling around. It is not really a world you want to end up on forever.

Uranus and Neptune

Once we get to this frigid neck of the Solar System, colonisation is much more possible on moons than planets. This is because, just as with Jupiter and Saturn, Uranus and Neptune lack much in the way of a solid surface under their layers of ice and gas on which to settle. The pressures below the thick atmosphere on Uranus are enormous and would instantaneously crush any life form. Also, there is no process inside Uranus, such as volcanism on Earth, that would give colonists a form of energy to use as a replacement for the very distant Sun. Out of the 27 moons orbiting Uranus, two prime targets for colonisation would be *Titania* and *Miranda*. Not a huge amount is known yet about these moons, but it is thought that they have a solid surface on which a mission could at least attempt to touch down. All of Uranus's moons lack weather systems and surface pressure due to non-existent atmospheres, and it is probably a safe assumption to say there is a multitude of as yet unknown hazards waiting on them. They are also very cold, with the average temperature of Titania, for example, hovering around −203°C (−330°F). Furthermore, all the moons spend 42 years in darkness and 42 years in faint sunlight, which would not exactly prove ideal for the human body or mind.

Humanity could also happily bypass Neptune and move on to its largest moon, *Triton*. Little is known about this moon either, as only a single spacecraft (*Voyager 2*) has ever whizzed by. We know it is made of rock and nitrogen ice and has both cratered and smooth regions. The smooth areas are formed when geysers of dust and nitrogen gas erupt out of the moon's crust. The dust then drifts gently back down, coating the surface of the moon. It has a slight atmosphere and might feel strangely similar to standing on the Moon or Mercury. It's unclear, however, how dangerous the geysers would be but, as with any unpredictable eruption, establishing a settlement next to or near one would never be a smart move. Triton is currently the coldest known object in the Solar System with an average temperature of −235°C (−390°F), so a continuous energy source would be needed to keep a colony warm.

Pluto

This once-upon-a-time planet has been shrouded in mystery for so long that science can only speculate about what setting foot on it might be like. Depending upon where it is on its 248 Earth-year orbit, freezing temperatures can be expected down to −233°C (−387°F), and so we can kiss goodbye to the chance of liquid water. It has a tenuous atmosphere, created through the seasonal sublimation of ices on the surface, but is not thick enough to give the surface much pressure to work with – just 0.003atm (0.3 MPa/3mbar) – and due to its small size has only 1/15th the gravity of the Earth. However, NASA's *New Horizons* probe has given Pluto a much-needed confidence boost (it was owed nothing less after the whole 'not a *real* planet' demotion) by revealing an incredibly geologically diverse and active world, even out in the farthest reaches of the Solar System. Should humanity ever figure out how to travel there in person, Pluto would display a number of useful attributes. This newly viewed second Red Planet is reddish owing to layers of haze stretching 160km (100 miles) into the atmosphere, while the surface is covered in flowing nitrogen-rich ice, similar to the movement of glaciers on the Earth, as well as ice volcanoes and snowfall. There may even be an underground ocean. Although setting up and maintaining a settlement on Pluto would be enormously complex and communications would be frustratingly slow, it would, scientifically at least, be well worth the endeavour.

Living in Space

At our current level of technology, the building of a space colony would present a set of extraordinarily great challenges. Space settlements would have to provide for all the material needs of hundreds or thousands of people, in an environment that would be very hostile to human life as we know it. Colonists would require systems such as controlled life support, which have yet to be developed in any meaningful way, and would be obliged to deal with isolation and confinement over many years, potentially for the entirety of their lives. The huge cost of sending anything from the surface of the Earth into orbit (roughly £15,000 per kilogram) gives an insight into the astonishing costs associated with building and launching a space colony.

As mentioned previously, humanity is already living in space and life on the *International Space Station* (*ISS*) provides a glimpse into some of the major challenges humans would face should we venture further into the Solar System. The *ISS* is a habitable satellite that orbits the Earth at an altitude of 355km (220 miles) once every 90 minutes, meaning that the Sun sets and rises for the crew nearly 16 times a day. It's a vast project with shared ownership by NASA (USA), Roscosmos (Russia), JAXA (Japan), ESA (several European countries) and CSA (Canada), who all pitched in to build it. For the last 15 years there have been up to 10 astronauts at any one moment living in the vacuum of space above our heads, for up to a year at a stretch. Astronauts from all contributing space agencies have spent time there and the first British-ESA astronaut, Tim Peake, arrived for a six-month getaway in December 2015.

There are so many scientific and spiritual benefits of spending time in space, but it is the challenges and dangers that these real-life superheroes overcome to achieve these that tend to capture the public's imagination and most certainly deserve our respect. The best-known attributes of the cosmic environment are that there is no oxygen or pressure in the vacuum of space. Daring to take an unprotected breath in space removes oxygen from the blood without replenishing it, so after 9–12 seconds, the deoxygenated blood would reach the brain, resulting in loss of consciousness. Two minutes later, death would follow. Blood and other bodily fluids would boil as the pressure instantly dropped, causing the body to swell to twice its normal size, but it would not explode, as commonly depicted in films – this is a myth. Another myth to debunk is that portrayed by the image of a frozen drifting corpse. In the vacuum of space, there is no medium for removing heat from the body, so in fact an astronaut is very unlikely to freeze to death. A vacuum flask is exceedingly good at insulation and keeping coffee hot, and it would also be true of your body warmth in space. Rapid evaporative cooling of skin moisture in a vacuum may create frost but this in itself is not fatal.

Without the protection of Earth's atmosphere and magnetosphere, astronauts are exposed to high levels of radiation. A year in low-Earth orbit results in a dose of radiation 10 times that of the annual dose on Earth, which damages the lymphocytes in the blood – cells that are heavily involved in maintaining the immune system – and DNA itself. This damage contributes to the lowered immunity experienced by astronauts and potentially gives them a slightly higher risk of developing cancer later on in life. Thankfully, the crews living on the *ISS* are partially protected from the space environment as they are in a low enough orbit still to be embraced by Earth's magnetic field, which deflects the solar wind around the Earth and the *ISS*. Nevertheless, a solar flare ejected from the Sun is still powerful enough to warp and penetrate these magnetic defences, and be hazardous to the health of the crew. Beyond the limited protection of Earth's magnetosphere, however, interplanetary manned missions are much more vulnerable.

The greatest challenge, other than funding, facing human space exploration is not the technology required to achieve it, but the fragility of the human body to withstand it. To survive for a prolonged or even indefinite period of time in space, the effects and impact of long-term space travel on the human body must be properly understood, and for that there needs to be some voluntary test subjects – the astronauts. Technology has proven its ability to shield their bodies from many of the dangers of space, either by creating a life-support system to provide air, water and food and maintain comfortable temperatures and pressures, or by building a spaceship hull and habitat for shelter and protection against hazardous radiation and incoming micrometeorites. One aspect of a space-based life that cannot be avoided or protected against, however, is that of microgravity. If you have ever ridden a roller coaster and felt your body rise up as you crested the first huge hill and then plummeted towards the ground, you have experienced weightlessness. Imagine that feeling for maybe an entire year – no wonder over 40 per cent of astronauts feel nauseous. One astronaut, Jake Garn, was so unwell with space sickness that a new unit of measurement was named after him. The Garn Scale is now used as a gauge of how space-sick an astronaut is – the top level indicates when he or she just wants to give up and go home. What is surprising, however, is that the human body manages to adapt remarkably well to living in zero-g or, more precisely, microgravity. But the effects go far beyond the initial trip. Temporarily, weightlessness causes many key systems of the body to relax, as there is no longer the need to work against the pull of gravity. Astronauts experience disorientation as their sense of up and down becomes confused, which is why the ISS has all of its writing on the walls pointing in the same direction. Also, ISS occupants have reported losing track of where their limbs are and of feeling as if they are not there anymore. Spacecraft design takes into account all the effects of microgravity by putting extra foot- and handholds everywhere. A random fact: some materials – including human facial hair – tend to be more flammable in lower gravity. Thankfully, handling hazardous combustible materials on the ISS is taken very seriously and carried out with great care, so the risk of astronauts burning off their eyebrows is pretty low.

The longer astronauts spend in space, however, the greater the enduring impact the lack of gravity has on their bodies. Most famously, they experience deterioration of bone mass. The calcium in their bones oozes out through their urine, weakening the bones over time and simulating accelerated osteoporosis. This condition is thankfully mostly reversible once back on solid ground and in Earth's gravity. Consequently, astronauts are much more susceptible to breaking their compromised bones should they slip and fall (those extra handholds come in useful). Sadly, an astronaut's muscles also lose mass because while floating around is all very pleasant, a space traveller would literally waste away if that were all he or she did. Although astronauts have to exercise for two hours a day in orbit in an effort to counteract this muscle-wasting, they still require months of rehabilitation to build muscle back up again once they have returned to Earth. Astronauts also grow an inch taller while in space owing to their spine elongating, and they can develop a swollen *moon-face* as the body's fluids move upwards. Unfortunately, this shift in fluids can also cause eyesight problems in astronauts, defined mainly by their seeing flashes and streaks of light. Much of this can gradually be reversed once back on Earth – but what if an astronaut were not returning to Earth? What would happen to the body then? The first one-year mission to the *ISS* launched in March 2015 conducted a unique experiment as US astronaut Scott Kelly has a twin brother, Mark, who remained on Earth. The brothers were then studied to observe the effects on Scott's body in long-term weightlessness versus his brother's on Earth.

A Space Oddity

Life in the cosmos also means dealing with a very distinct lack of personal space. Best-known of the challenges facing astronauts are long-term isolation, monotony, limited mobility and living in extremely close quarters with the same small group of people. The ISS is vastly larger than any previous space structure, about the size of a five- or six-bedroom house, but even so, staying inside your house for six months is hard to cope with both mentally and physically. Astronauts have cramped living quarters, privacy is a luxury, and they have to share everything with their fellow crew members for months at a time. The constant noise of people and machinery and the irregular light patterns make it difficult to sleep on board the space habitat, with astronauts commonly experiencing fewer hours of regular sleep and/or poor-quality snoozing. Combine that with the disruptions of the natural Earth day/ night cycles en route and the result is stressed and fatigued personnel. Maintaining Earth standards of personal hygiene is also almost impossible as water is precious and showering in microgravity is not an option – but apparently this is a minor irritation and the *ISS* actually doesn't smell too badly.

Surprisingly, although astronauts are physically removed from the Earth, they actually experience less isolation than scientists living in Antarctica in the height of winter. Regular contact with Earth, chatting with mission control, family and friends, as well as surprise calls from celebrities, via both video and voice chat and email keeps these space-dwellers thinking positively and feeling connected, giving them a respite from day-to-day chores and providing a sense of comfort and normality in an alien environment. The Internet and the advent of blogging and Tweeting, for example, may also ease the feelings of isolation faced in space, knowing that in cyberspace there is always someone listening. For five months, from December 2012 to May 2013, Canadian astronaut Chris Hadfield served as the commander of the *ISS* and gained a reputation as the 'most social media savvy astronaut' by sharing his daily life with the world, posting over 45,000 photos on Tumblr and Twitter and recording videos for YouTube. His guitar-playing and vocal performance of the late David Bowie's *Space Oddity* and exchange of tweets with William Shatner of *Star Trek* legend were remarkable, considering it all was sent from space. For the first time, the *ISS* felt like simply an extension of the Earth. Hadfield himself said that posting the photos, and the immediacy of the reactions and collective sense of wonder he could share with people from all over the world, made him feel connected with the planet and to other people, even as he floated hundreds of kilometres above them. All those who have lived in space say they took great comfort in the view of and in communication with the Earth, but what if the journey meant that Earth became barely a dot on the horizon and communications nearly impossible?

Life in space has the potential to lead to depression, interpersonal conflict, anxiety, insomnia and even psychosis. Astronauts are living a life of risk. One rogue meteor or solar flare and it's all over. But the considerable preparations made by astronauts aim to help them fight any negativity caused by months of living in fear and isolation. They train together for years as a team and as a family, so they already have camaraderie, a mutual understanding and trust, and to some extent intimacy with each other. Since outer space is considered an extreme environment, most training simulations and camps are also located in remote and harsh environments. The NEEMO mission sends *aquanauts* to the underwater *Aquarius* research station off the Florida Keys and several other analogue missions have been conducted on the Earth to simulate living in space or indeed on Mars. Most of these are research-based and were described in Chapter 5, but one – Hi-SEAS – is focused on the daily lives of people living off-world. Hi-SEAS (Hawaii Space Exploration Analog and Simulation) is a self-contained habitat found at an elevation of around 2,590m (8,500ft) on the slopes of Mauna Loa volcano on the Big Island of Hawaii. *Terranauts* live in a geodesic dome simulating life in a close-knit colony on Mars, including communication delays, isolation, cramped living quarters and, most importantly, food preparation. It's no secret that pre-packaged, dehydrated space food is bland and the extent of seasoning involves pepper suspended in olive oil to stop it flying up and scattering around the station. Eating the same foods day in, day out can cause a syndrome known as *menu fatigue*, a common affliction at the *ISS*. The gastronomically bored astronauts end up consuming fewer calories, and ultimately lose weight and can become malnourished. NASA continually examines the daily lives of the crew on the *ISS* to see how they're coping in a harsh and isolated environment, and to improve the agency's plans for future long-term missions in space. Despite all the risks, there is no shortage of applicants for astronaut positions and virtually everyone who has had the chance to live in space is keen to return.

Fly Me to the Moon

We mentioned before the bodies in the Solar System where humans might one day make footfall, or at least how they might accomplish it should technology allow, but skipped over our nearest and dearest celestial relative, the Moon. Designs for and ideas about how humans might live on the Moon have existed since long before the dawn of the Space Age, but what is actually feasible today? And why the Moon?

The Moon is an ideal staging post where we can accumulate materials, equipment and personnel outside the confines of Earth's gravitational pull, and it could be used as a test bed for the technologies needed to place humans on other worlds. From the Moon, we can send missions onwards to Mars or into deep space, set up astronomical observatories to view the cosmos without the interference of an atmosphere or Earth's radio chatter, utilise lunar resources (mining deposits such as titanium and helium-3) and even support a bustling space tourism industry – who wouldn't want to take a weekend break on the Moon? Humanity already has the means to get there and there are technologies that have proven advanced enough to sustain human and plant life in space. We just need the commitment and finance to proceed with it.

To build a habitat on the Moon is no easy feat. It requires consideration of how building materials will respond to the Moon's vacuum; the extreme temperature variations between day (120°C/248°F) and night (down to −153°C/−243°F); impacts by micrometeorites (travelling at up to 10km/s or 6.2 miles per second); outward forces resulting from the habitats being pressurised for human survival;

radiation damage; lunar dust contamination; and the gravity that is one-sixth of that of the Earth. These lunar habitats will be a lifeline for future colonists and as such will have to provide oxygen for them to breathe, water to drink, an environment in which to grow food, protection from the harsh radiation of the Sun, as well as light, warmth and power during the 14-day nights. They will also need to keep people comfortable in all temperatures. There are two types of water on the moon: first, from water-bearing comets striking the surface; and second, originating on the Moon itself. These could provide a potential source of drinking water, fuel, breathable air and protection for inhabitants: it just needs digging up. In 2009, India's probe *Chandrayaan-1* discovered more than 40 permanently darkened craters near the Moon's north pole containing an estimated 600 million tonnes of water ice. Despite this huge potential store of water, over 90 per cent of that used in a future lunar habitat would be recycled. Recycled water would produce carbon dioxide (CO_2), which could be pumped into a greenhouse for use by plants that would in turn produce oxygen as a waste gas, which could then be pumped back into the habitat. Power requirements of a habitat would require a stable and continuous supply of energy that could easily be generated by lunar solar farms. On Earth, solar power generation is limited at night, but on the Moon there would be the option of 24/7 continuous clean energy generation (which could in theory be channelled back to the Earth, as well as being used on the Moon).

With such a low gravity compared to that of the Earth, building a habitat for living and working would become quite a feat. On the positive side, engineers would be able to build structures less hampered by gravity and moving large objects would be far easier; they would just need to make sure they kept hold of these objects. Conversely, the low-g environment would pose difficulties for construction workers and their ability to move around easily. The lack of an atmosphere, however, would prove most damaging.

Ignoring the obvious issue of a lack of air for inhabitants to breathe, without the buffering of air around drilling tools huge amounts of heat would be generated, causing drill bits and rock to fuse. Should demolition tasks be needed, explosions in a vacuum would create countless high-velocity missiles that would tear through anything in their path (including habitats and astronauts) and there would be no atmosphere to slow them down. Likewise, additional protection of habitats and inhabitants from meteorite impacts would need to be considered with no atmosphere to burn up incoming space debris. Also, ejected dust would obscure everything and settle statically, contaminating machinery, not to mention the huge health risk if the dust were somehow breathed in. The launch costs from Earth to bring building supplies would be astronomical, so local materials could and should be used wherever possible. Lunar regolith (fine grains of pulverised Moon rock), for example, could be used to cover parts of habitats to protect settlers from cancer-causing cosmic rays and to provide insulation. It is estimated that a regolith thickness of least 2.5m (8ft) would be required to shield the human body and reduce radiation exposure to a *safe* background level. High energy efficiency would also be required, so the designs would need to incorporate very effective insulating materials to ensure minimum loss of heat.

One design put forwards so far is a stereotypical inflatable dome, which would be lightweight and relatively easy to erect on the Moon's surface. However, this would need good protection against incoming space debris, micrometeorite attacks, solar radiation and the vacuum of space. *Lunarcrete* or *mooncrete* could be made from lunar regolith, water and cement with the cement manufactured from lunar rock with a high calcium content. Water would either be supplied from sources off the Moon or by combining oxygen with hydrogen produced from lunar soil. Another option could be to manufacture habitats via 3D printing. In September 2014, a 3D printer was sent to the *ISS* to help astronauts print tools, parts and other much needed supplies. For the Moon, ESA has a plan. Prior to a human mission, they propose to send in a shuttle with an inflatable dome that would be erected on the surface as the founding unit of a future base. A robot and 3D printer would also be sent to create an exoskeleton that would line the outside of the dome and provide protection. Using dust available from the surroundings, ESA estimates it would take three months to get the base constructed and secure for up to four astronauts to inhabit.

Habitats could also be erected within ancient lava tubes. These form when the upper layer of a basaltic lava flow cools and hardens, and molten rock continues to flow beneath it. Once this drains, it can leave behind a hollow tube-shaped cavity. These natural cave systems provide a structure within which habitats could be built and easily sealed, the rock itself providing protection from the harsh surface environment and impacts. Such lava tubes are commonly interconnected, which would provide scope for the habitat to grow. A tube 1km (just over half a mile) in size or bigger would be ideal. The presence of lunar tunnels has yet to be confirmed unequivocally but spacecraft have revealed cave entrances known as *skylights* that may open into hidden lava tubes. Because of the Moon's lower gravity, these are expected to be larger than those already discovered on our planet.

When prospecting for the ideal site for a lunar outpost, it should provide good conditions for transport operations, a range of useable natural resources and a number of targets of scientific interest. Yet, the success of a lunar settlement will heavily depend on the efficiency of its transport structure. It seems likely that transportation around the Moon will rely on wheeled methods, following from terrestrial vehicles and tried and tested *Moon buggies* from the *Apollo* missions in the 1960s and '70s. To avoid mission-ending dust issues, it would be necessary to construct roads or potentially even a lunar cable car. One lunar colony could utilise the Shackleton crater at the Moon's south pole, using the crater walls to enclose a domed city with a 1,520-m (5,000-ft) ceiling and a diameter of 40km (25 miles). A colony settled in that location would have access to large deposits of water ice and be situated on the boundary between lunar sunlight and darkness. Its proponents estimate that a Shackleton dome colony could support 10,000 settlers after just 15 years of assembly by autonomous robots.

Something to consider packing when moving to the Moon would be a good batch of microorganisms. Microbes are currently used in mining to help recover metals such as gold, copper and uranium as they can catalyse extraction of minerals faster than chemicals. In fact, more than one-quarter of the world's copper supply is currently harvested from ores using microorganisms, in a process called *bio-mining*. Microbes could also be an important food source on the Moon. They grow faster than plants and generate more breathable oxygen than the same volume of vegetation, and they have a simpler growing process and are cheaper to transport as they take up less space. A peanut butter and microbe sandwich, anyone?! On Earth, *Anabaena cylindrica* is a nitrogen-fixing cyanobacterium and an extremophile to boot. When tested on rocks on Earth that are similar to lunar regolith, this microbe was able to extract calcium, iron, potassium, magnesium, nickel, sodium, zinc and copper from the material. It could also survive for 28 days under the extremely low temperatures and pressures found on the Moon, as long as it was shielded from UV radiation. This useful organism could also tolerate a decrease in water availability, so could happily be freeze-dried for transport.

Humans may not have set foot on the Moon since *Apollo 17* over 40 years ago, but that doesn't mean other life forms won't grace the lunar surface again. NASA is teaming up with students and private space companies to grow the first plants on the Moon's surface. The self-contained *Lunar Plant Growth Habitat* will resemble a glorified coffee can and will contain enough water, nutrients and air to grow 10 turnip seeds, 10 basil seeds, and 100 arabidopsis seeds on the lunar surface – *Arabidopsis thaliana* (Thale cress) was the first plant to have its genome sequenced. This experiment will test whether plants can survive the radiation, flourish in partial gravity, and thrive in a small, controlled environment – the same obstacles that will need to be overcome in order to build a greenhouse on the Moon, and ultimately for humans to be self-sufficient on its surface. When the mini-habitat lands on the Moon, it will automatically release enough water to wet a piece of nutrient-laden filter paper. That, along with the natural sunlight on the Moon, should trigger the germination of the plants. Completely sealed, the container will only contain enough air for about one week, but that will be enough to show whether the seeds germinate successfully. Interestingly, as a control, which every experiment needs, NASA are crowd-sourcing by sending schools across the USA their own set of habitats so they can grow the same plants that are being sent to the Moon. If the seeds successfully germinate on the lunar surface, this will be the first terrestrial plant life transported to and grown on another planetary body. The experiment is destined to hitchhike on board the robotic spacecraft of whoever wins the Google Lunar X Prize, saving millions of dollars in travel costs. The current price tag rings up at a mere $2 million – quite modest for an experiment that could help us figure out how to sustain life on other planets.

In the meantime, during his year in orbit on board the *ISS*, Scott Kelly successfully grew red romaine lettuce and a flower in space – an orange zinnia. Kelly had agreed with NASA to tend the plant as if it were in his garden on Earth, rather than according to a strict scientific regime. The zinnia soon flourished and put out several buds: a thrilling indication that cultivation of crops for food and medicine may be possible beyond our biosphere.

A Mission to Mars

Should colonisation missions head for the Moon first or Mars direct? Although the Moon is closer, easier to access from the Earth and has near-instant communication options, Mars is the world that seems to have captured humanity's imagination as a future human outpost. Its formation and evolution are so similar to that of the Earth that we can't help but want to study it, to learn more about our own history and future. Robotic explorers have studied Mars for more than 40 years – it is the only planet inhabited solely by mechanised beings – but a human presence is still a long way off. Mars today, despite its sub-zero temperatures, thin, non-breathable carbon dioxide-rich atmosphere, high UV radiation and savage global dust storms, actually has, as we have already explained, the most clement and almost welcoming environment in the Solar System after the Earth. It also contains habitable environments that could support microbial life, both in the past and even today in isolated areas.

At their closest point, a mere 54.7 million km (34 million miles) separates Mars from the Earth. One of the greatest barriers to humans making this trip, however, is the ability to carry the fuel needed. To travel these distances requires more fuel than just making a quick stop on the Moon, which means there is more weight to carry, and the greater the weight of a spacecraft the more fuel is needed to transport the weight. The total journey time from Earth to Mars could take between 150–300 days, depending on the distance between the planets at the time of launch and the rockets being used, so first on the to-do list would be to find a way to protect crews from radiation exposure on the trip. In May 2013, NASA scientists reported that a possible manned mission to Mars might involve a great radiation risk, based on the level of energetic particle radiation detected by the Radiation Assessment Detector on *Mars Science Laboratory* on its journey to Mars in 2011–2012. The

Curiosity Mars' rover received around 0.66 sieverts during its 253-day cruise to Mars – the equivalent of receiving a whole body CT scan every five or six days. In addition to this, large solar flares and cosmic radiation, although they can be prepared for, may still deliver a lethal radiation dose to a crew. Nonetheless, as mentioned in Chapter 7, a human crew to the Red Planet would be likely to receive only just above the limit of radiation currently deemed acceptable over an astronaut's lifetime, and so the risk is judged tolerable in relation to the potential benefit to humanity resulting from their work.

Living in microgravity on the journey will cause the same physical effects as seen on the *ISS*, but these astronauts would then have to land on Mars and adjust to its gravity as quickly as possible. There will be no one waiting for them on the ground to help them out of the craft and to support them to start walking. The best way to assist the astronauts would be to remove the problem and produce artificial gravity by spinning the spacecraft as it travelled to Mars, adjusting the gravity slowly to help the astronauts adapt before arrival to life on Mars.

Another worry is the risk of supersonic space dust. In 1967, a stream of micrometeorites ended the three-year-long *Mariner 4* mission, while in 2012 a micrometeorite slammed into one of the *ISS*'s giant windows. Space shuttles have all returned to Earth with mini impact craters on their hulls. The *ISS* now has a micrometeorite shield on the exterior of the *Zvezda* Service Module, which any Mars shuttle would also need. Finally, although this is not the end of the list of worries by a long shot, there is the issue of landing. The current success rate for setting down safely and in one piece on Mars is only 30 per cent. With a human at the controls, the rate may be higher – NASA did not lose any of its *Apollo* landers during touchdown on the Moon. However, unlike the Moon, Mars has an atmosphere and its gravity can make a soft landing much more challenging.

Building an outpost on Mars will require a great deal more planning, even though we would have far better conditions to work with than are present on the Moon. The benefits of moving to Mars are that it has a similar length of day and the planet is tilted on its axis at an angle comparable to that of the Earth, which creates similar seasons; and it has an atmosphere, water ice, and habitable environments. There is a number of geological landforms, such as impact craters and lava tubes, which could be used to house habitats, as proposed for the Moon, and there is a never-ending list of scientific investigations that could be carried out. Larger habitats would be required for long-term living (the only real way to live on Mars), which could be built in stages during a series of launches, taking inspiration from the piece-by-piece construction of the *ISS*. The parts for a Martian base could be delivered by landing modules in a series of missions, which could then be assembled by a human crew either already on the surface or arriving later, by robots or even by a crew based on a nearby Martian moon. Buzz Aldrin, the second person to walk on the Moon and a great advocate of Mars colonisation, suggested sending three people to spend 18 months on the moon Phobos, using this as a headquarters from which to remotely construct a base for Mars.

The environment on Mars is the main challenge to overcome for any human or habitat as its 95 per cent carbon-dioxide-filled atmosphere is toxic to humans and promotes low atmospheric pressures (0.006atm/0.0006MPa/6mbar). Additionally, it only has 38 per cent of the Earth's gravity, is always cold (−85°C to −5°C/−120°F to 23°F), and there are no liquid bodies of water on its surface. As for habitats on the Moon, oxygen would need to be generated for humans to breathe and suits would need to be worn whenever the inhabitants left the outposts. Owing to the time taken to travel between Mars and the Earth (not to mention the cost), a habitat on Mars would need to be self-sustaining from day one, growing its own food, extracting its own water and producing its own oxygen. Even though many studies are being conducted into the logistics of how this might be achieved, it is still very likely that a spacecraft would stay in orbit with food and supplies for a journey home, and also for a *safe haven* in case something went wrong on the surface. With costs of £50,000 to ship 4 litres (7 pints) of water to the Moon, imagine the cost, let alone the logistics, of shipping water and food to Mars on a regular basis. The only logical key to long-term human habitation of Mars is space agriculture or *astro-gardening*.

The first Martians will therefore be two species – plant and human – who are actually perfect travelling companions. Humans consume oxygen and release carbon dioxide. Plants return the favour by consuming this carbon dioxide during photosynthesis and releasing oxygen. Humans can use edible parts of plants for nourishment, while human waste and inedible plant matter can (having been broken down by microbes in tanks called *bioreactors*) provide nutrients for further plant growth. Plants need water, oxygen, sunlight, nutrients and relatively comfortable temperatures, but none of these are currently found on Mars in quantities that suit the growth of a garden. With a lower gravity than the Earth and ravaged by global dust storms, this is a world that would not support most known plant life. Plants are a canary in a coal mine for human habitation – if they cannot find a way to survive, then we cannot either. Gardening on Mars would provide a long-term food source for future human colonies and could provide over half their required calorie intake through the growth of tomatoes, potatoes and other fruit and vegetables. Plants that thrive in the carbon dioxide rich atmosphere of Mars include seeds of radish, alfalfa and mung bean, while asparagus, potatoes and marigolds have been shown to grow in Mars-like soils. If Mars gardeners are to use Martian soil, then knowledge of how crops respond to its contents, such as sulphates and perchlorates, will be required. Gardens help to recycle nutrients, and provide drinking water and in the longer term could provide building materials such as wood and bamboo. Any garden would need protection in the form of a greenhouse or geodesic dome that could keep the crops sheltered from extreme UV radiation, while still allowing in enough sunlight for growth. This dome would need to be securely anchored into the regolith to provide support and stability against the fearsome Martian dust storms and dust devils. The crops would also have to be kept warm while surrounded by the cold climate of Mars. This heating of the greenhouse would require energy, potentially from solar panels arranged outside the habitat and heating filaments beneath it; although that energy source too would require protection against the Martian environment. Accessing liquid water is a given since it would be needed both for irrigation of the plants and for human consumption.

Terraforming

When humans finally make it to Mars, we will live in a similar manner to how we do in Antarctica. Mini enclosed Earth-like environments will arise on the Martian surface that could include not only gardens and homes, but also parks, forests and lakes, all maintained under an Earth-like air pressure through a process known as *paraterraforming*. While it would cost a great deal of money to construct, paraterraforming sections of Mars with a sample of Earth's biosphere inside pressurised domes and underground caverns is something that humanity could achieve within mere years of arrival. Eventually, however, there would be an even more ambitious goal that might take millennia – full-scale *terraforming*. This is the process of 'transforming a hostile environment into one suitable for *human* life', as defined by NASA, although this is a dated and distinctly Homo sapiens-centric view. I prefer terraforming as the process of *making a hostile environment suitable for life* – not necessarily human life, which needs very specific conditions that are hard to achieve. Essentially, we are saying that one day we could bring Mars back to life. But why would we want to do this? Is it for the art of doing it, for the science, for the economic necessity or is it to leave a legacy for the planet Earth?

Terraforming Mars would entail three major interlaced changes: building up the atmosphere, keeping the planet warm enough to allow liquid water to remain stable on its surface and, finally, protecting the atmosphere from being lost to outer space. Most of the legwork would be done by life itself. You would not build Mars ... you would just warm it up, throw in some seeds and allow life to take over. First, the atmosphere would need to be thickened and enriched with nitrogen and oxygen while the average temperature of the planet would need to be increased substantially. *Perfluorocarbons*, potent greenhouse gases, could be synthesised from elements in Martian dirt and air and then blown into the atmosphere. Through warming, the planet's frozen carbon dioxide in the ground would be released, which would amplify the temperature and boost atmospheric pressure to the point at which liquid water could flow. Terraformers might then seed the red rock with a succession of microbial ecosystems to increase the amount of methane in the Martian air, because methane is a much stronger greenhouse gas than carbon dioxide. First, bacteria and lichens (which have survived in Antarctica) would be grown, then later mosses. As dark plants and algae spread across the surface, they would darken the planet so that it absorbed more sunlight, and after a millennia or so, forests would be growing. With the right combination of plants and well-selected microorganisms, planetary engineers could generate the critical oxygen and nitrogen needed for human inhabitants to roam the surface without a space suit. Throughout this process, colonists would continue to inhabit Mars and expand the system of enclosed mini Earth-like habitats.

However, before we start this irreversible process of Martian environmental change, we need to be sure that we are not treading on the toes (if they have any) of any hidden life forms on the red planet. As we push Mars towards being more Earth-like, are there organisms present that might push back? We know that Mars has organic compounds that could be used by life, but a pessimist would say that any life that did exist there has not survived intact today. So if we are to bring Mars back to life, should it not be with native Martians rather than with Earthlings? The ingredients of the biosphere, if at all possible, should have Martian DNA at its core. Perhaps if we could find the relics of past Martian life frozen beneath the surface, in the polar ice caps, or living in some sub-surface refuge as we do on Earth, we could reconstruct it and let it once again control biogeochemical cycles on Mars. We could give Mars back its heartbeat. Sending life from Earth to colonise Mars should be an absolute last resort. Only if Mars has no genome should we consider sharing ours with it.

Epilogue

If the message has not been emphasised enough already, there are hundreds, most likely thousands, of possible habitable environments on worlds throughout our Solar System and beyond. But before we visit these places and possibly consider making changes to them so that they can host humanity, we may want to start by paying them the courtesy of protection from us while we investigate them. Space agencies all over the world have signed up to a very important programme of *Planetary Protection*, which scientists hope will preserve any possible life forms that do exist outside our planet from contamination by terrestrial organisms hopping a ride on incoming spacecraft. In turn, we are also committed to protecting the Earth from contamination by alien life should such a craft laden with samples return home. This responsibility is not taken lightly by humanity. We understand and appreciate the need to ensure that we are not interfering with these natural pristine environments while still powering forwards with our exploration of the cosmos. Missions to Mars are especially singled out by *The Committee on Space Research* (*COSPAR*). Since it has special regions within which terrestrial organisms could readily propagate, and areas thought to have an elevated potential for existence of Martian life forms. This applies to any region on Mars where liquid water occurs, or can occasionally occur, and is of course based on our current understanding of the requirements and conditions that are *just right* for life.

This talk of extraterrestrial life, habitable environments, moving to the Moon, humans colonising the Galaxy, and growing flowers and eating asparagus on Mars is fantastical and exciting, but we must not overlook and forget about our *just right* planet, to which we owe our very existence. We are designing habitats that will enable us to survive on

Mars and the Moon and technologies to search for alien life forms despite the fact that we do not yet understand how life came to be on the Earth and have been unable to colonise some of the most remote places on our own planet that are lush in comparison to those found throughout the Solar System. Humanity is not using the only truly habitable planet we know of to its fullest potential, but are instead taking a liberty with the lessons it has to teach us. Yet planetary exploration and planetary preservation have the same goal. If we can find means by which to colonise and inhabit the most inhospitable places on the Earth, it will aid our exploration of other worlds, and in so doing will help us to better use and preserve our own.

Whether we are searching for just the right home to live in, just the right school to send our children to, just the right moment to take the next step forwards in our lives, or just the right planet to house another form of life in the cosmos, humanity is constantly searching for its *just right*, as Goldilocks did. We are exploring the Solar System but found that Mercury and Venus may be too hot and Mars and the outer icy worlds may be too cold. We have eagerly turned our eyes to the exoplanets and exomoons of distant solar systems, hopefully watching and listening for any signs of life. Yet the *just right* for humanity and life as we know it today is the Earth – who knows what it might be in the future.

Acknowledgements

They say writing is a lonely and solitary process and yet I found it to be far from either of these. Although the act of putting finger to keyboard was of course done alone, behind the scenes I had an army of extraordinary people cheering me on, offering thoughts and suggestions, and sharing my excitement with the project. To start with I have to thank those without whom this book would never have been published: the incredible team at Bloomsbury Sigma and their fearless leader Jim Martin. Jim, you took a huge leap of faith by asking me to write my first book for you and I thank you from the bottom of my heart – your tweet could not have come at a better time. Thank you for always sharing in my vision for the book, especially its cover, and thank you for always replying to emails quickly and with a great sense of humour. To Sigma's assistant editor Anna MacDiarmid for taking *Goldilocks* through to publication, Lucy Clayton and to the rest of the Sigma team; this labour of love would not have been possible without you. The Bloomsbury Sigma family has brought me into contact with so many wonderful scientists and science communicators whom I am now honoured to call friends, and I am tremendously proud to be a part of this group. To my illustrator Sam Goodlet – I wish I had your talent! You are such a gifted and easy woman to work with. Thank you for sharing in my vision for the illustrations and I think everyone will agree you have produced some phenomenal drawings that bring the book to life. To Monica Byles, my brilliant copy editor – your comments have been invaluable and insightful and *Goldilocks* is the better for you.

A deep and heartfelt thank you goes to my huge support network of family, friends and trusted readers who have stood by my side and listened to my many ramblings about aliens and extremophiles: Natalie Bell, Fiona Bond,

Chloe Chin, Denise Houcke, Matthew Houcke, Tony Houcke, Jules Howard, Barbara James, Irina Kasatkina, Suzanne Kenny, Katherine Kotian, David Lambert, Kersten Malhan, Gemma Metcalfe-Beckers, Sophie Murray, Alexandra Pontefract, Ann Preston, Anke Schnedler, Linda Seward, Alaura Singleton, Lynne Whoolley and my TED Fellows family. I have enjoyed every second of writing this book and all of your support has made it possible. To those of you who gave up your time to read and edit my book – offering helpful suggestions, brutal comments and infantile humour over the use of certain words – this book is the better for you! I also owe a massive thank you to my favourite *coffice* (coffee office), Artisan, for patiently allowing me to steal a corner of its lovely cafe for hours on end. Thank you for the fantastic coffee, unshakeable Wi-Fi and delicious raspberry lamingtons, and especially to Jessica, whose steadfast optimism helped inspire me every morning. Thank you to Max Richter for providing the soundtrack to my mind and Netflix for letting me stream episode after episode of multiple TV shows, providing me with focus. Yes, I watch TV and write at the same time – I have no idea how or why – it just works.

To my parents, I say a huge thank you for … well … everything. Thank you for supporting and encouraging a seven-year-old girl who was just as interested in becoming a geologist and climbing volcanoes as she was in playing with Barbie dolls and running a delicious, yet make-believe, hamburger diner. Together and separately you have given me every possible opportunity to experience the best the Earth has to offer, and quite possibly sealed my fate in becoming a space scientist by orchestrating my first trip to the Kennedy Space Centre. Dad even masqueraded as a teacher to get me the Kennedy Space Centre educational pack – my hero. Throughout my life they have taught me to work hard and push my limits so I know this book would never have been written if it weren't for them.

Finally to Dan, my husband and best friend for the last 15 years, a thank you is simply not enough. Never was there a man who more supported a woman wholly determined to make a living doing a job she loved. Who patiently read her book on his commute to work every day and shared in her vision of the story she wanted to tell. Thank you for being my rock (pun intended) through the last few years and for giving me our wonderful little boy. I hope all the months of emotional and financial backing were worth it and I have made you proud. Oh, and I should also admit – he came up with the title – without him, there would be no *Goldilocks and the Water Bears*.

Index